Man's Natural Environment

DISCARDED

Man's Natural Environment

A Systems Approach

Edited By

Lorne H. Russwurm
Edward Sommerville

Duxbury Press
North Scituate, Massachusetts

Duxbury Press
North Scituate, Massachusetts
A Division of Wadsworth Publishing Company, Inc.

ISBN-0-87872-070-7

L.C. Cat. Card No. 74-75715

Printed in the United States of America

1 2 3 4 5 6 7 8 9 10 —— 78 77 76 75 74

Man's Natural Environment was edited by Maryellyn Montoro and designed by
Duxbury Press.
The cover was designed by Oliver Kline.

CONTENTS

Preface   vii

1. **A SYSTEMS APPROACH TO THE NATURAL ENVIRONMENT**   1
    Lorne H. Russwurm

2. **UNITED OF THE NATURAL ENVIRONMENT**
    Introduction   17
    The Life Layer – *Arthur N. Strahler*   19
    Ecosystem Theory in Relation to Man – *Eugene P. Odum*   31
    Man The Newcomer – *Paul B. Sears*   43

3. **WEATHER–CLIMATE: FLOWS AND EXCHANGES OF
    ENERGY AND MOISTURE**
    Introduction   56
    Challenges in Climatology – *A.D. Tweedie*   61
    Microclimate and Bioclimatology – *E.R. Biel*   68
    Man-Made Climatic Changes – *Helmut E. Landsberg*   87

4. **THE INTEGRATING FLOWS OF WATER**
    Introduction   110
    Water Resources: A Global Problem with Local Roots –
        Raymond L. Nace   114
    The Hydrology and Limnology of Lake Tahoe – *J.R. Crippen
        and B.R. Pavelka*   123
    The Ecology of Flowing Waters in Relation to Management –
        H.B.N. Hynes   141

5. **LANDFORMS: PROCESS AND PATTERN**
    Introduction   150
    Erosion of the Land – *Sheldon Judson*   154

Rivers – *Luna B. Leopold*   169
A Cycle of Sedimentation and Erosion in Urban River
    Channels – *M. Gordon Wolman*   189

6.   **SOILS: THE BIOTIC – ABIOTIC SYSTEMS LINK**
Introduction   203
The Living Soil – *E.A. Paul and J.W.B. Stewart*   206
Outline of a Generalized Theory of Soil Genesis – *Roy W. Simonson*   221
Man as a Factor of Soil Formation – *O.W. Bidwell and F.D. Hole*   232

7.   **BIOTA: THE COMPLEX WEB OF LIFE**
Introduction   240
A World Pattern of Plant Energetics – *Carl F. Jordan*   244
Effects of Pollution on The Structure and Physiology of Ecosystems –
    G.M. Woodwell   262
The Ecological Decline of Lake Erie – *Dean E. Arnold*   272

8.   **APPLICATIONS OF SYSTEM PRINCIPLES**
Introduction   284
Man's Efficient Rush Toward Deadly Dullness – *Kenneth E.F. Watt*   288
The Ecosystem as a Criterion for Public Land Policy – *Lynton K.*
    Caldwell   295
Barrier Beaches of Eastern North America – *Christopher J.*
    Schuberth   312
Optimum Population and Environment: A Georgia Microcosm –
    Eugene P. Odum   321

Index   331

PREFACE

In recent years there has been a rapid growth of public concern over the degradation of both manmade and natural environments. Citizens protest development and redevelopment schemes, large power projects, lack of public access to beaches, and numerous other problems concerning their environment. Intensified popular awareness about the importance of healthy and pleasant biophysical surroundings has led to political pressure for measures to restore, maintain, and improve environmental conditions. Action to improve the environment is being undertaken by government, industry, civic groups, and individuals.

In the long run, the success of any effort to restore, maintain, and improve the environment will largely depend on two things: (1) our basic knowledge about the behavior of environmental systems and (2) better understanding of man's role as an agent of biophysical change.

We believe that this book will give its readers the kind of information needed to deal with environmental change. The book is organized according to a systems approach. The systems approach provides a realistic yet simplifying framework for viewing the many scientific facts and principles relating to the environment. Scientific knowledge about the workings of nature is presented not as a multitude of facts, but as a meaningful explanation of the complexities of each natural subsystem. Facts go further when they fit into a meaningful framework.

In selecting articles to be included in this book, we were governed by the needs and interests of students enrolled in introductory physical geography and environmental science courses. While the book reflects our view of physical geography, we are aware that geography is only one of the many disciplines involved with the natural environment. Accordingly, we have selected articles from a wide variety of sources and disciplines. In our chapter introductions we have tried to integrate the articles with a view to the systems framework. We have eliminated footnotes, but have included with each article a carefully chosen set of readings to permit student and instructor to follow up specific topics quickly.

Over the past seven years, students in introductory physical geography courses at the University of Waterloo have given us many helpful comments on our systems approach and on the readings used in the courses. We would like to thank all of them. We also thank our colleagues in the Geography Department for their assistance; our secretaries for their cheerful, competent work; and the University's librarians, who always managed to find what we needed.

It is the authors of the readings who must be given primary credit for whatever success this book achieves. As editors of the volume, we have tried to provide an integrating framework for the articles. We have taken the strong points of individual articles to build a stronger whole. That has been our intent; hopefully we have succeeded.

CHAPTER 1

A Systems Approach to the Natural Environment

Lorne H. Russwurm
Department of Geography, University of Waterloo, Waterloo, Ontario

In this chapter the systems approach will be explained and the various systems of the natural environment will be discussed.

THE ESSENTIALS OF A SYSTEMS APPROACH

In a system, each part is related to each other part. The natural environment is a system that can be broken down into a set of five integrated parts or subsystems — weather-climate, water, landforms, soils, and biota. The environmental system is too complex for us to deal simultaneously with all its subsystems. By studying the various subsystems separately we can achieve a greater understanding of the whole and of its parts. But we must always remember that the system as a whole is something different from the sum of its parts.

A systems approach provides a single conceptual framework within which all the processes and forms of the natural environment can be explained. Within this framework one can study the whole, move from the whole to the parts, and move back again to the whole. In the systems approach the primary emphasis is on the *flows* of energy, water, nutrients, and other matter within each subsystem and between subsystems. Reading after reading in this book will emphasize the importance of flows of energy and matter. Flows of energy and matter interconnect and unify the subsystems of the natural environment; they suggest interrelationships and interdependence. In the systems approach, attention is given to interrelationships because all subsystems and all components of each subsystem are interrelated and interdependent.

As an example we might consider the erosive work done by a river system. Erosion results from the kinetic energy of the movement of a mass of water, that is, from the flow of energy and matter. All the systems of a river — water, soil and rock particles in the water, chemical matter in solution in the water, geologic material constituting the bed and sides of the river channel — are interdependent. Should the rock underlying the river bed be strongly resistant to erosion, the river will wear down its bed quite slowly. But should the slope of the river bed be steep, the potential energy of gravity for the moving water will be great and consequently the erosion potential will be considerable. In this example the relationships between the flows of energy and matter and the geologic structure are revealed. Such interdependencies and interactions are the basis for the organization and wholeness of the system.

THE SYSTEMS OF THE NATURAL ENVIRONMENT

For purposes of study, the natural environment can be divided into five easily recognizable subsystems. This division is somewhat arbitrary, and other analysts may divide the environmental system along other lines. But we believe that the division into five subsystems provides the simplest yet clearest breakdown, and this book has been organized accordingly. The first three subsystems, weather-climate, water, and landforms, comprise the abiotic (non-living) physical environment. They provide the setting, the physical support, and sustenance for the remaining two subsystems, soils and biota. The biota consists of plants, animals (including man), and microorganisms living together as sociobiological communities. Soils are the link between the biotic and abiotic environments. Life depends on the continuous flow of energy and matter among the five subsystems.

In any given place, biota and soils together with landforms, weather, and water form an ecosystem. A pond, a cornfield, a beech-maple forest, a city — each is an ecosystem. For analytical purposes, we divide an ecosystem into its five component subsystems, but in reality they form one whole. In dealing with natural systems, man often forgets that each part (or subsystem) affects all other parts of the system. For example, when a dam is built across a river, the flow of water and sediments is changed. Water in the lake behind the dam becomes warmer and fish species change. Water below the dam, now freed of its sediment load, has more potential energy and the river bed is scoured and down cut. Nesting sites for fish in this stretch of the river are destroyed. When the Aswan Dam was built on the Nile River in Egypt, little or no thought was given to its possible effect on fisheries in the Eastern Mediterranean. The output of the fisheries was reduced because of changed nutrient flows and thus an unexpected, unforeseen linkage came to light. In a systems approach we attempt to consider all possible linkages and to allow for unknown ones. In this book we will emphasize the link between the environmental subsystems and man, for man's activities can play an important role in modifying the natural environment.

Analysis of the Natural Environment

The five subsystems of the natural environment can be thought of as horizontal or vertical segments of the whole system. A vertical segment is the ecosystem occurring in a given place, and it involves the integration in place of the five subsystems—weather-climate, water, landforms, soils, and biota. A horizontal segment is any one of the five subsystems. Table 1 illustrates the horizontal-vertical way of looking at the environmental system. The five rows are the horizontal segments representing specific subsystem outputs; the three columns represent three forest ecosystem types found on the glaciated landscapes of the Northeastern United States and Eastern Canada.

Subsystems can be further divided into lesser subsystems and the elements which comprise them. Thus, the global landform system might be divided into glaciated and non-glaciated subsystems; the glaciated system might be further divided into moraines, drumlins, eskers, and outwash plains. In the systems approach, subsystems and elements are dealt with as functional wholes that provide inputs for other subsystems from which they, in turn, receive inputs.

The purpose and detail of any given analysis will determine what are subsystems and what are elements. The level of analysis chosen is known as the resolution level. On a spatial scale, we use three resolution levels—global, regional, and local. On a time scale, comparable resolution levels are long, intermediate, and short run.

THE IMPORTANT CONCEPTS OF SYSTEMS THEORY

Although complex systems like those of the natural environment can never be fully comprehended, we can attempt to learn as much as possible about them by concentrating on the flows of energy and

Table 1. Horizontal and vertical subsystems.

	Ecosystem Type One: Flood Plain Forest	Ecosystem Type Two: Swamp Forest	Ecosystem Type Three: Upland Forest
Biotic Subsystem	Deciduous floodplain species (e.g.: Red Maple, Willow, Elm).	Deciduous and coniferous swamp species (e.g.: Spruce, Tamarack, Ash, Elm, Peat deposits).	Deciduous upland species (e.g.: Sugar Maple, Beech, Oak, Hickory).
Soil Subsystem	Entisols	Histosols	Alfisols
Landform Subsystem	River Valley	Outwash Plain	Moraine Hills
Water Subsystem	Seasonal oversupply with inconsistent drainage	Oversupply with very poor drainage	Regular supply with good drainage
Weather-Climate Subsystem	Humid temperate climate with a regular supply of precipitation but a seasonal variation in energy input		

matter that unify systems. They are best illustrated by three sets of concepts that throw light on the nature and extent of these flows. The three concepts are: (1) exchanges between systems and environments; (2) energy and entropy; (3) diversity, stability, equilibrium, and feedback.

Exchanges Between Systems and Environment

A system is a functional whole composed of organized, interacting, interdependent parts (subsystems and elements). All natural systems cycle matter and energy within themselves and exchange matter and energy with their external environment. In these exchanges with their environment, there are boundaries, real or arbitrary, across which energy and matter flow.

Intersystem Exchanges

How can we dissect the natural environment for study purposes while continuing to view the system as a whole? In figure 1 we present a schematic drawing which illustrates the *inputs* (of energy or matter) to a natural system, the *processes* by which the system maintains itself or changes, and the *outputs* (or results) produced by a given set of inputs and processes. By means of various internal processes, natural systems transport, transform, and use flows of energy and matter (especially water and nutrients) received from their environment. A process is a succession of events dependent on characteristic energy agents. For instance, the process of erosion depends on the potential energy of gravity and the kinetic and heat energy of water, wind, and ice. In this process, geological materials are weathered, transported, and deposited elsewhere by water, wind, and ice.

In figure 1, six inputs from the external environment of a given ecosystem are diagrammed. These inputs flow into the ecosystem and are largely beyond control of the system. They can be thought of as independent variables. The primary inputs are matter and solar radiation

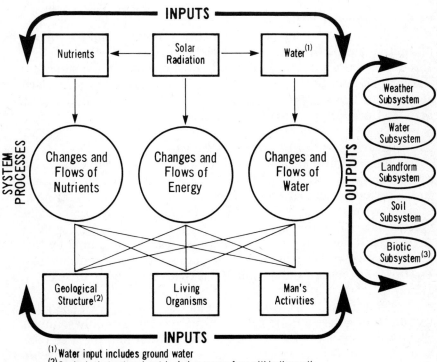

(1) Water input includes ground water
(2) Geological structure input includes energy from within the earth
(3) The biotic subsystem includes man

Figure 1. The natural environment system.

(solar energy). They act on and through the secondary inputs (geological structure, living organisms, and man's activities) to drive the processes of life on earth. In figure 1 solar radiation is centrally placed because it is the energy input which keeps all earthly processes operating. Two types of matter, nutrients and water, are specifically identified in figure 1 because of their overwhelming importance to life. Nutrients provide the chemical energy (food) needed by living organisms. The most needed chemicals are oxygen, hydrogen, carbon, nitrogen, phosphorous, potassium, calcium, magnesium, and sulphur. Water is the integrating link, and is the basis of most physical, chemical, and biological processes of the ecosphere.

Exchanges between a system and its environment are always important. A river system depends on precipitation inputs from the weather system; an agricultural system depends on nutrient and moisture inputs from the soil, and heat and matter inputs from the atmosphere. Inputs are handled according to the physical, chemical, and biological laws operating within the system, and according to the nature of the system (its structure and function). But a system can tolerate only a certain range in the quantity, quality, and pattern of inputs. Thus, a river system of a certain size can handle a given amount of waste without changing its existing equilibrium state. But if too much polluting waste arrives at once rather than over regularly spaced time periods, the system may have difficulty maintaining itself and deterioration may result.

Cycling and Intrasystem Exchanges

In the internal environment of any system, energy and matter are transformed and flow in characteristic pathways. Energy is used in the system when matter is transported or is transformed through system processes, that is by chemical reactions or by changes of state (gas, liquid, solid). Energy cannot be reused, and the system would deteriorate if the energy input became less than that required by the system processes. Natural (and manmade) systems can continue to exist only because of the seemingly inexhaustible supply of solar energy.

Natural systems, while having an infinite supply of energy (solar energy), have a finite supply of matter. There is only so much phosphorus, carbon, or water on the earth, and it must be used over and over again. As the various natural systems evolved, they developed different strategies for dealing with exchanges of matter. There are two extremes: (1) exchange as much matter as possible; cycle and store as little as possible or (2) exchange as little as possible; cycle

and store as much as possible. There are many variations between
these extremes. Oceanic ecosystems employ the first strategy; mature
forest ecosystems use the second. The first system is a very open
system and is dependent on the stability of its external environment.
The second system is a closed one that can draw on its internal resources to weather a disruption in supply. In such a system, matter is
cycled over and over again for reuse. The earth itself is a closed system,
for it receives almost no matter from its external environment, that
is, from the rest of the universe.

Cycling is the transformation of matter within a system until
it is again available for reuse in its original form. Such transformations
depend on the use of energy as it flows through the system. Thus, in
the calcium cycle of an almost mature upland deciduous forest (figure
2), the calcium taken out of the available nutrient pool (soilwater and
soil clay-humus particles) by trees and other plants is returned as
calcium to this pool after the decomposition and leaching of vegetative
debris (leaves, stems, twigs, bark, roots). This calcium flow is a good
example of cycling and intrasystem flow. With some variations, the
pattern of relationships is similar for most nutrients. Three possible
sources of calcium exist within the internal environment of the ecosystem: (1) minerals from the rock (primary) and from the soil (secondary), (2) vegetative biomass and vegetative organic debris, and (3) available nutrients from the soil. A fourth but minor source is calcium deposited from the atmosphere on plants and on the ground. This source
requires an intersystem flow.

In figure 2, two basic intrasystem flows occur. The major one
is the flow of calcium from the nutrient pool available in the soil
to the plants and its return after organic debris has decomposed. This
cycling flow is almost at steady state, for uptake is 49.3 kilograms
per hectare per year while the return is 49 kilograms per hectare per
year. Each hectare contains 690 kilograms of calcium, but only one-
fourteenth (690 ÷ 49) of this available calcium is used annually. The
minor flow is from weathered rock and soil minerals into the nutrient
pool of the soil. Some return loss (no numeric data are available)
from the nutrient pool occurs as soluble minerals become fixed in
a form not available to plants.

The almost mature ecosystem in figure 2 is efficient in retain-
ing and circulating calcium. It uses only a slight portion of the available
calcium each year. Exchanges with the external environment are also
rather slight. This ecosystem is a relatively closed system for calcium.
Calcium input to the system from the atmosphere is 2.6 kilograms
per hectare per year, while calcium output from the system is 12.0

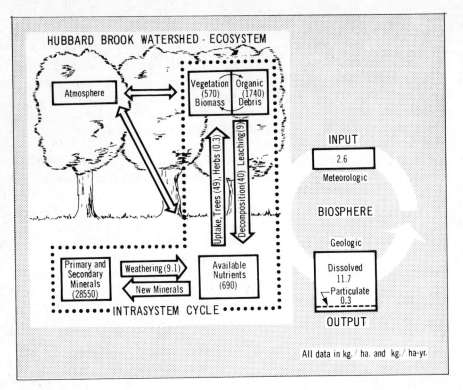

Figure 2. Major parameters of the calcium cycle in the Hubbard Brook watershed ecosystems. (Adapted from G. E. Likens and F. H. Bormann in *Ecosystem Structure and Function,* p. 53.)

kilograms per hectare per year. Most of this output is dissolved in stream outflow where it becomes part of the larger erosion cycle. The system's net annual calcium loss is 9.4 kilograms per hectare, or only 1.3 percent of the total available calcium. Actually, most of this loss is replaced by weathering of minerals (9.1 kilograms per hectare per year). Detailed research on this almost mature forest eco-system indicates similar input-output findings for other nutrients.

It must be emphasized that the more closed the system, the more critical the intrasystem cycling; conversely, the more open the system, the more critical its exchanges with the external environment. Exchanges with the internal and external environments are related to the growth of a system. The growth or development of a natural system can occur in two ways. One is by storage of energy and matter within the system as inputs exceed outputs. Another is by the increasing organization of the system, which results in better use of energy and matter. An example is vegetation development in which succeeding stages become increasingly organized as energy and matter are stored and cycled. The flow-through of energy is slowed down and matter is captured from the external environment. A system begins deteriorating whenever inputs of matter and/or energy are exceeded by outputs.

Energy and Entropy

Flows of energy and matter are the underlying causal forces in the operation of all natural systems. Energy is the capacity for doing work. Matter is a specialized form of energy which has the attributes of mass and extensions in space and time. Unlike matter, regular energy can be used but not reused; when energy is used it is changed to a different form. Energy flows through natural systems while matter is recycled. Energy is used to do the work involved in recycling matter. But each change in the form of energy means dissipation as heat energy or thermal waste. In this form energy cannot be used to do further work. The two basic laws of thermodynamics apply: (1) in a system of constant mass energy cannot be created or destroyed, but only transformed; (2) energy is dissipated in heat energy (thermal waste) as work is done. Entropy is the term used to refer to the dissipation of energy. It is a measure of the amount of original energy available which has been dispersed as heat. When maximum entropy is reached, all the energy is randomly dispersed (disorganized) and no more energy is available (is organized) to do work.

What is the interconnection of energy and matter? Except for radiant (solar) energy, energy can exist only in the presence of matter. Commonly recognized forms of energy include chemical energy (food), kinetic energy (motion), potential energy (gravity), electrical energy, and nuclear energy. Conversion from one to another of these forms occurs only through the presence of matter and involves energy loss through dissipation as heat energy. For example, electrical energy is transmitted through wires. As electricity flows through the wires, friction is generated and causes the electrical energy to be dissipated as heat energy. Hence, at some point so much heat energy is lost that it is no longer economically feasible to transmit the electrical energy any further distance.

To be available for work, energy must be concentrated. Once energy is dispersed evenly, no more work can be done and maximum entropy is attained. Thus, a stretch of river flowing across a flat plain has little potential energy compared to a stretch of river with the same volume of water flowing down the slope of a hill. Maximum entropy refers to a completely random dispersion of energy. Such a random state is the more probable state. In this state no energy gradient exists and no more work can be done. The more organized a system, the more effective is its use of energy and matter, and entropy is minimized. More gets done with the same amount of energy; the system is well ordered. The earth can maintain a high level of organization and a low level of entropy only because of the continuous input of energy from the sun.

Mature ecosystems are characterized by minimal entropy, for they possess greater diversity than less well-developed ecosystems. They have more species, more niches are filled, and thus they are more able to capture matter and to slow down the dissipation of energy. Flows of energy and matter are used more effectively for the long-run maintenance of the system. Great diversity within a system seems to delay the increase of entropy (or dissipation of energy). Apparently, diversity and stability go hand in hand in natural systems.

Diversity, Stability, Equilibrium, and Feedback

It is so easy to get buried in the multitude of detailed facts that are needed to describe any complex natural system. But it is not the multitude of facts which provides understanding of a natural or manmade system. What is vitally important is recognition of the feedback and diversity processes by which the system maintains its stability and equilibrium.

In the study of ecosystems, stability and diversity are commonly used measures of organization. Diversity is more easily measurable than stability. It is at a minimum when all the elements in a system belong to the same class, and at a maximum when each element belongs to a different class. If all the elements were the same, there would be no diversity; if all elements were different, there would be no organization. It is generally accepted that the greater the number and variety of species in an ecosystem, the more stable that ecosystem will be. For all types of systems, increased diversity tends to mean more stability because (1) the system possesses more means to counteract or otherwise deal with changing inputs and (2) risk to the system is more widely spread. If one element is wiped out, chances are greater if the system has considerable diversity that another element can assure its function.

Mature forest ecosystems like those occurring in the Appalachians have a relatively low productivity given their large amount of biomass, but they have considerable diversity and stability. When a dominant tree species, the American chestnut, was lost though disease, it was quickly replaced by oak species. The threat of severe damage by pests looms much larger in a low diversity forest such as the Canadian and Eurasian boreal forests than in a forest characterized by great diversity of species.

There is little diversity of species in our commercial agricultural systems. Species are bred for productivity and size or attractiveness. Through breeding, they lose much of their resistance to disease, as it is sacrificed for the aforementioned qualities. High levels of production and high levels of protection (preservation) are desirable attributes, but they cannot occur simultaneously, as we are learning more and more often. Our commercial agricultural ecosystems have high productivity but little inherent stability.

Stability in a system implies persistence of its structure over time. Stability demands that change occur in such a way that the system's structure remains recognizable. If it is stable, today's deciduous forest will be recognizable as a deciduous forest thirty years from now. Some trees will die, others will mature. The numbers of individual species may change; some species may be replaced. But it will continue to be a deciduous forest.

In a stable system a high level of diversity implies the presence of energy well-organized to do work. The level of entropy is quite low. Together stability and diversity imply organization and some kind of equilibrium over time.

Equilibrium is the maintenance of some kind of balance over a given time span. Equilibrium implies a dynamic or changing balance; it does not require absolute sameness of balance. There is action and counteraction, as in a teeter-totter. A system may be in equilibrium although some of its subsystems or elements may be in disequilibrium. Some subsystems may be storing energy and matter; others may be losing energy and matter. If a system is to continue to exist it must maintain some kind of equilibrium; gain and loss must balance around some mean figure. There are limits to the amount of change that a system can tolerate. Because such tolerance limits exist, stabilizing factors will go into operation when the processes of change place strains on a system. Hence equilibrium can be understood as the interaction of the processes of change and the processes of stability.

In figure 3 the three major types of dynamic equilibrium trajectories are graphically illustrated. The trajectories represent a course through time. The wobbles around each mean trajectory represent a dynamic equilibrium; level, upward, and downward trajectories are

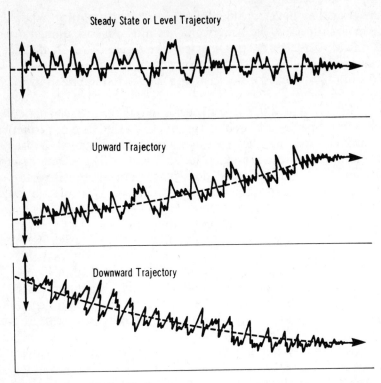

Figure 3. Dynamic Equilibria.

presented. Slow but increasing pollution of a lake could change its
energy and matter balances, and ultimately reduce its productivity—
an example of a downward trajectory. Gradual climatic change
causing more precipitation and a higher biotic output could illustrate
an upward trajectory.

The concept of dynamic equilibrium suggests that significant
change can occur without causing breakdown of a system. Change
occurs within bounded limits (limits of tolerance) as illustrated in
figure 4. In a system on a level trajectory, losses are replaced by inputs of the same or similar kinds of matter or energy. For example,
old maple trees die in a forest and young ones replace them in equal
amounts of biomass. When a system's inputs of energy and matter
change, the outputs change equally if the system is on a level trajectory. Replacement equals loss.

If the system is changing its trajectory upward or downward, its
structure and function will gradually change until a new steady state

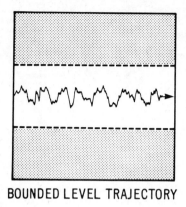
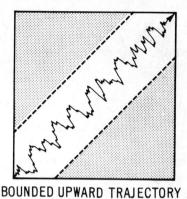

BOUNDED LEVEL TRAJECTORY   BOUNDED UPWARD TRAJECTORY

Figure 4. Bounded dynamic equilibrium.

is reached. In parts of the Appalachian forests, the destruction of the
American chestnut by blight in the early 1930s caused a downward
trajectory in biomass output. Gradual replacement of the chestnuts
by oak species is filling the niche left open. This implies an upward
trajectory for the 1950s and 1960s and a levelling off sometime in the
next few decades.

A change from level equilibrium to downward or upward
occurs when there is a significant change of input or a significant
change in the ratio of input to output. Critical limits of change, below which little may happen but above which equilibrium may be
altered, are referred to as thresholds; the interval during which no
effects are apparent is referred to as a lag. For example, the harmful
effect of DDT on the reproduction of eagles, brown pelicans, condors,
and falcons became obvious only after a lag of about ten years following the first major applications of this pesticide and only after a
threshold level of DDT concentration in the birds' tissues was attained.

In any system, adjustments that maintain the balance of a
dynamic equilibrium take place by means of feedback mechanisms.
All complex systems possess feedback mechnisms that are constantly
in operation, helping to maintain a dynamic equilibrium. Any disturbance to a system stimulates a response from these feedback mechanisms. Figure 5 diagrams the feedback mechanisms. There are two types
of feedback. The more common type is called negative feedback or
deviation counteracting. This feedback counteracts the effect of the
input—as when a thermostat controls the temperature of a room. The
thermostat detects that temperature has reached the limits of equilibrium. It sends a message to the furnace, the effector, to reduce or

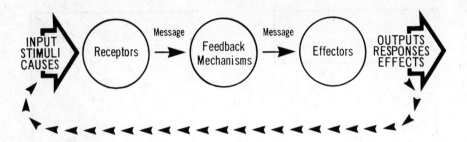

Figure 5. Minimum essentials of feedback mechanisms.

increase input. Negative feedback is responsible for system maintenance; it regulates the system so that it will maintain its status quo.
Negative feedback processes also counteract change-generating forces
(positive feedback) in order to keep change within the tolerance limits
of the system. The other type of feedback (or response) is called
positive feedback or deviation amplifying. Instead of counteracting
change, it reinforces it. Positive feedback strengthens the thrust of
the input. The changes may be harmful or beneficial to the system.
If beneficial, the positive feedback mechanisms will probably cause
an upward equilibrium trajectory which may lead to a changed steady
state. If harmful, the system could break down; at the least there is a
downward equilibrium trajectory. Harmful positive feedback is popularly called a vicious circle or the snowballing effect; changes occur in
the same direction at a compounding rate. The equilibrium trajectory
of a system always represents the interaction of positive and negative
feedback.

   An example of the deterioration of a system through harmful
positive feedback is provided by Holling and Goldberg (see Suggested
Readings). A successful malaria control program based on DDT was
being used among the isolated Dayak people of Borneo. These people
live in long houses with up to five hundred under one roof. The Dayak
people share the thatched huts with a small biological community —
cats, cockroaches, and geckos (small lizards). The cockroaches picked
up the DDT; geckos ate the cockroaches and concentrated the DDT.
The cats sustained themselves partly by eating geckos, and the concentrated DDT killed the cats. When the cats died, rats began invading
the villages — a harmful positive feedback. The cats had acted as negative feedback mechanisms controlling both geckos and rats. With the
rats came a new biological community of fleas, lice, and parasites. The
result was a serious outbreak of sylvatic plague among the Dayaks —
another harmful positive feedback. In an attempt to produce a bene-

ficial positive feedback, the authorities parachuted cats into the villages. Meanwhile, in another harmful positive feedback effect, the DDT had also killed the parasites and predators of a small caterpillar that lives by eating thatched roofs. The caterpillar thrived and roofs disappeared! This example illustrates the many interacting pathways involved in feedback processes. When we tamper with natural systems, knowledge of their complexity is absolutely essential.

What should we look for when seeking to understand feedback processes? (1) Resistance to change is not the same for all parts of the system. In the Borneo example, compare the effects of the loss of the geckos and the cats. To manage natural systems successfully we must identify critical points of strength or weakness. (2) The more highly developed the system, the greater the number of feedback possibilities – and the greater the possibility of unexpected results. Hence the absolute necessity of understanding how energy and matter flows in the system and what these flows mean. (3) We must understand how inputs enter a system, determine their range of magnitude, and assess the ability of the system parts to expand their storage capacity. Man's attempts to manage natural systems usually involve manipulation or buffering of inputs that either reinforce or counteract tendencies existing in the system. Before undertaking such manipulation man should understand how a given input is assimilated or how it changes a system. Understanding feedback mechanisms is a prime requisite before we attempt to maintain or to change any facet of our natural environment.

Concluding Comments
Every action results in one or many reactions. These reactions are predictable only if we understand the system flows and feedback mechanisms involved in those flows.

Often, for practical reasons, man can work with only a part of a system. At the same time, however, he should try to base his actions on a knowledge of the workings of the whole system. The use of a systems approach to study the natural environment forces us to model as carefully as possible (conceptually, mathematically, empirically, or however) the complexities of the real world. To do so successfully demands a sound theoretical framework and solid empirical knowledge. The systems approach provides the framework into which the multitudinous empirical facts necessary to comprehend our natural environment can be fitted. By combining the factual knowledge furnished by scientific research with the broad framework contributed by the systems approach, we can better understand the workings of the parts and of the whole. The real world operates as a system; to better understand it requires the use of a systems approach.

SUGGESTED READINGS

Chorley, R. J. and Kennedy, B. *Physical Geography, A Systems Approach.* London: Prentice-Hall International, 1971.

Foote, D. C. and Greer-Wootten, B. "An Approach to Systems Analysis in Cultural Geography." *The Professional Geographer* 20 (1968): 86–91.

Holling, C. S. and Goldberg, M. A. "Ecology and Planning." *Journal of The American Institute of Planners* 37 (1971): 221–230.

Kates, R. W. "Links Between Physical and Human Geography: A Systems Approach." In *Introductory Geography: Viewpoints and Themes.* Commission on College Geography, Publication No. 5. Washington: Association of American Geographers, 1967.

Likens, G. E. and Bormann, F. H. "Nutrient Cycling in Ecosystems." In *Ecosystem Structure and Function,* edited by J. A. Wiens. Corvallis: Oregon State University Press, 1972.

Margalef, F. "Diversity and Stability: A Practical Proposal and a Model of Interdependence." In *Symposium on Diversity and Stability in Ecological Systems.* Biology Department, Brookhaven National Laboratory, Springfield, Va.: Clearinghouse for Federal Scientific and Technical Information, 1969.

Maruyama, M. "The Second Cybernetics: Deviation Amplifying Mutual Causal Processes." *American Scientist* 51 (1963): 164–179.

McDaniel, R. and Eliot Hurst, M. E. *A Systems Analytic Approach to Economic Geography.* Commission on College Geography Publication No. 8. Washington: Association of American Geographers, 1968.

Meadows, D. H., Meadows, D. L., Randers, T. and Behrens III, W. W. *The Limits to Growth.* New York: Universe Books, 1972.

Odum, H. T. *Environment, Power, and Society.* New York: Wiley, 1971.

Schaake, J. C. Jr. "Water and The City." In *Urbanization and Environment,* edited by T. R. Detwyler and M. G. Marcus. Belmont, Calif.: Duxbury Press, 1972.

Wilbanks, T. J., and Symanski, R. "What is Systems Analysis?" *The Professional Geographer* 20 (1968): 81–85.

CHAPTER 2

Unity of the Natural Environment
Introduction

The unity of the natural environment is expressed in energy and matter flows which cross the interfaces of the weather-climate, water, landform, soil, and biotic subsystems. Interfaces are the physical discontinuities, the boundaries between air, water, land, and organisms. There are continuous flows of energy and matter within each subsystem, and continuous exchanges of energy and matter among the various subsystems. Some of the subsystems store and slowly use the energy and matter inputs they receive, while in other subsystems there is a brisk and continuous inflow and outflow of matter and energy.

If we study them in terms of energy and matter flows, we will find that weather-climate systems, for example, demonstrate a rapid flow-through of energy and matter. Conversely, water systems are characterized by storage of energy and matter, since the oceans contain vast amounts of heat and nutrients as well as 97.3 percent of the earth's water. Land systems primarily store matter and energy, while the living systems, soil and biota, tend to experience rapid throughflows of moisture and nutrients. These differing patterns of flow are easily noted. In our daily experience, the brisk changes of the weather (atmospheric flows) contrast with the more sluggish changes of the oceans. Meanwhile, the land remains a static receiver of heat and water inputs.

Storage provides a system with a reservoir of matter and energy

and a buffer against rapid change. It is essential for system maintenance. Just as a sizeable bank balance may give us security, so a sizeable
balance of matter and energy can protect a system. Our agricultural
systems are characterized by flows, our mature forest ecosystems by
storage.

The articles by Strahler and Odum emphasize energy and
matter flows as expressed in the structure and function of the subsystems. Differing heat, nutrient, and water budgets are the key to
understanding why ecosystems vary across the earth's surface. Strahler
examines the natural environment from the viewpoint of geoscience
or the physical environment, while Odum studies it in terms of the
biological community or ecoscience.

Man is an integral part of the natural environment. The main
message of Sears's article is that man is enjoying the advantages of an
earth that was a long time preparing for him. In Sears's words, "Man
has evolved in relation to and by virture of a highly organized and
specialized environment." This symbiotic relationship must be maintained if man is to survive.

The Life Layer

Arthur N. Strahler
Adjunct Professor of Geology, Columbia University

Reprinted with some deletions by permission of the author and the publisher from
The Journal of Geography 69 (1970), pp. 70–76.

ENVIRONMENTAL SYSTEMS OF PLANET EARTH

The biosphere, or total realm of plant and animal life, occupies
a very shallow surface layer on our planet Earth. Yet this layer is one
of greater diversity and complexity than planetary layers both above
and below it. It is a dynamic layer which experiences great fluxes of
energy and matter, organized into physical systems whose rhythms
are dictated by a spherical earth form and a given periodicity of
earth rotation and revolution.

Interaction between the biosphere and its total environment
constitutes *ecology* in its broadest sense. The relationship of Man to
his physical environment and to all other life forms is the special concern of human geography. It is to the description and explanation of
the physical environment of Man that this paper addresses itself.

Grouped into a workable arrangement, popularly known as
physical geography, those areas of environmental science of most
direct interest to the geographer are selected from the larger body of
the *earth sciences,* consisting of all phenomena of the solid earth
(*lithosphere*), liquid earth (*hydrosphere*), and gaseous earth (*atmosphere*). The geographer must be selective in setting up a course in
physical geography; he must concentrate attention upon the surface
zone that is the environment of life. Consequently, certain planetary
regions receive little or none of his attention. For example, the earth's
interior, the deep ocean waters and their basins, and the upper atmospheric layers are described only in the briefest of reference frameworks. Similarly, the vast recesses of geologic time in which continents
grew and life evolved, comprise a part of the earth sciences of secondary priority with respect to man's environment. Instead, emphasis
must be on the last million or so years, in which modern man evolved
and the landforms of his environment were shaped.

Selective as it may be, physical geography encompasses an
enormous amount of information, both about formative processes
and the global distributions of landforms, soils, natural vegetation,
and climate. Should we be so foolhardy as to attempt a complete
coverage of all that is known, we would soon find that the rate of
accumulation of new knowledge is greater than the ability of any

single individual to absorb it. Certainly, then, a purely substantive approach can lead only to frustration. Selection of a few topics for description, disregarding the rest, is one answer that some have accepted. As textbooks become larger, more detailed in treatment, and more demanding in terminology and vocabulary, the problem of selection becomes more acute.

Perhaps a change in direction is in order at all levels of education in the area of physical geography. The solution I propose here is that we adopt a systems approach, wherein a single conceptual framework can encompass the essential explanation of all the diverse processes and forms that together comprise the physical environment. A systems approach requires abandonment of the topical-substantive organization of information. We shall no longer base our organization of content upon categories of things, such as a topical list that might run thus: *rocks, mountains, lakes, shorelines, clouds, hurricanes, rainforest, tundra.* In most cases these things are only the byproducts of processes operating on a much larger scale of magnitude.

Physical systems that sustain the planetary environment are *energy* systems, that is, energy as well as matter is in flux within the system. It is the inclusion of energy as a primary consideration that makes the systems approach a dynamic analysis, as contrasted to a static description. Once the nature of a system is understood, the observable forms, which are its products, fall into their proper places. For example, a specimen of igneous rock which we examine as a truly cold and dead object, acquires interest only after the system of radiogenic heat production on a vast scale within the earth is explained. The prevailing westerlies, instead of being merely a wind belt found at a prescribed latitude, are discovered to be the logical consequence of a vast planetary circulation system in which heat energy is transported poleward across parallels of latitude to sustain the earth's heat balance.

Systems of the physical environment are further distinguished as being *open* systems; they involve the inflow, transformation, storage, and outflow of both energy and matter through boundaries. Energy can take many forms — kinetic, potential, latent, radiant, atomic. Masses taking part in the flux may be gases, liquids, solids, or charged particles. In view of this wide range in forms of energy and matter, the various systems can take highly diverse forms. Timing, or periodicity, of the system operations can also vary widely, from daily or annual cycles of repetition, found in the atmosphere and oceans, to cycles of thousands or millions of years, as found in geological episodes of mountain-making or continental denudation. An important concept

in understanding the physical environment is that highly unlike systems
may have linkages, wherein the matter and energy of the one system
feeds into the other. An example might be the manner in which the
hydrologic cycle, through precipitation of rainfall, provides water
and potential energy to energize the geomorphic cycle of landmass
denudation.

Systems of the planetary environment are typically bounded
or subdivided by *interfaces*. These are physical discontinuities, across
which energy and matter are exchanged. For example, the surface of
the sea or the land serves as an interface with the lower atmosphere.

Basic to the theme of open systems is the concept of *steady
state,* as contrasted with the unchanging condition of a closed system.
An example of steady state can be found in the monotonously uniform temperature regime of the equatorial climates. Actually, this
belt receives much more heat energy from incoming solar radiation
than is lost locally by radiation to space and would become increasingly hotter if heat were not exported by some other means. Heat is exported to higher latitudes by circulation of the atmosphere and oceans.
Because this system has achieved an overall steady state of operation,
the air temperatures near the equatorial surface do not change appreciably either throughout the year, or from one year to the next. What
might otherwise be merely an uninteresting climatic statistic proves,
under systems analysis, to be a remarkable state of balance in an enormous global action system.

Once an energy system is identified and its workings understood, the resulting forms follow with simplicity and inevitability.
The energy-systems approach logically examines cause first and effect
second; it seeks to unify and simplify the complex forms of nature .
by referring them to vast but simple physical mechanisms in orderly
operation.

Principles and concepts will become apparent as we review
in succession selected major physical systems of planet Earth and evaluate each for the role it plays in sustaining the surface environment.

THE EARTH-SUN-SPACE RADIATION SYSTEM

Our sun, as a star with very high surface temperature, emits a
large quantity of energy in the form of the electromagnetic radiation
spectrum. Traveling radially outward, this energy is intercepted by
its planet, Earth, which both reflects and absorbs the incident shortwave
energy. (Figure 1) Radiation absorbed by the Earth becomes sensible

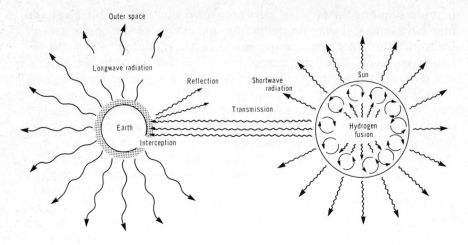

Figure 1.

heat in the atmosphere and in the surface layer of the oceans and continents. The Earth in turn, emits longwave radiation, part of which passes out into space where it is lost forever.

Source of energy for this system is in the sun's interior, where hydrogen is converted into helium by processes of nuclear fusion. For a vast span of time into the future, the rate of production of energy by the sun will remain almost constant, as it has throughout much of the geologic past. At the earth, the quantity of energy intercepted each minute by a horizontal surface of unit area, above the limits of the atmosphere, is known as the *solar constant*. Although slight variations in the value of the solar constant are postulated to occur, its constancy is the key to origin and evolution of life and to the maintenance of all present day life.

In analyzing the sun-earth-space radiation system, we note first that it is an open system through which flows energy, but not matter. It is a one-way system, not a closed circuit. There is one energy source, one energy transformer, and one energy sink. The condition of steady state for the earth as a planet is referred to as the *radiation balance*. Physical climatologists evaluate the various forms of radiation and absorption that take place in the atmosphere and at the earth's surface. Through a basic equation that includes all radiation phenomena, the climatologist shows that on the average, over long periods of time, the quantity of outgoing longwave and reflected shortwave radiant energy must exactly equal the incoming shortwave radiation. In physical geography today, increasing emphasis is being placed on the radiation balance as a dynamic concept.

Transport System: Atmospheric and Oceanic Circulation

Continually in action are two global circulation systems in which fluids move in closed circuits, transporting sensible heat and redistributing it over the globe. (Figure 2) In the broad definition of states of matter, both air (a gas) and water (a liquid) are fluids and have much in common in physical behavior. Easily set in motion, the lower layer of the atmosphere and the upper layer of the oceans are shaped into vortices of great horizontal extent. Where flow is poleward across parallels of latitude, heat is transported from equatorial regions of radiation surplus. If it were not for such heat transport, the equatorial belt would become heated to extremely high levels, while the polar regions would be chilled to severe extremes of cold. The circulation system of atmosphere and oceans is thus the primary regulator of the thermal environment of Man, and as such it must be heavily emphasized in the teaching of physical geography.

Physical climatologists evaluate the quantities of sensible heat entering and leaving unit columns of the atmosphere and oceans; they evaluate the flux of sensible heat across the parallels of latitude. They are thus able to evaluate the earth's *heat balance* through the premise that in the long run, the average air and water temperatures of a given belt of latitude hold constant. This steady state is characteristic of open systems, which are self-regulatory in nature.

Upon further analysis, it becomes evident that the circulation systems of atmosphere and oceans are powered by the imbalances of incoming and outgoing radiation. The latter is therefore the primary, or driving system; the circulation that results is a secondary flow system. But looking even deeper, we find that the prevailing winds, by exerting a drag upon the ocean surface, set the currents in motion. Therefore the oceanic circulation is to a large degree secondary to the atmospheric circulation. In other words, there exists a hierarchy among the earth's natural systems. Here we find the concept of *interface* strikingly evident; the surface of separation between atmosphere and hydrosphere is a system boundary through which energy is exchanged between physical systems.

Details of the atmospheric and oceanic circulation, such as belts of prevailing winds and calms, cyclones and anticyclones, and jet streams, fall into place as consequences of a thermally driven circulation on a rotating earth. In this presentation we do not begin by enumerating the circulation zones (doldrums, trades, horse latitudes,

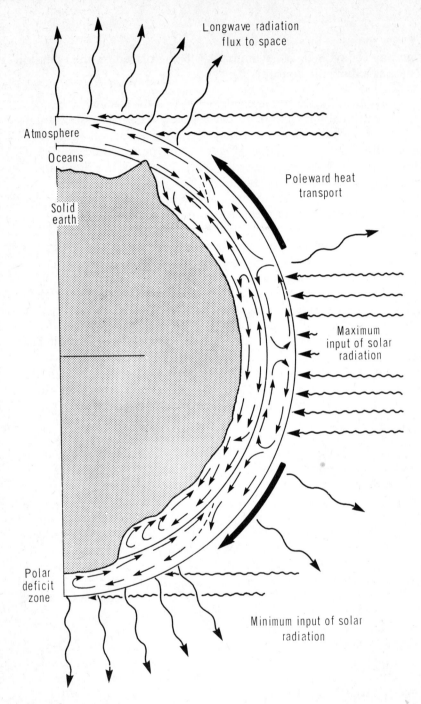

Longwave radiation
flux to space

Atmosphere

Oceans

Solid
earth

Poleward heat
transport

Maximum
input of solar
radiation

Polar
deficit
zone

Minimum input of solar
radiation

Figure 2.

westerlies, polar easterlies), and memorizing their latitudinal positions. Instead, we derive these morphological features as consequences of a total circulation system. The Hadley cell circulation of equatorial and tropical latitudes can be deduced from the requirements of simple convection and earth rotation. When these requirements are met, the need for a belt of high pressure cells and a trade-wind belt emerges through deductive analysis.

Transport System: Changes in State of Atmospheric Water

The presence of water vapor in the atmosphere adds a new ingredient to the atmospheric circulation. The ingredient of matter is added to the energy of sensible heat. Water vapor also entails another form of energy, that of latent heat of vaporization and fusion. To the transport of sensible heat by the earth's atmospheric circulation system must be added the transport of latent heat present in the water vapor held in that air.

Here, again, the interface between atmosphere and oceans comes to the fore. Evaporation from the ocean surface, and from moist land surfaces, feeds water vapor and its latent energy into an otherwise dry atmosphere. Much of this evaporation is from the dry belt under the subtropical high pressure cells. (Figure 3) The latent heat is carried both equatorward and poleward, where it is released in condensation in the convectional (thunderstorm) activity of the doldrums and in cyclonic and frontal activity in middle latitudes. The heat balance equation is modified to take into account latent heat gained and lost by evaporation and condensation.

Physical climatologists evaluate the transport of water in the atmosphere and its exchange with land and water surfaces in terms of the *water balance.* Man's physical environment is thus largely dependent upon two fundamental ingredients: heat and water. If the ingredient of heat dictates the *thermal environment,* the ingredient of water can be said to dictate the *hygric environment.* Climate, soils, and natural vegetation, which, with landforms, are the environmental entities by which the earth's continental surfaces are differentiated, are the products of the local state of the heat balance and the water balance. For any particular small area of the earth's surface there is a particular combination of heat budget and water budget which, with geological controls over earth materials and landform configuration, produces the unique environment of that area.

Transport Subsystem: Gravity Flow of Water on the Lands

The total flow system of water in all its forms and states, and in all places that water is found, is unified by the concept of the *hydro-*

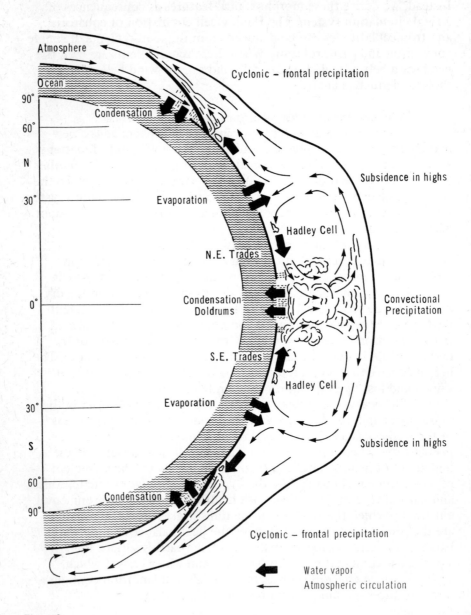

Figure 3.

logic cycle. Many possible flow circuits and subcircuits exist in the hydrologic cycle. . . .

Within the hydrologic cycle, water is brought by atmospheric precipitation to elevated positions on the surfaces of the continents. In such positions, the water constitutes a mass possessed of potential energy. Under gravity, this water flows to lower levels in the liquid state as overland flow and stream flow. It also enters the ground and moves in flow paths as ground water, which emerges at lower levels. In cold environments at high altitudes, precipitation is in the solid form of snow, giving rise to glaciers. These bodies of ice also possess potential energy and move under gravity to lower levels.

Thus we can identify the system of gravity flow of water on the lands as one of the major natural open systems of our planet. But the flow of water also entrains particles of mineral matter, which are brought to positions of rest at low levels. Thus the gravity flow system of water performs a geologic function of lowering the continental masses and creating deposits of sedimentary strata.

Streams are organized into networks, each serving to drain excess precipitation out of a clearly defined watershed, as shown in Figure 4. Each drainage basin is itself an open subsystem in which the function of water and sediment collection from sloping surfaces must be combined with the function of transport by the channels. We can predict that the relief of this drainage system will be reduced with time, since the solid matter carried by the overland flow and stream channels is derived from the surface itself. Consequently, elevation of landmass diminishes with time. Reduced gradients of flow result in reduced rates of erosion and transportation. In essence, the system is one of spontaneous decay and proceeds to lower energy levels. This, then, is the broad view of the cycle of landmass denudation.

In analyzing the gravity flow system of water, we find that it is an open system in which both matter and energy enter and leave the system through clearly identifiable boundaries. But the operation of gravity flow of water is also dependent upon geological systems of entirely different nature which initially cause the earth's crust to be elevated above sea level. If it were not for repeated crustal uplifts, the gravity flow systems would have long ago reduced the continents to featureless plains, perhaps submerged as shallow seas.

The geologic work of streams and glaciers is a branch of geomorphology. Traditionally, in the teaching of physical geography, geomorphology is presented on a topical basis, in which the landforms are enumerated in succession, e.g., *valley, meander, flood-plain, entrenched meander, glacial trough, rock step, esker, kame.* Happily,

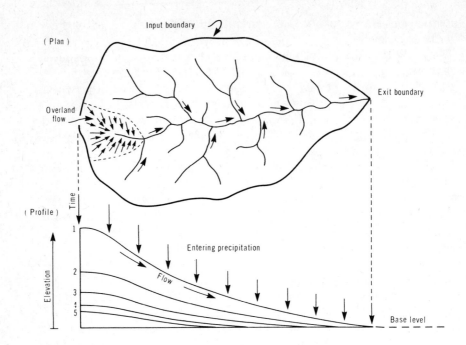

Figure 4.

most landforms are photogenic and can be represented as geometrical entities. Unhappily, this approach renders a landform as a static feature, which is the antithesis of the dynamic image it enjoys under the systems approach.

The evolution of landforms is for the most part a very slow process; it is difficult for us to capture the dynamic aspect. Whereas a cyclonic storm passes through its life cycle of changes in a few days' time and can be witnessed by direct observations and on weather maps, the life of a stream meander through its growth and eventual cutoff can be appreciated only through small scale laboratory models or through simulation in motion pictures.

Difficult as the dynamic view may be to carry out, we must try to make the study of landforms a study of change. The systems approach, focusing attention upon the flow of matter and energy, can help the teacher to keep the concept of change at the forefront. It is not necessary that the catalog of landforms be completely covered.

It is necessary that the geomorphic processes be grasped in depth through considerations of energy and mass transport.

Geologic System: Radiogenic Heat and Flow of Molten Rock

Radioactive elements, largely concentrated in the earth's crust and upper mantle, spontaneously generate heat. Where this heat accumulates in sufficient quantity, rock may be brought close to its melting point deep beneath the earth's surface. Where the solid rock enters the liquid phase it migrates, because of density differences, to positions higher in the earth's crust. Here it may solidify as an intrusive rock body. In some cases the molten rock pours out upon the earth's surface in volcanic extrusions. Radiogenic heat thus causes enormous masses to be lifted against the force of gravity, generating mountain masses and resulting in the transport of heat to the earth's surface. Here the heat is dissipated, eventually into outer space.

The radiogenic heat system in its broadest sense is one of inherited energy, since the radioactive elements were formed with the earth itself and cannot be added to. Radioactivity is a decay process which cannot be reversed, hence the system of geologic activity which it represents must be in the long run diminish to lower and lower levels.

Because its energy is internal in source, this geologic system creates a distribution of mountain belts and continental structures that is completely accidental with respect to the solar radiation and circulation systems of atmosphere and oceans. The result is a unique compartmentation of the planetary surface wherein the alternation of continent with ocean basin disrupts what would be the otherwise symmetrical arrangement of the earth's climatic zones.

Under the energy systems approach, a volcano and an outcrop of granite are secondary importance to the great transformations of matter and energy that operated in the earth's crust. Consequently, we do not begin our study of earth materials and landforms with a definition of a volcano and a description of its shape and rock composition.

Various other natural systems and subsystems enter into the total physical environment at the earth's surface. There is not space in this brief review of concepts to describe each one. It will suffice if the spirit of the approach has been grasped and clarified by examples. We have sought to reach an understanding of the environment of Man and all other life forms by considering great fluxes of energy and matter, rather than by creating a catalog of small things which often do not show change and do not relate to one another. . . .

SUGGESTED READINGS

Coates, D. R., ed. *Environmental Geomorphology.* Binghamton: Publications in Geomorphology, State University of New York, 1971.

Farb, P. *Living Earth.* New York: A Worlds of Science Book, Pyramid Publications, 1962.

Maunder, W. J. *The Value of the Weather.* London: Methuen, 1970.

Miller, D. H. *A Survey Course: The Energy and Mass Budget at the Surface of the Earth.* Commission on College Geography Publication No. 7. Washington: Association of American Geographers, 1968.

Odum, E. P. *Fundamentals of Ecology.* 3rd ed. Philadelphia: Saunders, 1971.

Othmer, D. F. and Roels, O. A. "Power, Fresh Water, and Food from Cold, Deep Sea Water." *Science* 182 (1973): 121–125.

Scientific American. *Continents Adrift.* San Francisco: Freeman, 1970.

Strahler, A. N. and Strahler, A. H. *Environmental Geoscience: Interaction Between Natural Systems and Man.* Santa Barbara: Hamilton (Wiley), 1973.

Tank, R. W., ed. *Focus on Environmental Geology.* New York: Oxford, 1973.

Ecosystem Theory in Relation to Man

Eugene P. Odum
Director, Institute of Ecology, University of Georgia

Reprinted with some deletions and modifications by permission of the author and
the publisher from *Ecosystem Structure and Function,* edited by J. A. Wiens, pp.
11–23. Corvallis, Oregon: Oregon State University Press, 1972.

The concept of the ecosystem is not only the center of professional ecology today, but it is also the most relevant concept in
terms of man's environmental problems. In the past two years the public has seized on the root meaning of ecology, namely *"oikos"* or
"house," to broaden the subject beyond its previously rather narrow
academic confines to include the "totality of man and environment,"
or the whole environmental house, as it were. We are witnessing what
I have called a historic "attitude revolution" in the way people look
at their environment for the very simple reason that for the first time
in his short history man is faced with ultimate rather than merely
local limitations. It will be well for all of us to keep this overriding
simplicity in mind as we face the controversies, false starts, and backlashes that are bound to accompany man's attempts to put some
negative feedback into the vicious spiral of uncontrolled growth and
resource exploitation that has characterized the past several decades.

As recently as ten years ago the theory of the ecosystem was
rather well understood but not in any way applied. The applied ecology of the 1960s consisted of managing components as more or less
independent units. Thus we had forest management, wildlife management, water management, soil conservation, pest control, etc., but
no ecosystem management and no applied human ecology. Practice
has now caught up with theory! Controlled management of the human
population together with the resources and the life support system
on which it depends as a single, integrated unit now becomes the
greatest, and certainly the most difficult, challenge ever faced by
human society.

An "anthropocentric" definition of the ecosystem might read
something as follows: Man as a part of, not apart from, a life-support
system composed of the atmosphere, water, minerals, soil, plants,
animals, and microorganisms that function together to keep the whole
viable. If you would like a more formal definition, I can give you
the one I am using in the third edition of *Fundamentals of Ecology*,
namely: "Any unit including all of the organisms (i.e., the "community") in a given area interacting with the physical environment so that
a flow of energy leads to a clearly defined trophic structure, biotic

diversity, and material cycles (i.e., exchange of materials between living and non-living parts) within the system is an *ecological system* or *ecosystem.*"

HISTORICAL REVIEW OF THE ECOSYSTEM CONCEPT

Although the term ecosystem was first proposed by the British ecologist A. G. Tansley in 1935 the concept is by no means so recent. Allusions to the idea of the unity of organisms and environment (as well as the oneness of man and nature) can be found as far back in written history as one might care to look, and such an idea has been a basic part of many religions, although less so in Christian religions, as recently pointed out by historian Lynn White. Anthropologists and geographers have long been concerned with the impact of man on his environment and early debated the question: To what extent has man's continuing trouble with deteriorated environments stemmed from the fact that human culture tends to develop independently of the natural environment? The Vermont prophet George Perkins Marsh wrote a classic treatise on this theme in 1864. He analyzed the causes of the decline of ancient civilizations and forecast a similar doom for modern ones unless man takes what we would call today an "ecosystematic" view of man and nature. In the late 1800s biologists began to write essays on the unity of nature, interestingly enough in a parallel manner in German, English, and Russian languages. Thus Karl Mobius in 1877 wrote about the community of organisms in an oyster reef as a "biocoenosis," while in 1887 the American S. A. Forbes wrote his classic essay on "The Lake as a Microcosm." The Russian pioneering ecologist V. V. Dokuchaev (1846–1903) and his disciple G. F. Morozov (who specialized in forest ecology) placed great emphasis on the concept of "biocoenosis," a term later expanded to geobiocoenosis (or biogeocoenosis), which can be considered a synonym of the word "ecosystem."

No one has expressed the relevance of the ecosystem concept to man better than Aldo Leopold in his essays on the land ethic. In 1933 he wrote: "Christianity tries to integrate the individual to society, democracy to integrate social organization to the individual. There is yet no ethic dealing with man's relation to the land" which is "still strictly economic, entailing privileges but not obligations." Thus, man is continually striving, with but partial success so far, to establish ethical relationships between man and man, man and government, and, now, man and environment. Without the latter what little progress has been made with the other two ethics will surely be lost. In the context of the 1970 scene Garrett Hardin says it in another way when he points out that technology alone will not solve the population and pollution dilemmas; ethical and legal constraints are also necessary. Environmental science is now being called upon to help determine a realistic level of human population density and rate of use of resources and power that are optimum in terms of the quality of human life, in order that "societal feedback" can be applied before there are serious overshoots. This requires diligent study of ecosystems, and ultimately, a judgment on the carrying capacity of the biosphere. If studies of natural populations have any bearing on the problem, we can be quite certain that the optimum density in terms of the individual's options for liberty and the pursuit of happiness is something less than the maximum number that can be sustained at a subsistence level, as so many domestic "animals" in a polluted feed lot!

My advanced ecology class recently attempted to determine what might be the optimum population for the state of Georgia on the assumption that someday the state would have to have a balanced resource input-output (i.e., live within its own resources). On the basis of a per capita approach to land use the tentative conclusion was that a density of one person per 5 acres (2 hectares) represented the upper limit for an optimum population size when the space requirements for quality (i.e., high protein) food production, domestic animals, outdoor recreation, waste treatment, and pollution-free living space were all fully considered. Anything less than 5 acres of life support and resource space per capita, it was concluded, would result in a reduction in the individual person's options for freedom and the pursuit of happiness, and accordingly, a rapid loss in environmental quality. Since the 1970 per capita density of Georgia is 1 in 8 acres, and for the United States as a whole, 1 in 10 acres, no more than double the present U.S. population could be considered optimum according to this type of analysis. This would mean that we have about 30 years to level off population growth. The study also suggested that permanent zoning of at least one-third of land and freshwater areas (plus all estuarine and marine zones) as "open space" in urbanized areas would go a long way towards preventing the overpopulation, overdevelopment, and social decay that is now so evident in many parts of the world today.

THE TWO APPROACHES TO ECOSYSTEM STUDY

G. Evelyn Hutchinson in his 1964 essay, "The Lacustrine Microcosm Reconsidered," contrasts the two long-standing ways ecologists attempt to study lakes or other large ecosystems of the real world. Hutchinson cites E. A. Birge's 1915 work on heat budgets of lakes as pioneering the *holological* (from *holos* = whole) or *holistic* approach in which the whole ecosystem is treated as a "black box" (i.e., a unit whose function may be evaluated without specifying the internal contents) with emphasis on inputs and outputs, and he contrasts this with the *merological* (from *meros* = part) approach of Forbes in which " we discourse on parts of the system and try to build up the whole from them." Each procedure has obvious advantages and disadvantages and each leads to different kinds of application in terms of solving problems. Unfortunately, there is something of a "credibility gap" between the two approaches.

As would be expected, the merological approach has dominated the thinking of the biologist-ecologist who is species-oriented, while the physicist-ecologist and engineer prefer the "black box" approach. Most of all, man's environmental crisis has speeded up the application of systems analysis to ecology. The formalized or mathematical model approach to populations, communities, and ecosystems has come to be known as *systems ecology*. It is rapidly becoming a major science in its own right, for two reasons: (1) Extremely powerful new formal tools are now available in terms of mathematical theory, cybernetics, electronic data processing, etc.; and (2) formal simplication of complex ecosystems provides the best hope for solutions of man's environmental problems that can no longer be trusted to trial-and-error or one-problem-one-solution procedures that have been chiefly relied on in the past.

Again we see the contrast between merological and holological approaches in that there are systems ecologists who start at the population or other component level and "model up," and those who start with the whole and "model down." The same dichotomy is evident in the very rewarding studies of experimental laboratory ecosystems. One class of microecosystems can be called "derived" systems, because they are established by multiple seeding from nature, in contrast to "defined" microcosms which are built up from previously isolated pure cultures. Theoretically, at least, the approaches are applicable to efforts to devise life-support systems for space travel. In fact, one of the best ways to visualize the ecosystem concept for students and laymen is to consider space travel, because when man leaves the biosphere he must take with him a sharply delimited enclosed environment that will supply all vital needs with solar energy as the only usable input from the surrounding very hostile space environment. For journeys of a few weeks (such as to the moon and back) man does not need a regenerative ecosystem, since sufficient oxygen and food can be stored while CO_2 and other waste products can be fixed or detoxified for short periods of time. For long journeys man must engineer himself into a complete ecosystem that includes the means of recycling materials and balancing production, consumption, and decomposition by biotic components or their mechanical substitutes.

In a very real sense the problems of man's survival in an artificial space craft are the same as the problems involved in his continued survival on the earth space ship. For example, detection and control of air and water pollution, adequate quantity and nutritional quality of food, what to do with accumulated toxic wastes and garbage, and the social problems created by reduced living space are common concerns of cities and spacecrafts. For this reason the ecologist would urge that national and international space programs now turn their attention to the study and monitoring of our spaceship earth. As was the case with Apollo 13, survival becomes the mission when the limits of carrying capacity are approached.

THE COMPONENTS OF THE ECOSYSTEM

From the energy or trophic standpoint an ecosystem has two components which are usually partially separated in space and time, namely, an *autotrophic component* (*autotrophic* = self nourishing) in which fixation of light energy, use of simple inorganic substances, and the buildup of complex substances predominate; and secondly, a *heterotrophic component* (*heterotrophic* = other-nourishing) in which utilization, rearrangement, and decomposition of complex materials predominate. As viewed from the side (cross section) ecosystems consist of an upper "green belt" which receives incoming solar energy and overlaps, or interdigitates, with a lower "brown belt" where organic matter accumulates and decomposes in soils and sediments.

It is convenient for the purposes of first-order analysis and modeling to recognize six structural components and six processes as comprising the ecosystem:

A. Components
1. *Inorganic substances* (C, N, CO_2, H_2O, etc.) involved in material cycles.
2. *Organic compounds* (proteins, carbohydrates, lipids, humic substances, etc.) that link biotic and abiotic components.
3. *Climate regime* (temperature, rainfall, etc.).
4. *Autotrophs* or *producers,* largely green plants able to manufacture food from simple substances.

5. *Phagotrophs* (*phago* = to eat) or *macro-consumers,* heterotrophic organisms, largely animals which ingest other organisms or particulate organic matter.

6. *Saprotrophs* (*sapro* = to decompose) or *micro-consumers* (also called osmotrophs), heterotrophic organisms, chiefly bacteria, fungi, and some protozoa, that break down complex compounds, absorb some of the decomposition products, and release inorganic substances usable by the autotrophs together with organic residues which may provide energy sources or which may be inhibitory, stimulatory, or regulatory to other biotic components of the ecosystem.

B. Processes
1. *Energy flow circuits.*
2. *Food chains* (trophic relationships).
3. *Diversity patterns* in time and space.
4. *Nutrient* (*biogeochemical*) *cycles.*
5. *Development and evolution.*
6. *Control* (cybernetics).

Subdivision of the ecosystem into these six "components" and six "processes," as with most classifications, is arbitrary but convenient, since the former emphasize structure and the latter function. From the holistic viewpoint, of course, components are operationally inseparable. While different methods are often required to delineate structure on the one hand and to measure rates of function on the other, the ultimate goal of study at any level of organization is to understand the relationship between structure and function. It is not feasible to go into any detailed discussion of these component-processes in this brief introduction, but we can list a few key principles that are especially relevant to human ecology. Figure 1 is a schematic diagram that may be useful in picturing the basic arrangement and functional linkage of ecosystem components.

1. The living (items A 4–6 above) and non-living (A 1–3) parts of ecosystems are so interwoven into the fabric of nature that it is difficult to separate them; hence operational classifications (B 1–6) do not make a sharp distinction between biotic and abiotic. Elements and compounds are in a constant state of flux between living and non-living states. There are very few substances that are confined to one or the other state. Exceptions may be ATP, which is found only inside living cells, and humic substances (resistant end products of decomposition) which are not found inside cells yet are characteristic of all ecosystems.

2. The time-space separation of autotrophic and heterotrophic

activity leads to a convenient classification of energy circuits into (1) a *grazing* food chain where grazing refers to the direct consumption of living plants or plant parts, and (2) an *organic detritus* (from *deterere* = to wear away) food chain which involves the accumulation and decomposition of dead materials. To build up a stable biomass structure there must be negative feedback control of grazing, a need too often neglected in man's domesticated ecosystems.

3. As is well known, available energy declines with each step in the food chain (so a system can support more herbivores than carnivores; if man wants to keep his meat-eating option open there will have to be fewer people supported by a given food base). On the other hand, materials often become concentrated with each step in the food chain. Failure to anticipate possible "biological magnification" of pollutants, such as DDT or long-lived radionuclides, is causing serious problems in man's environment.

4. It is becoming increasingly evident that high biological productivity (in terms of calories per unit area) in both natural and agricultural ecosystems is almost always achieved with the aid of *energy subsidies* from outside the system that reduce the cost of maintenance (thus diverting more energy to production). Energy subsidies take the form of wind and rain in a rain forest, tidal energy in an estuary (*see* Fig. 1), or fuel, animal, or human work energy used in the cultivation of a crop. In comparing productivity of different systems it is important to consider the *complete budget* — not just sunlight input.

5. Likewise it is increasingly evident that both *harvest* and *pollution are stresses* which reduce the energy available for self-maintenance. Man must be aware that he will have to pay the costs of added antithermal maintenance, or "disorder pumpout" as H. T. Odum calls it. It is a dangerous strategy to try to force too much productivity or yield from the landscape (as is being attempted in the so-called "green revolution") because very serious "ecological backlashes" can occur. These may result from: (1) pollution caused by heavy use of fertilizers and insecticides and the consumption of fossil fuels; (2) unstable or oscillating conditions created by one-crop systems; (3) vulnerability of plants to disease because their self-protection mechanisms have been "selected out" in favor of yield; and (4) social disorder created by a rapid shift of rural people to cities that are not prepared to house or employ them. (The tragedy here is that industrialized agriculture *can* result in increased food per acre but it can also widen the gap between rich and poor so that there are increasing numbers of people unable to buy the food!)

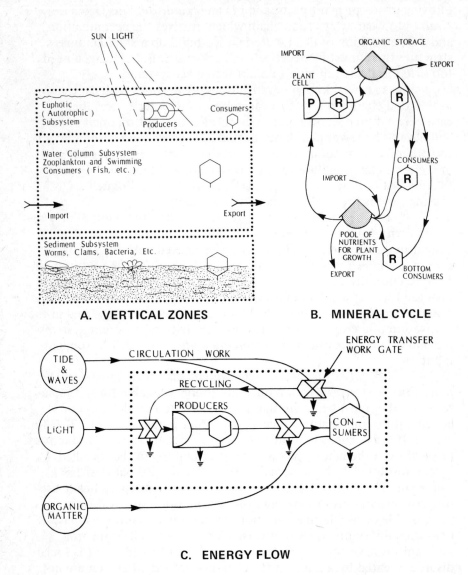

Figure 1. Three aspects of the structure and function of ecosystems as illustrated by an estuarine system.

6. While we generally think of production and decomposition as being balanced in the biosphere as a whole, the truth is that this balance has never been exact but has fluctuated from time to time in geological history. Through the long haul of evolutionary history, production has slightly exceeded decomposition so that a highly oxygenic atmosphere has replaced the original reducing atmosphere of the earth. Man, of course, is tending to reverse this trend by increasing decomposition (burning of fuels, etc.) at the expense of production. The most immediate problem is created by the increase in atmospheric CO_2, since relatively small changes in concentration can have large effects on the heat budget of the earth.

7. Ecological studies indicate that diversity is directly correlated with stability and perhaps inversely correlated with productivity, at least in many situations. It could well be that the preservation of diversity in the ecosystem is important for man since variety may be a necessity, not just the spice of life!

8. At the population level it is now clear that the growth form of the human population will not conform to the simple sigmoid or logistic model since there will always be a long time lag in the effects

A. Vertical zonation with photosynthetic production above (autotrophic stratum) and most of the respiration and decomposition below (heterotrophic stratum). B. Material cycle with circulation of plant nutrients upward and organic matter food downward. C. Energy flow circuit diagram showing three sources of energy input into the system. The bullet-shaped modules represent producers with their double metabolism, that is P (production) and R (respiration). The hexagons are populations of consumers which have storage, self maintenance, and reproduction. The storage bins represent nutrient pools in and out of which move nitrogen, phosphorus, and other vital substances. In diagrams B and C the lines represent the "invisible wires of nature" that link the components into a functional network. In diagram C the "ground" symbols (i.e., arrow into the heat sink) indicate where energy is dispersed and no longer available in the food chain. The circles represent energy inputs. The work gate symbols (large X) indicate where a flow of work energy along one pathway assists a second flow to pass over energy barriers. Note that some of the lines of flow loop back from "downstream" energy sources to "upstream" inflows serving various roles there, including control functions (saprotrophs controlling photosynthesis by controlling the rate of mineral regeneration, for example). The diagram (C) also shows how auxiliary energy of the tide (energy subsidy) assists in recycling of nutrients from consumer to producer and speeding up the movement of plant food to the consumer. Reducing tidal flow by diking the estuary will reduce the productivity just as surely as cutting out some of the light. Stress such as pollution or harvest can be shown in such circuit models by adding circles enclosing negative signs linked with appropriate heat sinks to show where energy is diverted away from the ecosystem. Both subsidies (+) and stresses (–) can be quantified in terms of calories added or diverted per unit of time and space. (From E. P. Odum, 1971, after H. T. Odum, Copeland, and McMahan, 1969.)

of crowding, pollution, and overexploitation of resources. Growth will not "automatically" level off as do populations of yeasts in a confined vessel where individuals are *immediately* affected by their waste products. Instead, the human population will clearly overshoot some vital resource unless man can "anticipate" the effects of overpopulation and reduce growth rates *before* the deleterious effects of crowding are actually felt. Intelligent reasoning behavior seems now to be the only means to accomplish this, as I emphasized at the beginning of this article.

9. Some of the most important "breakthroughs" in ecology are in the area of biogeochemical cycling. Since "recycle" of water and minerals must become a major goal of human society, the recycle pathways in nature are of great interest; there seem to be at least four major ones which vary in importance in different kinds of ecosystems: (1) recycle via microbial decomposition of detritus; (2) recycle via animal excretion; (3) direct recycle from plant back to plant via symbiotic microorganisms such as mycorrhizae associated with roots; and (4) autolysis, or chemical recycle, with no organism involved. Pathway 3 seems to be especially important in the humid tropics, which suggests that tropical agriculture might be redesigned to include food plants with mycorrhizae.

10. The principles inherent in limiting factor analysis and in human ecology can be combined to formulate the following tentative overview: In an industrialized society energy (power, food) is not likely to be limiting, *but the pollution consequences of the use of energy and exploitation of resources are limiting.* Thus, pollution can be considered the limiting factor for industrialized man — which may be fortunate since pollution is so "visible" that it can force us to use that reasoning power which is supposed to be our special attribute.

ECOSYSTEM DEVELOPMENT

Principles having to do with the development of ecosystems, that is, ecological succession, are among the most relevant in view of man's present situation. I have recently reviewed this subject[1]; accordingly a brief summary will suffice here.

In broad view ecosystems develop through a rapid growth stage that leads to some kind of maturity or steady state (climax), usually an oscillating steady state. The early successional growth stage is characterized by a high production/respiration (P/R) ratio, high yields (net production), short food chains, low diversity, small size of organisms, open nutrient cycles, and a lack of stability. In contrast, mature stages have a high biomass/respiration (B/R) ratio, complex food webs, low net production, and high diversity and stability. In other words, major energy flow shifts from production to maintenance (respiration).

The general relevance of the development sequence to land-use planning can be emphasized by the following "mini-model" that contrasts in very general terms young and mature ecosystems:

Young	*Mature*
Production	Protection
Growth	Stability
Quantity	Quality

It is mathematically impossible to obtain a maximum for more than one thing at a time, so one can not have both extremes at the same time and place. Since all six characteristics are desirable in the aggregate, two possible solutions to the dilemma suggest themselves. We can compromise so as to provide moderate quality and moderate yield on all the landscape, or we can plan to compartmentalize the landscape so as to maintain simultaneously highly productive and predominantly protective types as separate units subjected to different management strategies. If ecosystem development theory is valid and applicable to land-use planning (total zoning), then the so-called multiple-use strategy, about which we hear so much, will work only through one or both of these cases, because in most cases projected multiple uses conflict with one another.

REFERENCES

[1] E. P. Odum, "The Strategy of Ecosystem Development," *Science* 164 (1970): 262–270.

SUGGESTED READINGS

Hardin, G. "The Tragedy of the Commons." *Science* 162 (1968): 1243–1248.

Hutchinson, G. E. "The Lacustrine Microcosm Reconsidered." *American Scientist* 52 (1964): 331–341.

Leopold, A. "The Conservation Ethic." *Journal of Forestry* 31 (1933): 634–643.

Marsh, G. P. *Man and Nature: Or Physical Geography as Modified by Human Action.* 1864. Reprint. Cambridge: Harvard University Press, 1965.

Odum, E. P. "The Strategy of Ecosystem Development." *Science* 164 (1970): 262–270.

Odum, E. P. "Optimum Population and Environment: A Georgia Microcosm." *Current History* 58, (1970): 355–359, 365–366.

Odum, E. P. "The Attitude Revolution." In *The Crisis of Survival.* pp. 9–15. Glenview, Ill.: Scott, Foresman, 1970.

Odum, E. P. *Fundamentals of Ecology.* 3rd ed. Philadelphia: Saunders, 1971.

Odum, H. T. "Biological Circuits and the Marine Systems of Texas." In *Pollution and Marine Ecology,* edited by T. A. Olson and F. J. Burgess, pp. 99–157. New York: Wiley, 1967.

Odum, H. T. *Environment, Power and Society.* New York: Wiley, 1970.

Taylor, L. R., ed. *The Optimum Population for Britain.* New York: Academic Press, 1970.

White, L. "The Historical Roots of our Ecological Crisis." *Science* 155 (1967): 1203–1207.

Man the Newcomer:
The Living Landscape
and a New Tenant

Paul B. Sears
Professor Emeritus of Conservation, Yale University

Reprinted by permission of the author and the publisher from *The Ecology of Man.* Oregon State System of Higher Education. Eugene, Oregon: University of Oregon Press, 1957.

Man is a newcomer into our Earth that is old. This being true, prudence suggests that Man ought not be too self-centered. Instead of devoting himself completely to taking advantage of his surroundings, he might do well to spend some effort getting his bearings. Unfortunately, as matters stand now, science is being applied to competitive and exploitive ends in far greater measure than it is to establishing perspective. Even the humane and laudable business of prolonging life and increasing food supply through science seems to be raising as many questions as it solves.

We hear much these days about Man's conquest of Nature. Suppose as a first step, we examine the record. It is longer than we of the Western World had thought, for our ideas of eternity have reached into the future rather than the past, giving us a curiously bob-tailed notion of time. We may thank the astronomer, the geologist, the evolutionist and more recently the physicist for setting us straight. Due especially to measurements of radioactive change we now have some fairly good approximations of the age of the earth and the antiquity of various geological events.

What we know can be made graphic by taking a thick book of some 5,000 pages and assigning to each page the value of one million years, since the planet Earth seems to be some 5 billion (five thousand million) years old. We would scan the first half of this book before we came to any very clear evidence of life. Then we would begin to read the fragments that tell us of slow and painful development — marine to terrestrial, nonvascular to vascular, invertebrate to vertebrate, fish to mammal, marsupial to man. This is not all. We would read how, as old forms died out and new ones came on, there arose, both in plants and animals, not only more effective relations to environment, but more elaborate mechanisms whereby the parent assured the safety of the young.

We would see too an increasing interdependence among living things, and between them and their physical surroundings. The fossil

43

hunters of today are not content merely to describe single species. They go beyond this to identify social groups of extinct plants and animals. Yet in spite of this increasing fitness of living organisms we read no evidence in the record that any form of life ever had things completely its own way. All were subject to some great principle of give and take, leading toward a balance or equilibrium.

And finally if we took account of sediments and earth forms, of the chemistry and geometry of rocks, we would find clear evidence that living organisms have played an increasing part in geological proc- esses as time has gone on. We should see how the exclusively physical processes of erosion, deposition and crustal readjustments came to be supplemented by organic sedimentation, the stabilization of land forms by vegetation, and the modification of the flow of energy and inter- change of materials by many activities of plants and animals.

Since such interrelationships between life and environment are the peculiar business of ecology, a few words on that branch of bi- ological study are in order. The centennial of a landmark in Man's intellectual progress — the publication of Darwin's *Origin of Species by Natural Selection* — was celebrated in 1959. You will recall that the problem to which Darwin had addressed himself many years earlier was that of trying to account for the bewildering variety and astonishing fitness of living organisms, both plants and animals. Some measure of this task may be had if we recall that perhaps 300,000 species of plants and nearly a million of animals have been identified.

Darwin had at hand two powerful intellectual tools, one bor- rowed from geology, the other from political economy. The first was the principle of uniformity, which assumed that in nature events of the past have been determined by those forces that we see in operation today. The second was the idea that living beings have a far greater capacity to reproduce than to survive. Somehow their numbers, through the generations, are kept in balance with the space and means of subsistence available. Many are born that do not mature, or if you prefer to be Scriptural, many are called but few are chosen.

Fortunately Darwin was a naturalist, trained to observe nature in all her aspects. He noted, although he could not explain, the ten- dency of plants and animals to vary and showed that not all variations were equally well fitted to particular environments. And so he con- cluded that environment tends to eliminate the less fit while favoring their more suitable competitors.

Thus were the seeds of two new sciences planted — genetics to deal with variation and inheritance, ecology to investigate the inter- relation between life and environment. Curiously, a generation was to elapse before either gained much headway and when they did genetics raced ahead much the faster, for various reasons. Toward the close of the nineteenth century, the pioneer work in ecology filtered across the Atlantic to receive its warmest welcome at two youthful universities, both in the Midwest, Chicago and Nebraska. First to be developed was plant ecology, later came animal ecology and their combination bioecology. Human ecology, our present concern, is still in a tentative stage, but the ultimate goal is a general ecology, embracing that of all forms of life.

By this time ecology has proved its value in forestry, range, fish and game management, where specialists are free to employ it. Its greatest potential service to mankind, however, can only be possible through voluntary public policy, based on widespread common knowledge and consent. Ecology is, above all, a source of perspective in time and space and a means of understanding the great processes of which we are necessarily a part. We now face urgent problems in the allocation of population pressures, the use and care of environmental materials and energy, the planning of space and the elimination of war and other forms of waste. These all call for an ecological understanding beyond that now possessed by engineers, leaders in finance, industry and in politics.

Since increasing numbers are exposed to courses in biology in high school or college or both, it seems quite possible that the emphasis of these courses should be reviewed, to insure a proper presentation of important ecological principles. It is all very well to learn about anatomy and physiology in plants, animals and man. But no one would expect, for example, to deal through a knowledge of mechanics alone with the many public problems raised by the automobile. Indeed, viewing the extravagant missilelike design and immense waste power of the modern automobile, I wonder whether automotive engineering couldn't do with a little ecology of its own!

In any event, a practical way to test some of these notions and to prepare us for considering Man's place in nature is to examine some of the more elementary findings of the ecologist. Doing so, we must keep in mind that his essential business is to study *process,* in particular the process wherein life and environment interact. Obviously he must understand both living organisms and their environment — a task complicated by the fact that living organisms are themselves a part of the environment of other living things!

Now environment, any way we consider it, is a mighty complex system in itself. But there is an old rule and a good one that the way to tackle a complicated problem (in science, business, or

personal relations) is to take it a bit at a time, provided one doesn't
ever lose sight of the whole. Perhaps as useful a breakdown as any
is the following:

Earth — Lithosphere, studied by geologists, geographers, soil scientists.

Air — Atmosphere, studied by climatologists, meteorologists, etc.

Water — Hydrosphere, studied by oceanographers, limnologists, hydrologists, etc.

Life — Biosphere, studied by biologists.

To these might be added *Mind* — the Psychosphere, studied by psychologists, anthropologists and other social scientists.

Clearly no ecologist can become all of these various specialists rolled into one. But he must be enough at home in their various fields to draw upon them as he needs and even to contribute what he can. In particular he must learn to work the border lines between them, and in some degree become what has been called a "specialist in the general." To do this at the sacrifice of thoroughness or the ability to do scrupulously accurate, detailed work when necessary, would, however, be as fatal to him as to any other scientist.

By way of examples of some of the things that are of especial concern to him from each of these several aspects of environment let us take:

Earth (the solid lithosphere). Here he is interested in the obvious irregularity of surface forms and chemistry, both so significant for life. Mountains and valleys, ores and nutrient minerals are where we find them, not predictable on any simple geometrical plan. This means that the ecologist cannot, to the same extent as the chemist, safely rely upon universal formulas. Each situation must be studied on its merits. The rainfall which suffices to produce forest in a cool region may mark desert nearer the Equator. The failure of one plant to form seed in a given locality may be due to temperature or mineral deficiency; in another to the absence of a particular insect.

Yet behind all the diversity and irregularity there exist certain trends toward order and equilibrium. Rivers tend to seek base-level, extreme differences in elevation and mineral content to be reduced, soils to develop toward maximum fertility, and so on. Frequently though such trends may be interrupted or reversed, they are not to be ignored.

Air (the gaseous atmosphere). Gas, or *spiritus* in classical language, long the most mysterious and elusive of the states of matter proved in the end to be most amenable to experiment and the simplest for mathematical treatment. It was the study of gases that unlocked the gate to modern chemistry and physiology. The gaseous envelope of our planet is, like the soil, a reservoir of materials needed by plants and animals. It is also the medium through which solar energy reaches vegetation. But more than this, it is in constant turmoil, due primarily to that same solar energy. Its dynamic activity provides us with our daily weather while its behavior pattern in time and space we designate as climate, so important to the distribution and activity of living organisms.

Although atmospheric behavior is based upon the geometrically regular relations of sun and earth, the irregular pattern of land and water causes many interesting and important variations from place to place, from time to time. Great shifts have taken place over long periods of time as witnessed by the presence of coal in the polar regions and evidence of continental ice masses as far south as the Ohio River. Lesser fluctuations, for example the recurrence of dry years in groups, are known to be normal events and should be so regarded in planning regional economy, notably in the High Plains.

Water (the hydrosphere). Here we deal with three states of matter, liquid, solid, and gaseous. Although the prevailing temperatures on earth lie between the melting and boiling points of water — a very fortunate circumstance for life as we know it, of the utmost importance is the ability of water to form vapor at temperatures below its boiling point. Thus water rises from the oceans and moves inland as vapor, to fall upon the land as rain or snow, then flows back to sea. The rate of this return is of great ecological moment. In general the more gradual it is, the greater its opportunity to sustain life on land and the less it disturbs land forms through erosion and deposition. And here we encounter one of those many mutual relations that abound in the living landscape, for it is vegetation which, once established, chiefly restrains the rush and destructiveness of flowing water.

Truly water, one of the most familiar of substances is yet one of the most amazing; and its presence in atmosphere, lithosphere and living organisms as well, serves to remind us that environment is a great interwoven complex which we can take apart only mentally in our effort to understand it better.

Life (the living biosphere of plants, animals and some simple forms that may be either, or both). In the old days when physical scientists were called Natural Philosophers, and geologists and biologists were not ashamed to be called Naturalists, it used to be said that Nature abhors a vacuum. It might be said with equal truth that Nature abhors the absence of life on earth, in air or water. Life, whether visible to us or not, abounds everywhere, thanks to the variation, reproductive vigor and fitness through Natural Selection that Darwin pointed out to us.

Let us say that environment abounds in *Niches* or opportunities for particular organisms to carry on and that the course of evolution has been a process of filling these niches, meanwhile creating new ones at every step. Thus the oak tree, once established in its own niche, possibly a sunny, well-drained slope facing southwest, affords suitable niches to woodpecker, squirrel, fungi, and insects that find on it food or shelter, or both. We ourselves create niches for dogs, poultry, rats, maize and wheat, and an impressive list of smaller organisms whose number may vary inversely with our use of soap and water.

Any species moving into a Niche has an effect or reaction upon the situation. Let us call this its Rôle. The effect of this Rôle may vary widely. Thus the squirrel's habit of burying acorns is a means of planting many oaks, while its fondness for buds in early spring must be a more or less efficient substitute for the self-pruning that we see in the cottonwood. The Rôle of coyote in keeping a balance among rodents and thus protecting the grasses and other plants that sustain the whole native menagerie of the Yellowstone area I have observed myself. From years of studying such remnants of undisturbed nature as I could, I have concluded that, on the whole and in the long course of time, unless an organism in its niche performs a rôle that contributes to the balance of nature, it is likely to be eliminated.

Every organism we know about, with one interesting exception to be discussed later, is confined to a limited geographical area known as its Range. Within that Range it is usually restricted to certain favorable Habitats that afford it an appropriate Niche. These patterns are set by the operation of what are called Limiting Factors. Thus the commercial growth of maize is limited in the north by cold, in the west by dryness and to the east by a combination of topography, soil chemistry, and economics. Any plant or animal requires a certain constellation of favorable conditions to survive and does not thrive beyond the point where any one of these conditions becomes unfavorable or, as we say, limiting.

Some of the most interesting cases are those in which the limiting factor is the presence or absence of another species. Orchids may require certain fungi, cowbirds and cattle egrets follow grazing

herds, walnut roots poison tomato plants, and tsetse flies carry sleep-
ing sickness, thus keeping people out of an area and favoring certain
African mammals which otherwise man would exterminate.

The hunter and naturalist have long known that plants and
animals occur in characteristic communities or groups. To speak
of jack rabbits or prairie dogs is to suggest grassland. We would expect
to see squirrel in a woodland of oak and hickory, ptarmigan and coney
in the beautiful flowered alpine meadows above timber line. Even insects and microscopic forms of life may be known by the company
they keep.

Any community has both Structure and Composition. Structure depends on the form of dominant plant life, as forest, grassland,
or scrub. This tells us a good deal about local conditions such as moisture and length of growing season. Grass requires more moisture than
scrub, trees more than grass, as a rule.

To get further information we have to see what kinds of trees
make up a forest, what kinds of grass and other herbs form a given
prairie or steppe. Desert plants look much alike the world over but
are very different botanically, cactuses being 100 percent American.
Or rather they were until misguided people took them to North Africa
and Australia where they have become an unbounded nuisance. It has
become necessary, in fact, to send back to America for insects that
serve to keep cactuses in hand in Mexico and our own Southwest. As
we have said earlier, plants and animals through occupying Niches
and performing Rôles have a general tendency to maintain a balance
among themselves and with the physical conditions around them.

This balance is not a perfect thing, nor is it achieved immediately. The living organisms that first occupy a particular site change it by
shading, enriching and in other ways so that they actually write their
own finis, being succeeded by other species. This process, appropriately
known as ecological succession, continues up to the point where members of the community can perpetuate themselves as hemlock does
under hemlock, which for its part may have come in under fir or
spruce. And perhaps the fir or spruce has followed pine after the
latter had occupied bare ground. Thus it is that one can read climate,
soil moisture and quality, and history to boot by observing living
communities. It is important, not only to human enjoyment, but to
human understanding that we do not destroy completely the natural
communities which have preceded us and literally prepared the way
for us.

These communities have built up the soil to sustain far more
life than could the original bare ground, virgin soil being notably rich.

They have also regulated the flow of water and held the ground in place. They are the homes of plants and animals that are useful, interesting and enjoyable. They serve, far better than any instruments man has devised, to give us a measure of the capacity of an environment to sustain life. And, believe it or not, they afford us models for our own use of land. The most destructive practices, such as growing single crops in rows, are a far cry from what we find in nature. But grass and legume farming with livestock to consume the product and enrich the soil, winter cover crops to protect fields that otherwise would be bare and forests on rough ground are far better for the land and in the long run, for the man who lives on it. They accord better, too, with certain fundamental laws that govern the efficient use of energy and materials.

What we have tried to say thus far is that Man has enjoyed the advantage of an earth that was, so to speak, a long time getting ready for him. More specifically put, he has evolved in relation to and by virtue of a highly organized and specialized environment. The earth is fit for him and he for it not only because of what he found here but of what went on here during the millions of years before his advent. Surely it behooves him to think twice before causing too much disruption.

Now let us look at Man himself more closely. He is often called a Pleistocene mammal, which means that he appeared during the great glacial period in geological history. This was a time of storm and stress. Evaporation lowered the oceans to feed the growing polar and alpine ice. As the ice expanded it narrowed the biosphere into an equatorial girdle and within that girdle rainfall was probably heavy, favoring forests. At times the ice retreated, as it is doing now. Moisture lessened, temperatures rose, the living girdle widened towards the poles, and places which had been humid forest became desert. Such have been conditions during the past million years or so, the time that human beings have existed.

We are a novelty, if we do say so. Reach up to chin yourself, note the articulation of your shoulder joint and the ability of your hands to grasp a bar (or branch) strong enough to sustain your weight. Then ask yourself "What kind of a community — desert, grassland, or forest — did early men, my own ancestors, probably come from?" It seems clear that at first Man, like other species, was restricted in range and habitat by certain limiting factors, temperature and suitable food being among them.

But not for long. Why? Look again at your hands. Note the opposing thumb and fingers and compare their manipulative range

with that of any bird or beast you know. Think of your erect spine
that frees your fore-limbs from serving as legs, your head pivoted for
swinging about the horizon, and your eyes set to form between them
the base of a triangle. Any object you look at becomes the apex of
that triangle enabling you unconsciously to form some judgment of
its size or distance, or both. With such equipment an astonishing
range of experience becomes possible.

That is not all. You have a central nervous system that is
large to begin with and can continue its growth. Any experience,
we know, registers in this central nervous system, to be recalled or
recombined in future. Over and above what is called the "old brain"
in mammals, you possess a powerfully developed "new brain," the
busy nerve center of conscious activity. The "old brain" for its part
attends to many routine matters without bothering headquarters.

Finally, human beings are equipped with a remarkably versatile
vocal system, capable of producing an infinite variety of sound combinations. It is thus possible to have spoken symbols enough to com-
municate our experiences and thoughts to others. In this way knowledge
can be exchanged and accumulated, and handed down through the
generations, an immense advantage over the old do-it-yourself, learn-
the-hard-way, system that prevails so widely in nature. The upshot
was a true biological revolution, the birth of culture, carrying with
it the awful gift of conscious responsibility.

Man's unique power to manipulate things and accumulate experience presently enabled him to break through the barriers of temperature, aridity, space, seas and mountains that have always restricted
other species to specific habitats within a limited range. With the cultural devices of fire, clothing, shelter and tools he was able to do
what no other organism could do without changing its original character. Cultural change was, for the first time, substituted for biological
evolution as a means of adapting an organism to new habitats in a
widening range that eventually came to include the whole earth.

There is not much doubt that Man is an Old World product
and great interest centers just now on research in Africa where very
early humanoid primate material keeps turning up. We reason that
at first Man was a gatherer, eating what he could find and digest. To
judge by the thoroughness with which eatables, poisons and drugs
were known before the days of modern science Man must have tried
nearly everything — plant, animal and inanimate, that he found. We
can be fairly certain of one thing — early Man had to have considerable
space to pick over if he survived. Even when he had developed tools
and weapons for hunting it is estimated that some four square miles

per person were required to sustain a family. Until the domestication of cereals and other food plants mankind was spread thin. The State of Ohio, an area of about 40,000 square miles and now holding 7 to 9 million people, is estimated to have been populated by only 12 to 15,000 Indians even when some agriculture was combined with hunting, gathering and fishing in that very fertile land.

Now spacing is a crucial and constant problem with living organisms, plants as well as animals. It has a twofold aspect. We might say that it involves both contact and elbow-room. The individual must not become completely out of touch with his own kind. No matter how unsocial the species there must be communication for reproduction at the very least. Beyond that one finds all degrees up to the highly social and cooperative.

On the other hand the most dangerous potential competition of a species is that with precisely the same needs, namely its own kind. The sweet song of the nesting robin is more often a No Trespass sign than a love call. The jaeger, an Alaskan bird of prey that feeds on rodents gets along very well when food is scarce. But when the rodent population builds up the jaegers behave like a lot of claim jumpers around a gold strike. They encroach on each other's territory and between fighting over the abundance of food and squabbling over nesting space they fail to raise the normal broods to maturity and their population starts to decline before food runs out.

It seems reasonable to suppose that Man's progress over the earth was a matter of families or small groups living together for protection and cooperation, but spreading out and away from too close competition with other groups. If so, it affords a beautiful illustration of the principle that "competition with other species has a centripetal effect, driving each back into its own territory, while competition within a species is a centrifugal force, causing the species to scatter."

Man has always had to reckon with both kinds of competition. In the beginning, and until fire and weapons were available, the now extinct Pleistocene mammals doubtless kept him in bounds, never far from caves, perhaps treetops and other citadels. The effect was clearly centripetal. But the recent finding of extinct mammal remains in association with stone weapons shows clearly that he had discovered another refuge — the devices of his culture. He needed no longer to defend himself within a certain stronghold, but within a way of life. Modern Man having pretty well disposed of his larger competitiors, now finds himself pitted against rodents, insects, and fungi for control of food and other organic materials. He has also long been engaged in a confused competition for space with forests.

It is a safe guess that as he overcame pressure from other species, that from his own increased, thus setting the weaker and more venturesome both on the road. What he accomplished, on foot, with only the dog, fire, and stone tools to aid him, is one of the most remarkable of human achievements. It happened during the accordionlike action of the glacial age, when climate compressed the habitable regions as the ice advanced, releasing them to expand as it retreated. Through this experience Man learned to adjust himself to new vicissitudes of temperature and to utilize new forms of animal life from colder regions. The warm interglacials opened his path to the far north. Our observations in Greenland show us that glaciers can form only where both cold and moisture are present. There are and were many dry cold areas where early man, by now accustomed to the cold, could hang on in spite of the relentless advance of the continental ice masses.

This had spectacular consequences. As the ice grew from the moisture that fed it, the sea level was correspondingly lowered, until it was some 300 feet below where it is now. Then, of course, sea bottom was exposed in places, creating migration pathways. These served Man as they had served various Old World animals for an entry into the New World and allowed the horse, evolved in the Americas, to move westward into Asia. Just how and when these various shifts occurred is one of the intriguing problems of science, but we can say they did happen.

At any rate Man had spread his wide-meshed net of sparse populations into every continent before the next revolutionary step, his domestication of the cereals. We are pretty sure of our ground here because we can, by various methods, trace the use of cultivated plants outward from the centers of first use, and we know the general location of three such independent centers. These are Asia Minor (wheat), Southeastern Asia (rice), and Meso America (maize). In each instance a grass of weedlike readiness to grow in open bare ground and with fruits of good size and nutritious character played the star role. Around each was developed a complex of other plants, (in America squash, beans, peppers, tomatoes, etc.). It has been suggested, with good arguments, that the rich bare surface of household dumps, where bones, scraps, seeds, and doubtless manure accumulated, were Man's first gardens. The readiness with which tomato and melon vines spring up today out of garbage heaps makes this seem reasonable. So too does the fact that certain weeds of the amaranth and goosefoot family not only appear at the beginnings of agriculture in the Old and New Worlds both, but are still used as food in places. And unfortunately, the average single crop field happens to be the ecological equivalent of the pioneer, or weed stage in community development. If you will recall that at this stage of succession living organisms have, unlike the mature forest or prairie, a minimum stabilizing effect on the habitat, you will see why unskillful agriculture has often been its own undoing.

But the important things is that by domesticating food plants, Man reduced enormously the space required for sustaining each individual by a factor of the order of 500 at least. This meant that people could live closer together and in larger groups. It also meant that time was available for something beside the constant search for food. Cities and leisure for the arts were born, the offspring of agriculture. And yet, by a wry twist of fate, we see in history that repeatedly the status of the farmer has been lowered and with it the quality of his work and the response of the soil. Bad as it is for the offspring to look down on his parent, it is far worse for him to destroy that parent. Today, as a result of the present population explosion and resultant urban spread, choice garden, orchard and farm land is being converted into suburbs and lost to the production of food and fiber.

The human record becomes less vague — more continuous and clear — following the invention of agriculture and cities. Technical improvements in the use of minerals, fabrication of tools and utensils, the arts of writing, sculpture and architecture, and civic and military organization came on in succession, either by independent invention or often by transfusion. Much has been lost, much may be misunderstood, but the main trends are clear and growing more so every year.

It is not enough, however, to know the record. We need to know its meaning as well. Until very recently history told us much about Man, little about environment and practically nothing about their interrelation. In other words moral history was a thing completely apart from natural history. This, let us add, could scarcely be helped, for our discovery of the method of discovery, that is science, is something quite new, old though its roots may be.

What can and must be helped, however, is any further continuance of a bad situation. Now that we stand committed to universal education and the political responsibility of the individual we must close the gap between the humanities and the sciences. We must rewrite history and restudy human values with an eye to Man's long evolutionary background and his growing role as a natural force. What environment does to him and what he in turn does to it is of far more significance than the loves of monarchs and the quirks of generals. Conquests and migrations, campaigns and battles, creative arts and religious philosophies all take on a fuller meaning in the context of ecology.

Environment and life are inseparable, as Darwin showed them to be.

SUGGESTED READINGS

Caldwell, L. K. *Environment: A Challenge for Modern Society.* Garden City, N. Y.: Natural History Press, 1970.

Commoner, B. *The Closing Circle: Nature, Man and Technology.* New York: Alfred A. Knopf, 1971.

Dansereau, P., ed. *Challenge for Survival: Land, Air, and Water for Man in Megalopolis.* New York: Columbia University Press, 1970.

Darling, F. F. and Milton, J. P. eds. *Future Environments of North America.* Garden City, N. Y.: Natural History Press, 1966.

Detwyler, T. R. *Man's Impact on Environment.* New York: McGraw-Hill, 1971.

Dubos, R. *So Human an Animal.* New York: Charles Scribner's Sons, 1968.

Greenwood, N. and Edwards, J. M. B. *Human Environments and Natural Systems: A Conflict of Dominion.* North Scituate, Mass.: Duxbury Press, 1973.

Rowland, W. *The Plot to Save the World.* Toronto: Clarke Irwin, 1973.

Smith, R. L., ed. *The Ecology of Man: An Ecosystem Approach.* New York: Harper and Row, 1972.

CHAPTER 3

Weather-Climate: Flows and Exchanges of Energy and Moisture
Introduction

Weather refers to the physical state of the troposphere (the lower part of the atmosphere) in a particular place at a particular time. When we speak of changes in the weather, we are speaking about changes that occur minute by minute, hour by hour, day by day, in heat and moisture conditions. Climate, however, is an abstraction, a statistical average. It refers to the typical conditions expected at a particular place in a particular season. It represents the long-run, steady-state, dynamic equilibrium of the fluxes of heat and moisture in a given place.

Climate and weather can be studied at global, regional, local, and micro scales. At any scale, the climate and weather systems involve the interaction of solar radiation, atmospheric air, moisture, the earth's geologic structure, and its landforms, soils, and biota.

The Global Weather-Climate System

At the global scale, the energy balance of the earth and its atmosphere is maintained in a steady state. Although the tropics receive more solar radiation than they lose and the polar regions lose more than they receive, a heat balance is maintained at all latitudes by the transport of surplus heat poleward. Thus polar regions do not get colder and colder nor tropical regions warmer and warmer. The resulting energy gradient produces the vast system of global air flows usually referred to as the general circulation of the atmosphere.

Other factors influencing the global weather-climate system are (1) the rotation of the earth and (2) features of the earth's surface, particularly the location, size, shape, relief, and directional trend of major landforms, and the distribution of oceans and continents. Because of the irregular arrangements of these features of the earth's surface, there are various perturbations in the global air flows, resulting in temporal and spatial variations in weather and climate conditions. These perturbations in the global air flows are primary and permanent features of the general circulation system.

Regional Weather-Climate Systems

The large-scale primary circulation systems generate a series of secondary or regional-scale circulation systems. The secondary systems are certain to occur but they do so with considerable irregularity in space and time. They result from motion imbalances related to the earth's rotation rather than from heat imbalances, which are the generating force behind the primary circulation systems.

The Asiatic monsoon is the largest secondary circulation system. Depending as it does on the juxtaposition of a large mass of land and water and the largest area of high relief in the world, it comes close to being a primary circulation feature. Reversal of the upper air flows from westerly to easterly heralds the onset of the summer monsoon and a return reversal the onset of the winter monsoon. Despite its powerful regional forces, the monsoon circulation system is clearly linked into the primary circulation system.

Other secondary circulation systems which generate weather over large parts of the earth's surface are the mid-latitude cyclones and tropical cyclones (hurricanes). Associated upper air flow systems of a regional scale are those of the long (Rossby) waves and mid-latitude and subtropical jet streams.

Local Weather-Climate Systems

At the local scale there are short-lived air flow circulation systems such as thunderstorms, tornadoes, land-sea breezes, and mountain-valley wind systems. These local systems are generated in two ways: (1) through heat and/or motion gradients resulting from local imbalances occurring within air masses of secondary (regional) circulation systems; (2) as a result of intense locally developed heat gradients. Such local heat gradients can result from a mosaic of cover types having widely different thermal properties or from variations in local relief which produce differences in heating and cooling of air. Examples are the juxtaposition of dense forest and open fields, of large lakes and rock-covered land, of mountain cliffs and valleys.

We usually talk about weather at the local scale. A thunderstorm resulting from imbalances in a cyclonic system affects people and land in a local area. But the cyclonic system is related to the upper air long waves which tie into the general circulation system. Although we have separated the weather system into global, regional, and local levels for better understanding, we reemphasize two facts: (1) we are dealing with a single global system and (2) all of these perturbations, at the global, regional, or local scale, result from heat and/or motion imbalances in atmospheric flows.

The Microclimate

Important as the controlling global, regional, and local air flow systems are, it is at the micro scale that living organisms respond and adapt to weather-climate. Thus men wear clothing, animals seek cover under vegetation or underground, fish move as water heats up, tree leaves droop, grass becomes dormant. The microclimate zone is the layer of air whose heat and moisture content and aerodynamic characteristics are directly and often strongly modified by the particular surface over which it lies. It is largely at this scale that man's attempt at weather-climate modification is effective.

The earth's surface is a mosaic of natural and manmade cover types. Each possesses different energy-absorbing, energy-transforming, and energy-emitting characteristics. Each has widely varying water-holding capacities. Each possesses different aerodynamic roughness characteristics. It is not surprising that the air layer near the ground is characterized by a complicated microclimatic pattern. Forests and grasslands, corn fields and cotton fields, countrysides and cities have an impact on the energy, water, and momentum budgets of their immediate atmospheric environment. In effect, they create their own little weather-climate systems. But even these microclimates are ultimately controlled by the flows of the global and regional circulation systems.

At any scale, weather-climate systems are determined by energy and matter flows and by their exchanges of energy and matter with the other subsystems of the ecosphere.

These energy and matter exchanges and the related concepts of energy and matter budgets are the key explanatory principles used in the articles in this chapter. In the opening article Tweedie develops the concepts of energy and matter exchanges and budgets in a framework that can be used for any level of weather climate analysis. The second article by Biel illustrates the interaction with other natural environment systems at local and micro scales. In the concluding article Landsberg outlines in detail our current knowledge of the way in which man's activities have affected weather-climate patterns.

Our central theme of the causal importance of energy and moisture flows and exchanges is well illustrated by Tweedie. Using global, regional, and local examples, he demonstrates the applicability of the budget approach. This approach directs attention to the interfaces between the subsystems of the ecosphere and emphasizes the need for interdisciplinary research.

The interdependencies and interactions of the many elements that make up local- and micro-scale weather-climate systems are stressed by Biel. He shows how the unity of the natural environment is expressed at the local and micro scales as the various elements (air, landforms, soil, vegetation, and man) interact to determine the fluxes of energy and moisture. Although a systems framework is not explicit in his article, systems thinking is evident in the way Biel presents micro and bioclimatic findings. Soil, terrain, and plant interrelationships and energy-moisture exchanges are demonstrated and various practical applications are discussed.

Local- and micro-scale weather-climate systems are regularly experienced by all of us. Each of us has been too hot, too cold, too dry, or too wet. Each one of these physiological states represents an imbalance in our heat and moisture exchanges with the weather-climate system. All living organisms are subject to such imbalances. In order to survive, the negative feedback processes of the organism must be able to correct these imbalances. Thus we perspire to maintain our body temperature within tolerance limits, and we use clothing and housing to provide a shield against unwanted inputs of heat and moisture.

A comprehensive review article by Landsberg, an eminent meteorologist long concerned with the interactions of man, weather, and climate, concludes this chapter. Many, varied, and often complex are the interactions between human activity and atmospheric systems.

Although Landsberg has not written explicitly in a systems vein, the dominant theme of his article is the link between man's activities and weather-climate modifications. "How can we distinguish the changes that are the result of man's activities from the changes that result from the natural variability of the climate?" Obviously it is difficult. Landsberg believes that the detrimental effect of man's impact is minimal at the global scale, noticeable at the regional scale, but unmistakable at the local and micro scale, especially for urban air quality.

It is important to learn more about man's effect on the weather-climate system. His impact is often small at the local or micro scale. But since local and micro subsystems nest within regional and global systems, there may be unexpected long-term results. It is conceivable that man's activities could affect the amount of solar radiation arriving at the earth's surface. Even small changes in the receipt of solar radiation can have large effects, given the amount of energy involved. Positive feedback processes may produce undesirable effects on a global scale. Naturally generated changes during the geologic history of the earth have had many drastic effects on life. Let us not increase the possibility of such happenings in the future, for we do not know what the results of our activities may be.

Challenges in Climatology

A. D. Tweedie
University of Newcastle, Australia

Reprinted with some deletions and modifications by permission of the author and the publisher from *The Australian Journal of Science* 29 (1967), pp. 273–278.

Climate is a layman's term; and most layman's terms have a habit of altering their meaning with time, and often — to our confusion — with space. In employing the term "climate" to identify the weather he feels he has a right to expect as distinct from the weather he suffers, the layman of today is possibly only vaguely aware of the concept of permanence and continuity that underlies his thinking. Yet, it is in these terms that he plans his vacation, organizes his farming operations, and outfits his wardrobe. In thinking so and in reacting thus to his concept of climate, he is on common ground with the laymen of other times, for to the citizen of classical Greece *klimata* also suggested predictable situations and experiences. In the earlier use of the term, however, is an idea which has been lacking in the layman's expression of modern times. Today the layman thinks of climate as an aspect of atmosphere; it would surprise him to learn that his counterpart in classical Greece thought of *klimata* as a characteristic of the earth's surface.

Studies in climatology in recent decades, however, have again stressed this latter implication in the concept of climate. As they have developed in the post-war years climatic studies have continued to emphasize the idea of continuity and permanence which has always been inherent in the term. In focusing attention on the exchange processes which direct the flow of energy and of matter between the earth and its atmosphere, they develop this continuity as a special case of the laws of conservation of mass and energy. But in doing so the studies direct attention to the interface at which these exchanges occur, and climatology is again becoming concerned with the surface of the earth.

The initiation of the ideas behind these developments is no recent event. They advance the ideas expressed a century ago by such workers as Alexander Voeikov and George Perkins Marsh — workers who argued that in the identification and measurement of the exchanges of energy and matter at the surface of the earth lay one of the major fields of investigation in physical science. As with so many fruitful ideas of nineteenth century science, however, their fulfillment has had to await the development of modern methods, modern techniques and, in particular, modern instruments. The work is still far from complete. Many of the parameters have been identified and the framework of study has been constructed, but there are still a great many measurements to be made. . . .

ENERGY AND MASS EXCHANGE AT THE EARTH'S SURFACE

Essentially these are studies of special cases of the laws of conservation of mass and energy operating on what Voeikov termed "the active surface" of exchange between the earth and its atmosphere. As such, they could be considered to embrace the exchange of all forms of energy and the exchange of all forms of matter which occur at this interface. At the earth's surface, however, it is the conservation of heat which dominates the energy exchange processes. Despite the often impressive growth of vegetation which transforms our landscapes from year to year and from season to season, and despite the velocity of air movement in the limited area of a hurricane, the chemical and kinetic components of the energy exchanges at the earth's surface, compared with that of energy as heat, are of minor account. The chemical energy expressed in the annual growth of a dairy pasture in Denmark, for example, has a heat equivalent of less than 400 langleys, compared with the 82,000 langleys involved in the total energy exchange on that surface in a year. On the average windy day, the shearing stress that the moving atmosphere exerts on the earth's surface equates with only 10 langleys of heat energy — less than 2 percent of the energy involved in exchanges at the earth's surface at Melbourne on an average summer day.

Similarly, the exchange of mass between the atmosphere and the earth embraces several forms of matter. A visible and often impressive form of such exchange, for example, involves the atmospheric discharge of effluent from the modern city — an exchange which is of importance to an increasing proportion of the world's people. While there are now corrective technologies which in some instances have been applied to reduce the ash and carbon exchange from coal combustion, no modern city and its atmosphere are without the exchange of partly burned hydrocarbons and oxides of nitrogen that are exhausted from automobile traffic. Unlike the rapid fallout of the heavier particles of coal combustion, this essentially twentieth-century effluent engages in a complex interplay with matter and energy in the air so that its storage and chemical activity in the atmosphere is prolonged. The outcome is the reduced visibility and increased health hazards of the smog-bound city. For the resident of Los Angeles, these are the exchanges of matter which underlie the "eye irritant" forecasts which now accompany his weather reports. Despite the distress it may bring to the city dweller and the crop farmer immediately down wind, however, this is an exchange of matter which is still relatively restricted in areal extent. For the world as a whole it seems as yet to be of limited significance. That it will not always be so is the basis of Landsberg's comment that the city ventilation problems that this exchange creates are issues that will demand closer investigation in the not so distant future.

Less visible, possibly more significant and certainly more widespread are the exchanges of matter in gaseous state — the cycles of nitrogen, oxygen and carbon dioxide which play important roles in the creation of landscape character. Indeed in its origin, throughout its history, and in its present variety in both space and time, the atmosphere is essentially the outcome of exchanges of matter that have occurred at the earth's surface. In its turn, the varied face of the earth reflects these exchanges.

It is as water substance, however, that the most widely known and possibly the most significant of these exchanges of matter is made. This is the exchange which produces the most rapid and widespread variation in the content and character of the lower atmosphere, which sculptures the land surface, which develops character and variety in soils, and which underlies much of the variety of vegetation. This is the exchange of matter on which the study of climate still lays greatest stress.

THE CONCEPT OF BALANCE

Major attention in climatic study is thus still directed to heat and moisture, and continues in a sense the traditional emphasis on air temperature and precipitation as the most important of its "elements." The link, however, is a tenuous one, for the data in these recent studies are organized into a broader framework. With increased knowledge of the processes of radiant energy transfer, and the development that has followed of instruments to measure radiation, with the development of studies in the environment of plants and the new network of observation sites that have resulted, and with the more detailed studies in hydrology that have been prompted by national disasters of flood and drought, there has been a re-grouping of climatic data and a search for the measurement of other variables more significant for the exchange processes. Measurements of precipitation and of atmospheric temperature are now only part of a wider frame of reference. The existing record of precipitation finds a place in the new order, but the data

need to be rearranged, and new time units for the grouping of rainfall records are giving more reality to the climatic record. Attention
is being diverted from screen temperatures to measurements of solar
radiation and to the temperature of the earth's surface. For these are
the important parameters in the exchange processes that underlie the
heat and water budgets — budgets which by a common accounting
procedure stress the continuity of climate as a special case of the laws
of conservation of energy and matter.

In the heat budget, the conservation of energy is demonstrated
as we sum the fluxes of heat which reach the surface, and equate this
with those fluxes which move downward into the variable substrate
of vegetation, soil, solid rock and lake or ocean. Similarly is it so in
the water balance. Input which we measure as precipitation is equated
with the sum of the fluxes of output — evapotranspiration, infiltra-
tion, changing soil storage and run-off.

These are frameworks, moreover, which intermesh whenever
water changes its physical state for, in the course of this transformation, it takes part not only in the water balance but in the heat balance
as well. In such frameworks, in consequence, the traditional elements
of climate are no longer separate and discrete, but they are fused in a
single phenomenon. No longer are they a selection of the more easily
measured atmospheric variables strung together in a loose association
but rather they are aspects of a single process. In expressing this continuity, the balances unite the individual fluxes, the storages and the
transformations which contribute to them — fluxes, storages and
transformations which occur in the atmosphere, in the biomass, and in
the substrate of soil and ocean. Within these frameworks they become
interconnected exchange processes and provide a unified field of
study — climatology.

These frames of reference for the exchange of heat and moisture can be applied at any scale. The heat balance can be determined
for the world as a whole, for a clover pasture, for a city street, or for
a sheep. But always the reference is to a specific surface, for it is only
at the interface that the balance can be established.

Of the two budgets, that which traces the exchange of moisture
is possibly the more easily determined and the more readily understood. Much of the income and outflow is readily visible as precipitation and as stream flow, and certain aspects of this balance have been
measured with reasonable frequency and some accuracy. Storages of
water in the atmosphere and in the soil are more difficult to determine,
but the radiosonde and satellite-borne sensors and the neutron moisture meter now allow this with some precision, and the data are being
accumulated with increasing frequency. Transformation and outflow as
vapor is an even more elusive process to measure though the evapo-

tron and the weighing lysimeter give us a future prospect of the direct measurement of this aspect of the water balance. Previously we could assess it only as a residual in an accounting procedure, or as the outcome of the application of some empirical formula of varying degree of validity. . . .

The Water Balance

As with the heat budget, the fluxes, storages and transformations of water achieve a balance only in relation to some specific surface. The manner in which this operates in relation to the world's ocean surfaces, for example, has been demonstrated. The accounting procedures reveal an annual transfer of water from the Arctic and Pacific Oceans on the one hand, to the Atlantic and Indian Oceans on the other. Some 2.3×10^{12} acre-feet leave the Arctic Ocean through the Bering and Davis Straits each year to sustain the balance.

The frame of reference can also be applied to a continent. In the winter months, water vapor enters the North American air space from the south and west, and flows out eastwards as part of the mass of air which crosses the Atlantic seaboard. The amount of this vapor outflow, however, is only 60 percent of the inflow. The deficit is that water vapor which, by transformation, becomes a net addition of water to the surface of the continent. This water, the excess of precipitation over evapotranspiration, is in turn represented by the snow cover and the soil moisture which accumulates on, and the river flows which discharge from, the continent. In the summer months, inflow from the south and west is only 80 percent of the outflow to the north and east, a situation which can be sustained only by an excess of evapotranspiration over rainfall which now adds vapor to these atmospheric fluxes. Over the year in question, nine-tenths of the inflowing vapor was matched by the vapor outflow, the remaining tenth being the excess of precipitation over evapotranspiration which appears as river discharge to balance the water budget. Despite the often impressive volume of this surface flow, then, the great part of the total water balance of North America is worked out by the fluxes of vapor through its air space. Those interested in increasing the precipitation by artificial methods would appear to be correct in arguing that they have plenty of water substance to operate upon, though variations in its regional concentration and form still present practical problems of considerable difficulty. Significant for the present discussion, however, is the fact that it is only by exchanges with the land surface and by fluxes within it and upon it, that the water balance of the continent can be established.

At a smaller scale, the vapor fluxes, transformations and storages in the Mississippi Basin reveal that all but 6 percent of the

annual vapor inflow leaves as vapor in the air streams flowing outward. This 6 percent — the water equivalent of 200 mm. over the
drainage basin — is the excess of precipitation over evapotranspiration which can be measured as the river discharge into the Gulf of
Mexico. Again, only by reference to the surface of the earth can the
water balance of the region be established. A similar study discloses
that the net annual income of vapor into the air space of eastern
Australia can be balanced against the excess of measured precipitation
over computed evapotranspiration, an excess which, by implication,
leaves the area as river flow. The auditing of the balance which the
measurement of this last flux would allow, however, is hampered by
our incomplete knowledge of stream discharge.

At yet smaller scale, the accounting procedures and the concept of the water balance established at a section of the earth's surface
can be illustrated by the record of the water year as it has been recorded in Castle Creek Basin, California. During this time, a total inflow
of 55 inches of precipitation was balanced by the temporary storages
of snow accumulation and of soil moisture, and by the fluxes of
generated runoff and of evapotranspiration. The 2 inches of precipitation which had occurred between July and September in the 1946–
47 water year returned to the atmosphere within that time as the
vapor of evapotranspiration. By the end of February, however, the 33
inches of water input had a much more varied fate. It was accounted
for by the sum of 2 inches as runoff, 18 inches as accumulated snow,
5 inches as stored soil moisture, 5 inches as evapotranspiration and
3 inches intercepted by vegetation. By the end of August, all of the
inflow had been accommodated in the fluxes of evapotranspiration
and runoff and the temporary storages of snow mantle and soil moisture had been eliminated. The balance of the water year on this particular section of the earth's surface had been established.

It is in this manner of the organization of climatic data that
David Miller finds a fascinating intellectual challenge. The fact that
the heat and water balances have practical implications in evaluating
or predicting the results of development schemes whether these be
called "management" or "transformation of nature" is for him "beside
the point." Certainly here is a method which allows a uniform approach
to the study of climate and which offers a continuity of method from
the largest to the smallest surface of reference. Distinctions between
climatology and microclimatology are lost in this common study. Here
is an organization of climate which eliminates the awkward gap that
past studies frequently display between attempts to identify processes
and attempts to arrange the data into some empirical classification. . . .

Directed as they are to the study of the flows, storages and transformation of matter and energy, such studies of climate are investigations of the operation of the laws of conservation which are most readily demonstrated and understood in the controlled conditions of the physicist's laboratory. Here, however, they are concerned with the more complicated and uncontrolled situations that occur on the surface of the earth. As such they become the concern of a wide range of field sciences and the challenges they present are being met by workers trained in a wide range of disciplines — plant and animal physiology, soil science and meteorology, agricultural science and geography. In this form, climatology is no longer the sterile rearrangement of material from the meteorologist's archives but is characterized by a catholicity of interest and a broad front of endeavour. It becomes, as Hare has noted, a study of the "central integrating fact which permeates all the environmental sciences."

SUGGESTED READINGS

Benton, G. S. and Estoque, M. A. "Water-vapor Transfer over the North American Continent." *Journal of Meteorology* 11 (1954): 462–477.

Benton, G. S., Fleagle, R. G.; Leipper, D. F.; Montgomery, R. B.; Rakestraw, N.; Richardson, W. S.; Riehl, H.; and Snodgrass, J. "Interaction between the Atmosphere and the Oceans." *Bulletin of the American Meteorological Society* 44 (1963): 4–17.

Budyko, M. I. *The Heat Balance of the Earth's Surface.* Translated by N. Stepanova. Washington: U. S. Weather Bureau, 1958.

Gates, D. M. *Man and His Environment: Climate.* New York: Harper and Row, 1972.

Hare, F. K. "Energy Exchanges and the General Circulation." *Geography* 50 (1965): 229–241.

Hare, F. K. "The Concept of Climate." *Geography* 51 (1966): 99–110.

Landsberg, H. E. *Weather and Health, An Introduction to Biometeorology.* Garden City, N. Y.: Anchor Books, Doubleday, 1969.

Linton, D. L. "The Geography of Energy." *Geography* 50 (1965): 197–228.

Miller, D. H. "The Heat and Water Budget of the Earth's Surface." *Advances in Geophysics* 11 (1965): 175–302.

Reiter, E. R. *Jet Streams* Garden City, N. Y.: Anchor Books, Doubleday, 1967.

United States, Corps of Engineers. *Snow Hydrology, Summary Report of the Snow Investigations.* Portland: U. S. Corps of Engineers, 1956.

Wolman, A. "The Metabolism of Cities." *Scientific American* 213 (September, 1965): 178–190.

Microclimate and Bioclimatology

E. R. Biel
Professor of Meteorology, Rutgers University

Reprinted with some deletions and modifications by permission of the author and
the publisher from *American Scientist* 49 (1961), pp. 326–349.

Climatology is concerned with both physical and biological
problems. The explanations of most of the phenomena in which the
climatologist is interested, such as radiation geography, wind systems,
precipitation types, etc., have, of course, been offered by physicists;
the implications on plant growth, human comfort or discomfort,
economic potentialities in both favorable and hostile climates, etc.,
however, represent complicated problems which cannot be studied by
an exclusive analysis of data of the standard observational type which
Weather Bureaus have been collecting all over the globe. While the
physicist, for instance, requests temperatures to be measured at a
"representative" level above ground and within screens with thermom-
eters protected against insolation, re-radiation, and rain, the biologist
will rather request data on "experimental bodies" which are just as
exposed to the sun, to radiation from the ground, and to rain as plants
and animals are in Nature. The geographer, ecologist, engineer, and
hydrologist will demand detailed "ecological" rainfall maps for mountainous areas, even if their findings are partly based on plant geography,
stream discharges, an intelligent interpretation of terrain features and
other indirect evidence, and the purist objections of the meteorologist
who will want to exclude all evidence not based on rain gauge records
will mean little to him. This conflict of interests between the physical
and the biological approach is ever present no matter which instrument,
climatic element, or map is under discussion.
　　When, about ninety years ago, station networks were established
all over the globe, those charged with the responsibility to decide on
the principles of standardized observations were primarily interested
in the setting up of "representative stations" with a maximum useful-
ness for synoptical purposes. Forecasters had to eliminate the confusing
multitude of small and smallest-scale phenomena near the ground,
which to them were necessarily just obstacles obscuring the study of
large-scale synoptic situations. They had to ignore those very features
in which agronomists and ecologists are vitally interested: orography,
type, height and density of vegetative cover, soil texture, color and
moisture, etc. The decision to measure temperature and humidity six
feet above ground is understandable in terms of man's knowledge
around 1860; today, however, forecasters are studying data from the

middle and upper troposphere in order to analyze air masses and jet stream influences as steering mechanisms of surface weather, and the 6-foot observations are only of limited value to them. In a similar manner, it became also obvious during the last decades that these 6-foot observations were in many cases rather meaningless for the study of agroclimatic relationships, and that observations much closer to the ground and directly within the habitat of plants were indispensable. Thus, the standard level observations are primarily useful in evaluations of climatic environmental effects on man, his comfort, discomfort, health, etc., that is, in what could be called "anthropoclimatic" studies.

R. Geiger of Munich and W. Schmidt of Vienna were the pioneers in systematic studies of the atmospheric conditions in the very bottom layer a few inches above the surface. Geiger suggested the term "microclimate" as contrasted to the standard "macroclimatic" observations, which are very useful for large-scale surveys. The most important American contribution towards this new field is C. W. Thornthwaite's work, with its emphasis on the necessity to include top soil layer observations, since soil moisture conditions down to the root level are of utter importance to plant life. . . .

MICROCLIMATE

Temperature

The soil is referred to as "active surface" since it is heated by solar insolation and cooled by terrestrial radiation. The lowest layer of air close to the active surface is, in turn, heated and cooled from the ground, and the fact that daytime temperatures at the 2-inch level are higher and nocturnal temperatures are lower than those recorded at the 6-foot level is common knowledge. The order of magnitude of the thermal differences, however, is surprising and becomes spectacular in the dry and rarefied air of subtropical mountains. Even in central New Jersey the temperature gradient between the two levels amounts under clear skies and in the absence of strong winds to about $10°$F. in the early afternoon and to approximately $5°$F. around sunrise. Since the latitudinal summer temperature gradient in East America amounts to about $1°$F. per $1°$ of latitude (70 miles) the New Jersey 2-inch afternoon temperatures correspond to the macroclimate of Florida, while the early morning microclimatic readings in New Jersey correspond to the 6-foot readings in northern New England. The daily range recorded at the flower habitat level is about $15°$F. larger than that observed at the height of the human head. Macroclimatic records are, therefore, not representative at all of the living space of most plants. During July, 1955, for instance, temperatures near the ground exceeded 100°F. on 23 days in New Brunswick, N. J., but never at the standard level, and the maximum at the 3-inch level (114°F.) was 16° higher than that at 6 feet.

Humidity
Considerable differences between standard- and micro-level exist also with respect to humidity, and particularly so during the day. The surface, whether water, soil, plant cover, or snow, is the main source of evaporation, and the vapor content decreases sharply with height from a maximum in the bottom layer immediately above the active surface ("wet type"). Relative humidity (the ratio between actual and saturation vapor content at a given temperature), however, displays the "dry type" of increasing values from the soil upward, since the capacity of the warmed air close to the active surface to hold vapor increases much more rapidly than the actual vapor content increases by evapotranspiration. Within growing vegetation, on the other hand, relative humidity is conspicuously higher than above the plant cover: on fair afternoons near-saturation may prevail in the stagnant air within a field while the readings are 30 to 40 percent lower at the standard level.

Wind
The main reason for the existence of the rather spectacular climatic features in the layer near the ground is the sharp reduction in motion as a result of skin friction. A long series of observations made by G. Hellmann near Berlin indicated, for instance, that at the 6-foot level the number of hours with calms amounted to 7 percent of the total observational time, while the corresponding figure for the 2-inch level came close to 30 percent. Thus, the distribution of thermal characteristics, of water vapor, dust, etc., by turbulence, is drastically curtailed near the active surface. Since microclimatic features are most conspicuous under fair weather conditions, their potentialities should be studied during clear and calm days and nights, when clouds do not interfere with solar and terrestrial radiation and when the vertical wind profile is not influenced by approaching fronts. Microclimatology is, therefore, most important in climates with great frequencies of fair days. In the eastern United States, for instance, the number of clear and calm days and with them the intensity of microclimatic features increases sharply from the New England States towards subtropical latitudes, that is, from the main route and the convergence center of traveling disturbances in the Northeast toward regions distant from the primary storm tracks.

Soils

Soil properties (conductivity, moisture content, color) play a significant role in influencing the spot climate intensity near the surface. With a well-conducting soil a considerable percentage of the insolational energy is conducted into the substratum, and this stored heat will be available to the surface during the night. The surface temperature of the well-conducting soil is lower during the day, but higher during the night than the surface of a poorly conducting soil with its limited substratum heat storage and its resulting excessive thermal range. This differential conductivity may, in borderline cases, determine the occurrence or nonoccurrence of frost, the poorly conducting soil being more frost endangered. The higher the soil moisture content the better the conductivity, which is, therefore, increased after rain or during rainy seasons or spells, since ground air, an extremely poor conductor, is replaced by water.

Horizontal Differences

The fact should not be overlooked or underestimated that the horizontal microclimatic differences between nearby localities are just as important as the rather spectacular differences in the vertical profiles of temperature, humidity, and wind described above. While macroclimatic profiles through rather large areas of the size of, say, New Jersey from the Hudson to the Delaware River hardly record any important differences and are indicative of rather monotonous and uniform geographical distributions of most meteorological elements, the study of the microclimates along the same profile would reveal the existence of a great variety of types. Minute terrain features, differential exposures, marshlands, river edges, differences in wind exposure, etc., have a definite influence on the frequency, intensity, and duration of local fogs, spotty frosts, and snow covers; farmers, highway engineers, turnpike authorities, and city planners are aware of these facts. The drastic changes in suburban areas in terrain utilization, vegetative cover, wind exposure, and so on, are accompanied by drastic changes in microclimatic features as is, for instance, evidenced by the annual re-evaluations of snow fence locations. Many differences along horizontal profiles are not exactly "microclimatic" in nature, but are due to the effect of cities, industrial plants, small forests, etc. . . .

Orography

"Orographic microclimatology" is the study of the very conspicuous differences in spot climates encountered with rolling terrain as the result of concave and convex forms, air drainage, stagnation, differential exposures, and so on. It is a well-known fact that excessive temperatures are recorded in valleys and basins, while the thermal

conditions on nearby hilltops are much less extreme. Even within
hilly cities, enormous temperature differences have been encountered
between different sections (Toronto, Vienna). Pockets are subject to
very low night and winter minima and to very high daytime and summer maxima, while nearby convex forms of terrain (summits, hilltops)
record much more limited fluctuations. Similar differences between
valleys and ridges exist with respect to relative humidity, etc. In concave forms of terrain stagnation prevails and the air heated by insolation
or chilled by terrestrial radiation is not readily distributed by vertical
mixing as is the case with convex forms of terrain which are wind
exposed and where eddy turbulence results in rapid mixing of the
bottom layer with higher air. . . . J. N. Wolfe found tremendous microclimatic temperature differences within the Neotoma Valley of Central
Ohio based on 4-year studies of 100 to 300 observational points
within one mile. The number of frost-free days varied from location
to location between 124 and 276 per year, the dates of the last spring
frost from March 9 to May 25, those of the first fall frost from September 11 to December 13, etc. The differences between temperature
minima amounted to about $40°F.$ and those between maxima seem to
be even higher. Records were taken at ridges, cliffs, in pockets, crevices,
etc. . . .

Exposures

The fact that slopes facing at various angles of steepness toward
different directions receive vastly different amounts of solar energy
is of decisive importance in the study of microclimates in the mountains.
Vegetative life starts much earlier on slopes facing south than on
northern slopes; on the former the snowcover disappears much earlier
and the soil warms rapidly after snow melt, while on the latter snow-
covers persist due to their high albedo with a resulting dampening
effect on spring warming. In low latitudes, however, and in countries
with hot summers controlled by tropical air masses, the climatic advantages enjoyed by southern slopes do not last long and are followed
by conspicuous disadvantages. The southern slopes soon record very
high soil temperatures and heavy evapotranspiration. The daytime up-
slope breezes ("chimney winds") are very strong over hot soil and contribute toward the development of soil moisture deficiencies and
retarded growth rates. Along the northern slopes, on the other hand,
where temperatures are much lower and upslope breezes and evapotranspiration rates much weaker, soil moisture is considerably higher.
Consequently, the ratio between growth rates on southern and northern
slopes is gradually reversed in favor of the northern slopes, which,
moreover, are less endangered by forest or brush fires. . . .

Vegetation

The plant cover itself contributes toward its own microclimate. . . . "Horizontal," umbrella-shaped plants intercept a higher proportion of light than "vertical types." The cutting of tops of "horizontal" foliage crops, for instance, will change them temporarily into "vertical" types with an accompanying reduction in the interception of solar energy. In mixed stands, light competition between faster and slower growing species is bound to develop. In response to a complicated interplay of factors, thermal maxima are sometimes observed at the top of the plant cover and sometimes within the stand. With grass blades three feet in height, no less than 80 percent of the insolation is intercepted at the top of the vegetative cover and the soil surface of the meadow receives hardly one-fifth of the light intensity. In hilly terrain, very considerable differences exist between astronomically and orographically possible sunshine duration, and the terrain influences on direct insolation must not be overlooked in detailed ecological studies. Microclimate influences also the activity of soil organisms.

Forests

Foresters have always been aware of the great climatic differences between the interior and the surroundings of woodland. Previous to Geiger's pioneer work the explanations of these differences were based on comparisons between measurements taken within and outside forests. Geiger introduced tower observations with recordings made above, within, and below the canopy, in the trunk space, and close to the forest floor. The study of these vertical profiles proved that the irradiated and radiating surface is the canopy, while the forest floor is "deactivated." Canopy interference and wind-breaking effects of trees create special forest climates whose intensities vary with differences in canopy density (coniferous *versus* deciduous forests, seasonal variations in foliage, multi-layered tropical forests *versus* uniform-layered stands in forests under long cultivation, etc.). Very detailed surveys of crown densities in Austrian and Scandinavian forests contributed much toward a better understanding of forest ecology and floor vegetation; the interference with respect to incoming and outbound radiation varies tremendously, and temperature conditions, evaporation rates, vapor, and dust contents are controlled by screening and stagnation. Of particular interest are studies on canopy fogs and dew formation in tropical forests, on the canopy interceptions of precipitation (including comparisons between regions of different rainfall intensity) and on fog drip ("hidden" or "horizontal" precipitation) which, according to some authorities, becomes the decisive factor in the water balance of certain

heavily forested mountains. Studies on glade management indicate
that very considerable microclimatic differences exist between glades
of different sizes, since the main factors (canopy interference and wind
breaking effect) change very much with changes in glade diameters.
The wind scale used in meteorology becomes, of course, entirely meaningless in forest climatology. The importance of the rate of canopy
interference is well-illustrated by the fact that some foresters prefer to
define seasons phenologically by the dates of canopy formation
("start of spring"), the duration of a full canopy ("summer"), the
dates of leaf fall ("start of fall"), and the duration of the period without foliage ("winter").

Types of Active Surface
Different types of active surfaces display different types of
microclimates. Some differential soil properties and autecological
features have already been mentioned. Microclimate of water is highly
influenced by depth and state of motion. In the case of snow, depth
and density (age) are decisive factors. The examples of efforts to en-
force earlier snow melt given below are not only of practical importance
for the indicated specific purposes, but also of general climatic interest
with respect to both the duration of snow albedo microclimate and
to its sudden change to the basically different conditions of soil microclimate.

Human Interference
One of the most interesting aspects of the study of microclimates is the feasibility of influencing them by simple techniques.
Spot climates can be and very often are modified by human interference. Color changes and the applications of techniques that influence
wind speed result necessarily in changes of microclimates since the
response of the active surface to incident solar energy and the reduction in the intensity of turbulent mixing are the decisive physical
microclimatic factors.

In regions of tropical summer temperatures, dark soils often
become overheated and their tremendous evapotranspiration rates
result soon in moisture deficiencies. Applications of white powders
(India) or of aluminum foils (Hungary) increase the reflection from
the soil and reduce the rate at which insolation is absorbed; both
surface and subsoil temperatures are lowered (often down to the root-
ing level) and soil moisture is conserved. Benjamin Franklin had, as is
well-known, an amazing curiosity about the nature of many phenomena; he was the first to study, among numerous other meteorological

processes, the melting rates of snow covered with thin fabrics of different color. Today, large-scale darkening of snow and ice surfaces by dusting from airplanes is common practice in many countries. The resulting increased absorption is instrumental in enforcing rapid snow melt and in prolonging growing seasons in regions where their duration is marginal (northern and eastern Europe); in enforcing earlier thawing of frozen lakes in the interest of longer fishing seasons and of fish life preservation (northern prairies of the United States); in reducing spring flood dangers due to ice jams in rivers (Canada); in increasing the amount of water carried by mountain brooks from glaciers into valleys in regions where only the high altitudes receive abundant precipitation while the lower levels are semi-arid. In the western mountains of China heavy monsoonal precipitation is restricted to the summit regions and dusting of snow fields results in abundant supplies of irrigation water for vegetable production at lower levels.

If wind velocity near the ground is increased, an undesirable microclimate will be weakened and may even be eliminated. The cutting of trees, for instance, will often result in a considerable reduction of frost frequency, severity, and duration. Channelization of flow may have similar results ("bottleneck effect"). In other cases a reduction of wind speed may be desirable. In areas of marginal growing-season lengths where early planting is necessary (as is, for instance, the case with cotton in certain regions of Oklahoma), the spring velocity maxima that are typical of the Prairie States may cause soil blowing with light soils; delays in planting would mean a considerably increased danger of damages from early fall frosts; early planting, however, will be secure with shelter belts which stop soil blowing. Shelter belts have been in use for centuries in many wind-swept areas of the globe (southern France, southern Russia, the Viennese Basin, the east coast of the Adriatic Sea, etc.), in order to protect crops, and they are now increasingly used in the United States, in China, etc. The size of the protected area depends, of course, on the height, density, and shape of the belts and the number of rows. It is now more and more recognized that the belts change the microclimatic conditions in the protected area drastically. Evaporation rates are curtailed, snow is arrested on, and its melting waters are available to the fields, and the increasingly used term "moisture conservation program" describes this important effect; temperatures, on the other hand, are more excessive in the stagnant space behind the belt with an increase in frost danger. Experiments with hedges in the windy coastal regions of northwestern Europe indicate a conspicuous increase in dew formation and a reduction in runoff. Shelter belts around houses may result in very considerable fuel savings as tests in Michigan have indicated. In many regions, systems of neighboring shelter belts at close and carefully spaced intervals are in use in order to influence the microclimates of much larger areas than those relatively small sections that would be "protected" by a single belt.

Weathering

The weathering of building materials near to the ground is highly influenced and accelerated by the extreme conditions in the microclimatic layer where freezing and thawing temperatures with their detrimental effects alternate much more often than at the standard level, and where the humidity is much higher; snow-melt waters, the mechanical impact of splashing raindrops, and increased bacterial activity contribute in their turn towards more rapid deterioration of walls.

BIOCLIMATOLOGY

Frost

Since the terms "growing season" and "frostless season" were, unfortunately, for a long time used synonymously, much confusion was bound to result similar to that caused by the ill-defined term "killing frost." Plant growth starts, in general, when the average temperature rises above the "zero of vital temperature" of 43°F., while dormancy begins in autumn when the average temperature falls below this biologically important threshold. It is obvious that spring frosts occur long after the start of growth and that autumn frosts are recorded long before the start of dormancy. Thus, the vegetative growing season is much longer than the frostless season. In studies on specific crops, their "individual zeroes," that is the average temperatures at the average planting times, have to be used.

Figures 1 & 2 are taken from a series of self-explanatory maps prepared in the Department of Meteorology at Rutgers, the State University of New Jersey, to illustrate growing season problems. The differences within the small state are considerable: the vegetative growing season lasts about five weeks longer in the extreme south than in the northwest; the periods of frost dangers during the vegetative growing season last approximately forty days in the extreme south and along the coast and no less than about eighty days in the north. Figure 3 is of considerable practical importance to farmers since it indicates the length of the period of anxiety in spring during

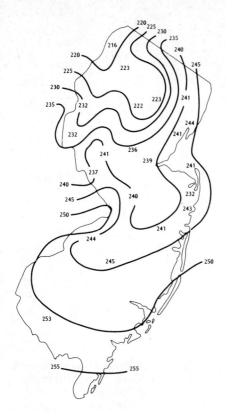

Figure 1. Duration of vegetative growing season in New Jersey (days).

which frosts usually occur *after* the start of growth. The rather striking differences in the length of this period of alertness follow a simple geographical pattern. The critical period lasts about two weeks along the coast, about five weeks in Central New Jersey and six weeks in the northwestern hills. The number of frosts which occur during this period is about five along a narrow coastal strip, while approximately twice as many are recorded in the interior. Cases with maxima of between 15 and 20 frosts during the critical period are on record for most stations in the interior.

Air drainage into pockets plays a very important role in frost frequency distribution. Sensitive plants are much less endangered when grown on the warmer "thermal belts" above bottoms (or above "sunken gardens" for that matter), which night after night are exposed to the gravitational flow of cold air that gradually piles up until it reaches its maximum depth around sunrise. German experiments proved that air drainage can be controlled to some extent by the setting

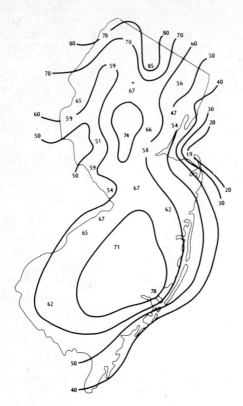

Figure 2. Differences between duration of growing season and frostless season in New Jersey (days).

up of barriers (groves, etc.) with a resulting sharp decrease in frost frequency and particularly in frost duration behind the obstacles.

The length of the period during which the temperature remains below the level of the plant's sensitivity plays an important role as to injury. A. V. Havens studied the problem of frost duration at several levels during critical nights in New Brunswick, New Jersey. Frost length increases sharply from the standard level down to the plant habitat. In one case, it was found that a species growing at the 3-inch level with an assumed critical temperature of 28° would have been exposed to sub-critical temperatures for more than thirteen hours, while at the standard level the minimum was 1.5°F. above the threshold sensitivity. The study of the frequency of genetic frost types is of considerable practical importance, since the efficiency of protective measures depends upon the vertical termperature profiles and other characteristics of the different types of frost. Anticyclonic radiation

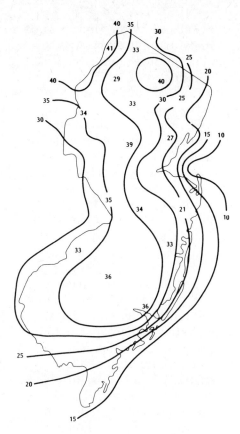

Figure 3. Average number of days from start of growing season to last Spring frost in New Jersey.

frosts occurring within a homogenous air mass during calm and fair nights are very shallow and spotty, and all known methods provide ready protection. Since the temperature increases sharply from the ground upward ("inversion"), propellers mounted on towers will rapidly mix the cold bottom air with the warmer air aloft, and air warmed by heaters will not rise above that level at which the ambient temperature is identical to that of the ascending current ("convection lid"). The sharper the inversion and the lower the convection lid the smaller the volume of air to be warmed by the heaters. Advective frosts ("freezes"), on the other hand, are the result of large-scale air mass transportations, whose arrival is accompanied by widespread frosts without inversions. Neither ventilation nor heating provide effective protection since no warmer air is available for mixing and since air heated by fires does not come to a standstill at a convection

lid. In recent years, infrared radiators introduced by the University of
Michigan have proved successful in a variety of applications with low
growing crops; since the presence or absence of inversions is irrelevant
to their successful operation they are "weatherproof" even during
moderate cold spells. In California most frosts are due to radiation;
east of the Rocky Mountains, however, the frequency of advective
frosts is, unfortunately, rather high. . . . The farmer should, therefore,
be familiar with the physical bases of several frost protective measures
in order to cope with different categories of frost, and he should know
what genetic type he is facing in each individual case in order to
avoid waste of efforts.

      Farmers and gardeners are often not aware of the fact that the
probability of frost occurrences after the so-called "last day of killing
frost" is still 50 percent, since average dates represent median values
(actually the chances of later frosts are much higher since the records
of the tables refer to standard level observation and not to the plant
habitat). If frost risks of this order of magnitude seem too high for
certain types of activities, tables should be consulted which indicate
the probabilities of low temperature occurrences after given dates,
and work should be scheduled according to the risk level of the farmers'
own selection. . . . More detailed tables are now becoming available
for many areas and for several low temperature thresholds. The New
Jersey data indicate that, even within relatively small areas, differences
of about five weeks exist between coastal locations (Long Branch)
and inland valleys (Layton). Since, under unfavorable terrain- and
soil-moisture conditions, the number of frosts near the ground may
be a multiple of the 6-foot value and since the "critical temperatures"
indicative of damage vary considerably with species, varieties and
phases of development (plant sensitivity increasing, in general, rapidly
with growth) the user of such data will have to study the particular
microclimatic conditions in his fields or orchards before he will be able
to take maximum advantage of the data.

      Winter killing of Ladino clover, an important forage crop in the
Northeast, is often rather widespread. Laboratory experiments carried
out by the Farm Crops Department of Rutgers, the State University of
New Jersey, proved that the rates of cooling rather than the minima to
which the temperatures drop are a decisive factor in injury. Field
measurements at the Agricultural Weather Station of the Department of
Meteorology indicated that cooling rates of the order of magnitude
which proved fatal to stolons in the laboratory occurred also in nature
(up to $15°F$. per hour).

      Figures 4 and 5 illustrate the daily variations of stolon tempera-
tures (measured with thermocouples), air temperatures (in a standard

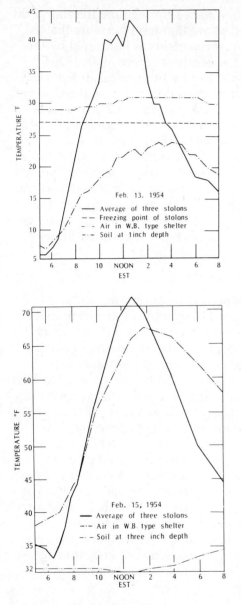

Figure 4. Temperature of the air, soil, and Ladino clover stolons on a day with light SW winds and some high cloudiness (N. J. Agricultural Experiment Station, New Brunswick, N. J.).

Figure 5. Temperatures of the air, soil, and Ladino clover stolons on a day with broken to overcast middle clouds and light to moderate SW winds (N. J. Agricultural Experiment Station, New Brunswick, N. J.).

shelter 4′ 6″ above ground), and soil temperatures (at 1″ and 3″ respectively) during two 24-hour periods in February, 1954. The first day, controlled by fresh air masses from Canada, displayed temperatures below freezing even during its warmest hours ("ice day"), while the stolons warmed up very rapidly under clear skies and in very dry air;

less than two hours after sunrise they passed through the freezing point of the tissues (27°F.) and remained above that level for more than seven hours. Very rapid thawing of frozen plants as illustrated by the warming rate of the figure results frequently in severe injury. The second example refers to a day controlled by subtropical air from the Gulf of Mexico and reveals amazing thermal differences in the clover habitat. While at the root level three inches beneath the surface sub-freezing temperatures prevailed, the simultaneously recorded stolon temperatures one-half inch above ground reached maxima of 72°F. A thermal gradient of more than 40°F. for a vertical distance of three and one-half inches is certainly indicative of extreme physiological stress. The fact that 70 percent of the Ladino clover in New Jersey was injured during February, 1954, a month whose average temperature was very conspicuously (more than 8°F.) above normal, can hardly be explained by an inspection of standard level data recorded within a shelter.

Dusting
Spraying and dusting operations (particularly dusting from airplanes) should be carried out only during hours of low wind speed, since otherwise the minute particles are bound to miss their targets. Since, on fair days, wind velocity displays a definite diurnal variation, the speed increasing with increased convection, the best hours for dusting are those immediately after sunrise and before sunset. The U. S. Department of Agriculture has prepared tables indicating at what rates particles of different sizes will settle in still air and how far they will be carried laterally with breezes of different speed. Since, moreover, particles display their greatest adhesivity to plants with high relative humidity, morning dusting is preferable to evening dusting because the relative humidity is at its maximum around sunrise. A further and important argument in favor of morning dusting is the daily variation of precipitation: in most continental areas heavy rainfall that would knock off the dust material occurs seldom in the morning, but showers and thunderstorms are rather frequent in the late afternoon and early evening. R. Geiger discussed the difficulties encountered in dusting forest canopies from the ground due to both meteorological and transportation factors.

Cattle
Since cattle grazing on our summer pastures are exposed to excessive tropical heat, experiments have been carried out by the U.S. Department of Agriculture for decades to produce a cross-breed that would combine as many desirable features as possible of both northern

European and tropical races. The former are excellent producers of milk and meat in their native environments, but their performance is rather poor under tropical conditions: their body temperature increases rapidly, their feeding habits become irregular and listless, their breathing changes into panting, etc. Tropical breeds, on the other hand, are well adjusted to summer heat, but their production is poor. Tests on the effects of exposure to the tropical sun on shadeless pastures, made at the end of a full grazing day, display conspicuous differences in body temperature and breathing rates between northern, tropical, and crossbred cattle and are indicative of the improved production performance of the cross-bred "American hot weather cow." Efforts have been made to provide optimum pasture climates by site selection, portable shades, abundant water supplies, and in other ways. The more wind-exposed the pasture (sea breezes, valley breezes, etc.), the greater the heat loss from the animal body ("cooling power") and the better the feeding habits. The heat burden can be considerably reduced by the use of portable shades with white reflecting tops and dark under-surfaces which absorb the heat radiated from ground and animal bodies, as found in very impressive California experiments. The cooler the available drinking water, the lower is the body temperature. Other studies indicate that, during heat waves, the animals rest mostly during the day and prefer night grazing, that insect attacks are particularly vicious and even dangerous with a rapidly falling and irregular barometer, etc.

Hay Drying

The quality and nutrition value of hay (protein content) is to the highest extent dependent upon meteorological parameters (sun, wind) during the curing period. Successful drying should result in a rapid reduction of the water content from 70 to 75 weight percent at cutting to the safe storage level of 20 to 25 percent. The main outdoor hay drying season in New Jersey is mid-May to mid-June. Some agronomists have described the weather conditions during the period under consideration as "unstabilized" and "unreliable" and analyses of 30-year records of precipitation frequency for three stations in the main hay growing regions of New Jersey indicate, indeed, that, with random cutting, the odds to "hit" a spell of three consecutive rainless days are 70 to 30 against the farmer ignoring forecasts. If cutting is done immediately after a rainy day under the rather primitive assumption that another rainy day is less likely to follow, the odds are improved by roughly 10 percent. If periods are selected during which the Bermuda High is well developed or during which ridges of high pressure drift slowly from the Middle West eastward, the probability becomes roughly 60 to 40 in favor of successful cutting. . . .

Dew

Research initiated in Israel indicates that, under subtropical conditions, the frequency and amounts of dew are by far higher than previously assumed. Improved methods of dew observation and the establishment of a dew-measuring network made it possible to draw dew maps for Israel. Studies in California indicate that great differences in dew utilization exist between different plant species; farming in semiarid areas will profit by the selection of species that are optimum dew users.

Soil Moisture

C. W. Thornthwaite's climatic classification with its bookkeeping system on precipitation-evaporation relations, on surpluses and deficiencies, and on the seasonal variations in depletion and recharging of soil moisture, formed an important point of departure for many studies on soil moisture calculations from climatic elements. Such work is of particular importance under the tropical heat conditions of our summers during which water requirements of crops are very high, and supplemental irrigation may be of great practical importance in spite of heavy amounts of rainfall. Two recent studies by W. E. Marlatt may be mentioned in this connection. Experiments at the Marlboro, N. J., Field Station with orchard grass of different cover density indicate that the evapotranspiration losses are by no means a linear function of plant density, but that maxima are recorded with cover amounts between 50 and 70 percent. It is now considered to be commercially feasible to grow certain vegetables under a plastic mulch which, by sealing off the soil, prevents both water losses by surface evaporation and the entering of rain into the ground. Studies on the difference in microclimate between an unmulched pepper plot and pepper grown with a mulched surface are promising, and findings of this kind could become of special interest for areas with small and irregular amounts of growing season precipitation.

Snow Ridging

"Snow ridging" as practiced by many farmers in windswept prairie regions where precipitation is often marginal is an interesting technique to change spot climates. After the first heavy snowfall at the beginning of winter the snow cover is ridged by snowploughs. The hillocks will survive during moderate warmer spells and will act as traps arresting between them later falling snow. Without these ridges, the snow would soon melt or it would be blown into ravines and gulleys. With snow ridging, however, the farmer tries to change, as it were, intermittent snow covers into a lasting snow cover with the advantages of prevention of deep soil freezes, and of snow melting in spring on the fields themselves. In years with a dry, early-growing season the influence of snow melting waters on soil moisture may be a very important factor as to yields.

Phenology

The study of the relations between cyclic natural phenomena and weather conditions (phenology) by observations on planting, emergence above ground, blossoming, heading and harvesting of crops, on leafing and coloring of trees, on insect life, on freezing and thawing of rivers and lakes, on movements of cattle to pastures at different altitudes in mountainous countries, etc., is very helpful for many practical purposes and represents, without any doubt, an important supplement to the recording of the traditional meteorological elements. Linnaeus, the great Swedish botanist, introduced the conception of phenology and was responsible for the establishment of a phenological network in northern Europe early in the 18th century, five generations before the establishment of weather bureaus.

Thermal sums (degree-day totals above various levels of "zero values") have been used since the 18th century (Réaumur) to explain differential growth in different years and between different regions. Phenometry, the quantitative study of the relations between atmospheric and soil moisture conditions, on the one hand, and different phases of growth and plant response, on the other hand, was rapidly developed. Thornthwaite and others included day length values and developed very reliable methods of precise harvest forecasting. It is somewhat surprising that not much progress has been made in systematic and large-scale phenological studies in the United States although one of the most important contributions to phenology was developed in this country: the "Bioclimatic Law" proposed by the U. S. Department of Agriculture entomologist, A. Hopkins, who studied the rates at which phenological events progress and retreat from lower to higher latitudes and altitudes in spring and fall respectively, and whose papers became known all over the world.

Interesting work on the phenology of common purple lilac (Syringa vulgaris L), a representative growth indicator whose blossoming dates were mapped in Europe as indices of the "start of spring" by Ihne and Kirchoff, has been organized by J. M. Caprio of the Agricultural Experiment Station in Bozeman, Montana, in cooperation with the U. S. Weather Bureau, farmers, and garden clubs. Isophanes (lines connecting place[s] of simultaneous occurrence of phenological events) were drawn for Montana and later for larger areas in the West in order to find regions of "early" and of "late" blossoming, of shorter or longer duration of the blossoming period, etc. In general, growth is retarded about one day for every 20 miles distance toward north and for every 100 feet in elevation. For instance, lilac starts to blossom on May 10 near sea level in northwestern Washington, while in southern Arizona blossoming occurs simultaneously at the 7,500 foot level. Caprio extended his phenological studies to fall- and winter-sown wheat. An analysis of the configuration of isophanes leads to a better understanding of differential spot climates and is helpful in the scheduling of farm operations and in growth forecasts.

Many and varied are the practical applications of micro- and bioclimatology.

SUGGESTED READINGS

Biel, E. R. "The Climate of New Jersey." In *The Economy of New Jersey,* edited by S. J. Flink. New Brunswick, N. J.: Rutgers University Press, 1958.

Budyko, M. I. *Climate and Life.* New York: Academic Press, 1973

Chang, J. *Climate and Agriculture.* Chicago: Aldine Publishing Co., 1968.

Geiger, R. *The Climate Near the Ground.* 4th ed. Cambridge: Harvard University Press, 1965.

Munn, R. E. *Descriptive Micrometeorology.* New York: Academic Press, 1966.

Sargent, F. D. "A Dangerous Game: Taming the Weather." *Bulletin, American Meteorological Society* 48 (1967): 452–458.

Sewell, W. R. D., Kates, R. W., and Phillips, L. E. "Human Response to Weather and Climate — Geographical Contributions." *Geographical Review* 68 (1968): 262–280.

Shaw, R. H., ed. *Ground Level Climatology.* Publication 86, American Association for the Advancement of Science. Washington, D. C.: 1967.

Man-Made Climatic Changes

Helmut E. Landsberg
*Research Professor, Institute of Fluid Dynamics and Applied
Mathematics, University of Maryland*

Reprinted with minor modification by permission of the author and the publisher
from *Science* 170 (1970), pp. 1265–1274. Copyright 1970 by the American
Association for the Advancement of Science.

Climate, the totality of weather conditions over a given area,
is variable. Although it is not as fickle as weather, it fluctuates globally
as well as locally in irregular pulsations. In recent years some people
have voiced the suspicion that human activities have altered the global
climate, in addition to having demonstrated effects on local microclimates. There have also been a number of proposals advocating various
schemes for deliberately changing global climate, and a number of
actual small-scale experiments have been carried out. For most of the
larger proposals, aside from considerations of feasibility and cost,
one can raise the objection that a beneficial effect in one part of the
earth could well be accompanied by deterioration elsewhere, aside
from the inevitable disturbances of the delicate ecological balances.

But the question "Has man inadvertently changed the global
climate, or is he about to do so?" is quite legitimate. It has been widely discussed publicly — unfortunately with more zeal than insight.
Like so many technical questions fought out in the forum of popular
magazines and the daily press, the debate has been characterized by
misunderstandings, exaggerations, and distortions. There have been
dire predictions of imminent catastrophe by heat death, by another
ice age, or by acute oxygen deprivation. The events foreseen in these
contradictory prophecies will obviously not all come to pass at the
same time, if they come to pass at all. It seems desirable to make an
attempt to sort fact from fiction and separate substantive knowledge
from speculation.

NATURAL CLIMATIC FLUCTUATIONS

In order to assess man's influence, we must first take a look at
nature's processes.

The earth's atmosphere has been in a state of continuous slow
evolution since the formation of the planet. Because of differences
in the absorptive properties of different atmospheric constituents, the
energy balance near the surface has been undergoing parallel evolu-

tion. Undoubtedly the greatest event in this evolution has been the emergence of substantial amounts of oxygen, photosynthetically produced by plants. The photochemical development of ozone in the upper atmosphere, where it forms an absorbing layer for the short-wave ultraviolet radiation and creates a warm stratum, is climatically also very important, especially for the forms of organic life now in existence. But for the heat balance of the earth, carbon dioxide (CO_2) and water vapor, with major absorption bands in the infrared, are essential constituents. They absorb a substantial amount of the dark radiation emitted by the earth's surface. The condensed or sublimated parts of the atmospheric water vapor also enter prominently into the energy balance. In the form of clouds they reflect incoming short-wave radiation from the sun, and hence play a major role in determining the planetary albedo. At night, clouds also intercept outgoing radiation and radiate it back to the earth's surface.

Over the past two decades Budyko has gradually evolved models of the global climate, using an energy balance approach. These models incorporate, among other important factors, the incoming solar radiation, the albedo, and the outgoing radiation. Admittedly they neglect, as yet, nonlinear effects which might affect surface temperatures but it seems unlikely that, over a substantial period, the nonlinear effects of the atmosphere-ocean system will change the basic results, though they may well introduce lags and superimpose rhythms. Budyko's calculations suggest that a 1.6 percent decrease in incoming radiation or a 5 or 10 percent increase in the albedo of the earth could bring about renewed major glaciation.

The theory that changes in the incoming radiation are a principal factor governing the terrestrial climate has found its major advocate in Milankovitch. He formulated a comprehensive mathematical model of the time variations of the earth's position in space with respect to the sun. This included the periodic fluctuations of the inclination of the earth's axis, its precession, and the eccentricity of its orbit. From these elements he calculated an isolation curve back into time and the corresponding surface temperature of the earth. He tried to correlate minima with the Pleistocene glaciations. These views have found considerable support in isotope investigations, especially of the $^{18}O/^{16}O$ ratio in marine shells deposited during the Pleistocene. Lower ^{18}O amounts correspond to lower temperatures. Budyko and others raise some doubts that Milankovitch's theory can explain glaciations but admit that it explains some temperature fluctuations. For the last 1700 years there is also evidence that the ^{18}O content of Greenland glacier ice is inversely correlated to a solar activity index based on auroral frequencies. Again, low values of ^{18}O reflect the temperature at which the precipitation that formed the firn fell.

The fluctuations of externally received energy are influenced not only by the earth's position with respect to the sun but also by changes in energy emitted by the sun. Extraterrestrial solar radiation fluctuates with respect to spectral composition, but no major changes in total intensity have yet been measured outside the atmosphere. The occurrence of such fluctuations is indicated by a large number of statistical studies, but ironclad proof is still lacking. Such fluctuations are of either long or short duration. They have been tied to the solar activity cycle. Inasmuch as details are yet unknown, their effect on climate is at present one factor in the observed "noise" pattern.

In the specific context of this discussion, we are not concerned with the major terrestrial influences on climate, such as orogenesis, continental drift, and pole wanderings. But other, somewhat lesser, terrestrial influences are also powerful controllers of climate. They include volcanic eruptions that bring large quantities of dust and CO_2 into the air, and natural changes of albedo such as may be caused by changes in snow and ice cover, in cloudiness, or in vegetation cover. The fact that we have not yet succeeded in disentangling all the cause-and-effect relations of natural climatic changes considerably complicates the analysis of possible man-made changes.

The Climatic Seesaw

It was only a relatively short time ago that instrumental records of climate first became available. Although broad-scale assessments of climate can be made from natural sources, such as tree rings or pollen associations, and, in historical times, from chronicles that list crop conditions or river freezes, this is tenuous evidence. But a considerable number of instrumental observations of temperatures and precipitation are available for the period from the early 18th century to the present, at least for the Northern Hemisphere. These observations give a reasonably objective view of climatic fluctuations for the last two and a half centuries. This is, of course, the interval in which man and his activities have multiplied rapidly. These long climatic series are mostly from western Europe, but recently a series for the eastern seaboard of the United States has been reconstructed from all available data sources. In this series Philadelphia is used as an index location, since it is centrally located with respect to all the earlier available records. Figures 1 and 2 show the annual values for temperature and precipitation for a 230-year span; there are some minor gaps where the data were inadequate. These curves are characteristic of those for

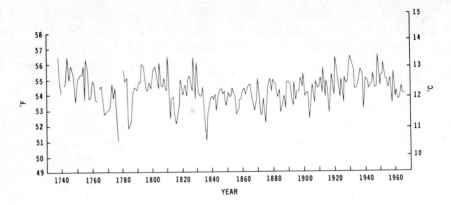

Figure 1. Annual temperatures for the eastern seaboard of the United States for the period 1738 to 1967 — a representative, reconstructed synthetic series centered on Philadelphia.

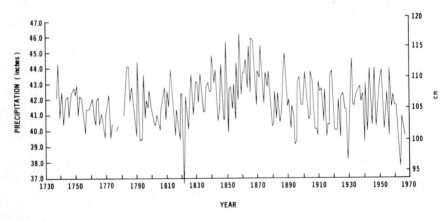

Figure 2. Annual precipitation totals for the eastern seaboard of the United States for the period 1738 to 1967 — a representative, reconstructed synthetic series centered on Philadelphia.

other regions, too. In particular they reflect the restlessness of the atmosphere. Many analysts have simply considered the variations to be quasi-random. Here I need only say that they do not reflect any pronounced one-sided trends. However, there are definite long or short intervals in which considerable one-sided departures from a mean are notable. On corresponding curves representing data for a larger area that encompasses most of the regions bordering the Atlantic, the major segments are those for the late 18th century, which was warm; the

19th century, which was cool; and the first half of the 20th century, in which there was a notable rising trend. This trend was followed by some cooling in the past 2 decades.

In the precipitation patterns, "noise" masks all trends, but we know that during a period in the middle of the last century there was considerably more precipitation than there is now. For shorter intervals, spells of drought alternate with high precipitation. Sometimes, for small areas, these can be quite spectacular. An example is the seasonal snowfall on Mount Washington, in New Hampshire; there the snowfall increased from an average of 4.5 meters in the winters of 1933–34 to 1949–50 to an annual average of 6 meters in the period 1951–52 to 1966–67. Yet these values should not be taken as general climatic trends for the globe, or even for the hemisphere. Even if we take indices that integrate various climatic influences, we still cannot make categorical statements. Glacier conditions are typical in this group of indices. For example, the glaciers on the west coast of Greenland have been repeatedly surveyed since 1850. In consonance with temperature trends for lower latitudes, they showed their farthest advances in the 7th decade of the 19th century and have been retreating ever since. This pattern fits the temperature curves to the 1950 turning point, but, although glaciers in some regions of the world have been advancing since then, this is by no means true of all glaciers. The question of whether these changes reflect (1) relatively short-term temperature fluctuations, or (2) alterations in the alimenting precipitation, or (3) a combination of these two factors remains unanswered.

Many of the shorter fluctuations are likely to be only an expression of atmospheric interaction with the oceans. Even if external or terrestrial impulses affect the energy budget and cause an initial change in atmospheric circulation, notable lag and feedback mechanisms involving the oceans produce pulsations which, in turn, affect the atmosphere. The oceans have a very large thermal inertia, and their horizontal motions and vertical exchanges are slow. Namias has investigated many of the fluctuations of a few years' duration. He concluded, for example, that drought conditions on the eastern seaboard of the United States in the 1960s were directly affected by the prevailing wind system and by sea-surface temperatures in the vicinity but that the real dominant factor was a wind-system change in the North Pacific. Such teleconnections (relations among conditions in distant parts of the globe) complicate interpretations of local or even regional data tremendously. The worldwide effect of changes in the Pacific wind system is obvious from Namias's estimate that accelerations and decelerations cause large-scale breaks in the regime of sea-surface temperatures. These seem to occur in sequences of approximately five years and may cause temperature changes of $0.5°C$ over the whole North Pacific. Namias estimates that this can cause differences of 8×10^{18} grams in the annual amounts of water evaporated from the surface. The consequences for worldwide cloud and rain formation are evident. It is against this background that we have to weigh climatic changes allegedly wrought by man.

Carbon Dioxide
The fact that the atmospheric gases play an important role in the energy budget of the earth was recognized early. Fourier, and then Pouillet and Tyndall, first expressed the idea that these gases acted as a "greenhouse". After the spectrally selective absorption of gases was recognized, their role as climatic controls became a subject of wide debate. The capability of CO_2 to intercept long-wave radiation emitted by the earth was put forward as a convenient explanation for climatic changes. Arrhenius made the first quantitative estimates of the magnitude of the effect, which he mainly attributed to fluctuating volcanic activity, although he also mentioned the burning of coal as a minor source of CO_2. The possibility that man-made CO_2 could be an important factor in the earth's heat balance was not seriously considered until Callendar, in 1938, showed evidence of a gradual increase in CO_2 concentration in the earth's atmosphere. But it was Plass who initiated the modern debate on the subject, based on his detailed study of the CO_2 absorption spectrum. The crucial question is, How much has CO_2 increased as a result of the burning of fossil fuels? It is quite difficult to ascertain even the mean amount of CO_2 in the surface layers of the atmosphere, especially near vegetation. There are large diurnal and annual variations. Various agriculturists have reported concentrations ranging from 210 to 500 parts per million. The daily amplitudes during the growing season are about 70 parts per million. Nearly all early measurements were made in environments where such fluctuations took place. This, together with the lack of precision of the measurements, means that our baseline — atmospheric CO_2 concentrations prior to the spectacular rise in fossil fuel consumption of this century — is very shaky. Only since the International Geophysical Year have there been some regularly operating measuring points in polar regions and on high mountains and reliable data from the oceans which give some firm information on the actual increase.

The best present estimate places the increase in atmospheric CO_2 since 1860 at 10 to 15 percent. This is hardly a spectacular change, but the rate of increase has been rising, and various bold extrapolations have been made into the 21st century. Much depends on the sinks for CO_2 which at present are not completely known. At present concentrations, atmospheric O_2 and CO_2 stay in approximate equilibrium, through the photosynthetic process in plants. It is estimated that 150×10^9 tons of CO_2 per year are used in photosynthesis. A corresponding amount is returned to the atmosphere by decay, unless the total volume of plant material increases. This volume is one of the unknowns in the estimates of CO_2 balance. Perhaps satellite sensors can give some bulk information on that point in the future. The oceans are a major sink for CO_2. The equilibrium with the bicarbonates dissolved in seawater determines the amount of CO_2 in the atmosphere. In the exchange between atmosphere and ocean, the temperature of the surface water enters as a factor. More CO_2 is absorbed at lower surface-water temperatures than at higher temperatures. I have already pointed out the fact that surface-water temperatures fluctuate over long or short intervals; most of these ups and downs are governed by the wind conditions. The interchange of the cold deep water and the warm surface water through downward mixing and upwelling, in itself an exceedingly irregular process, controls, therefore, much of the CO_2 exchange. Also, the recently suggested role of an enzyme in the ocean that facilitates absorption of CO_2 has yet to be explored. Hence it is quite difficult to make long-range estimates of how much atmospheric CO_2 will disappear in the oceanic sink. Most extrapolators assume essentially a constant rate of removal. Even the remaining question of how much the earth's temperature will change with a sharp increase in the CO_2 content of the atmosphere cannot be unambiguously answered. The answer depends on other variables, such as atmospheric humidity and cloudiness. But the calculations have been made on the basis of various assumptions. The model most widely used is that of Manabe and Wetherald. They calculate, for example, that, with the present value for average cloudiness, an increase of atmospheric CO_2 from 300 to 600 parts per million would lead to an increase of $2°C$ in the mean temperature of the earth at the surface. At the same time the lower stratosphere would cool by $15°C$. At the present rate of accumulation of CO_2 in the atmosphere, this doubling of the CO_2 would take about 400 years. The envisaged $2°C$ rise can hardly be called cataclysmic. There have been such worldwide changes within historical times. Any change attributable to the rise in CO_2 in the last century has certainly been submerged in the climatic "noise." Besides, our estimates of CO_2 production by natural causes, such as volcanic exhalations and organic decay, are very inaccurate; hence the ratio of these natural effects to anthropogenic effects remains to be established.

Dust

The influence on climate of suspended dust in the atmosphere was first recognized in relation to volcanic eruptions. Observations of solar radiation at the earth's surface following the spectacular eruption of Krakatoa in 1883 showed measurable attenuation. The particles stayed in the atmosphere for 5 years. There was also some suspicion that summers in the Northern Hemisphere were cooler after the eruption. The inadequacy and unevenness of the observations make this conclusion somewhat doubtful. The main exponent of the hypothesis that volcanic dust is a major controller of terrestrial climate was W. J. Humphreys. In recent years the injection into the atmosphere of a large amount of dust by an eruption of Mount Agung has renewed interest in the subject, not only because of the spectacular sunsets but also because there appears to have been a cooling trend since. The Mount Agung eruption was followed, in the 1960s, by at least three others from which volcanic constituents reached stratospheric levels: those of Mount Taal, in 1965; Mount Mayon, in 1968; and Fernandina, in 1968. Not only did small dust particles reach the stratosphere but it seems likely that gaseous constituents reaching these levels caused the formation of ammonium sulfate particles through chemical and photochemical reactions. The elimination of small particulates from the stratosphere is relatively slow, and some backscattering of solar radiation is likely to occur.

As yet man cannot compete in dust production with the major volcanic eruptions, but he is making a good try. However, most of his solid products that get into the atmosphere stay near the ground, where they are fairly rapidly eliminated by fallout and washout. Yet there is some evidence that there has been some increase in the atmospheric content of particles less than 10^{-4} centimeters in diameter. The question is simply, What is the effect of the man-made aerosol? There is general agreement that it depletes the direct solar radiation and increases radiation from the sky. Measurements of the former clearly show a gradual increase in turbidity, and the same increase in turbidity has been documented by observations from the top of Mauna Loa, which is above the level of local contamination. From these observations the conclusion has been drawn that the attenuation of direct solar radiation is, in part at least, caused by backscattering of incoming solar radiation to space. This is equivalent to an increase in the earth's albedo and hence is being interpreted as a cause of heat loss and lowered temperatures. But things are never that categorical and simple in the atmosphere. The optical effects of an aerosol depend on its size distribution, its height in the atmosphere, and its absorptivity.

These properties have been studied in detail by a number of authors.
It is quite clear that most man-made particulates stay close to the ground.
Temperature inversions attend to that. And there is no evidence that
they penetrate the stratosphere in any large quantities, especially since
the ban, by most of the nuclear powers, of nuclear testing in the
atmosphere. The optical analyses show, first of all, that the backscatter
of the particles is outweighed at least 9 to 1 by forward scattering.
Besides, there is a notable absorption of radiation by the aerosol. This
absorption applies not only to the incoming but also to the outgoing
terrestrial radiation. The effectiveness of this interception depends
greatly on the overlapping effect of the water vapor of the atmosphere.
Yet the net effect of the man-made particulates seems to be that they
lead to heating of the atmospheric layer in which they abound. This
is usually the stratum hugging the ground. All evidence points to
temperature rises in this layer, the opposite of the popular interpretations of the dust effect. The aerosol and its fallout have other, perhaps much more far-reaching, effects, which I discuss below. Suffice
it to say, here, that man-made dust has not yet had an effect on global
climate beyond the "noise" level. Its effect is puny as compared with
that of volcanic eruptions, whose dust reaches the high stratosphere,
where its optical effect, also, can be appreciable. No documented case
has been made for the view that dust storms from deserts or blowing
soil have had more than local or regional effects.

　　　Dust that has settled may have a more important effect than
dust in suspension. Dust fallen on snow and ice surfaces radically
changes the albedo and can lead to melting. Davitaya has shown that
the glaciers of the high Caucasus have an increased dust content which
parallels the development of industry in eastern Europe. Up until
1920 the dust content of the glacier was about 10 milligrams per liter.
In the 1950s this content increased more than 20-fold, to 235 milligrams per liter. So long as the dust stays near the surface, it should have
an appreciable effect on the heat balance of the glacier. There is fairly
good evidence, based on tracers such as lead, that dusts from human
activities have penetrated the polar regions. Conceivably they might
change the albedo of the ice, cause melting, and thus pave the way for
a rather radical climatic change — and for a notable rise in sea level.
There has been some speculation along this line, but, while these dusts
have affected microclimates, there is no evidence of their having had,
so far, any measurable influence on the earth's climate. The possibility
of deliberately causing changes in albedo by spreading dust on the
Arctic Sea ice has figured prominently in discussions of artificial modification of climate. This seems technologically feasible. The consequences

for the mosaic of climates in the lower latitudes have not yet been assessed. Present computer models of world climate and the general circulation are far too crude to permit assessment in the detail necessary for ecological judgments.

All of the foregoing discussion applies to the large-scale problems of global climate. On that scale the natural influences definitely have the upper hand. Although monitoring and vigilance is indicated, the evidence for man's effects on global climate is flimsy at best. This does not apply to the local scale, as we shall presently see.

Extraurban Effects

For nearly two centuries it has been said that man has affected the rural climates simply by changing vast areas from forest to agricultural lands. In fact, Thomas Jefferson suggested repetitive climatic surveys to measure the effects of this change in land use in the virgin area of the United States. Geiger has succinctly stated that man is the greatest destroyer of natural microclimates. The changeover from forest to field locally changes the heat balance. This leads to greater temperature extremes at the soil surface and to altered heat flux into and out of the soil. Cultivation may even accentuate this. Perhaps most drastically changed is the low-level wind speed profile because of the radical alteration in aerodynamic roughness. This change leads to increased evaporation and, occasionally, to wind erosion. One might note here that man has reversed to some extent the detrimental climatic effects of deforestation in agricultural sectors, by planting hedges and shelter belts of trees. Special tactics have been developed to reduce evaporation, collect snow, and ameliorate temperature ranges by suitable arrangements of sheltering trees and shrubs.

The classical case of a local man-made climatic change is the conversion of a forest stand to pasture, followed by overgrazing and soil erosion, so that ultimately nothing will grow again. The extremes of temperatures to which the exposed surface is subjected are very often detrimental to seedlings, so that they do not become established. Geiger pointed this out years ago. But not all grazing lands follow the cycle outlined above. Sometimes it is a change in the macroclimate that tilts the balance one way or another.

Since ancient times man has compensated for vagaries of the natural climates by means of various systems of irrigation. Irrigation not only offsets temporary deficiencies in rainfall but, again, affects the heat balance. It decreases the diurnal temperature ranges, raises relative humidities, and creates the so-called "oasis effect." Thornthwaite, only a decade and a half ago, categorically stated that man is incapable of deliberately causing any significant change in the climatic patterns of the earth. Changes in microclimate seemed to him so local and trivial that special instrumentation was needed to detect them. However, "Through changes in the water balance and sometimes inadvertently, he exercises his greatest influence on climate."

What happens when vast areas come under irrigation? This has taken place over 62×10^3 square kilometers of Oklahoma, Kansas, Colorado, and Nebraska since the 1930s. Some meteorologists have maintained that about a 10 percent increase in rainfall occurs in the area during early summer, allegedly attributable to moisture reevaporated from the irrigated lands. Synoptic meteorologists have generally made a good case for the importation, through precipitation, of moisture from marine sources, especially the Gulf of Mexico. Yet ^{3}H determinations have shown, at least for the Mississippi valley area, that two-thirds of the precipitated water derives from locally evaporated surface waters. Anyone who has ever analyzed trends in rainfall records will be very cautious about accepting apparent changes as real until many decades have passed. For monthly rainfall totals, 40 to 50 years may be needed to establish trends because of the large natural variations.

This century has seen, also, the construction of very large reservoirs. Very soon after these fill they have measurable influences on the immediate shore vicinity. These are the typical lake effects. They include reduction in temperature extremes, an increase in humidity, and small-scale circulations of the land- and lake-breeze type, if the reservoir is large enough. Rarely do we have long records as a basis for comparing conditions before and after establishment of the reservoir. Recently, Zych and Dubaniewicz published such a study for the 30-year-old reservoir of the Nysa Klodzka river in Poland, about 30 square kilometers in area. At the town of Otmuchow, about 1 kilometer below the newly created lake, a 50-year temperature normal was available (for the years 1881 to 1930). In the absence of a regional trend there has been an increase in the annual temperature of 0.7°C at the town near the reservoir. It is now warmer below the dam than above it, whereas, before, the higher stations were warmer because of the temperature inversions that used to form before the water surface exerted its moderating influence. It is estimated that precipitation has decreased, because of the stabilizing effect of the large body of cool water. Here, as elsewhere, the influence of a large reservoir does not extend more than 1 to 3 kilometers from the shore. Another form of deliberate man-controlled interference with microclimate, with potentially large local benefits, is suppression of evaporation by monomolecular films. Where wind speeds are low, this has been a highly effective technique for conserving water. The reduction of evaporation has led to higher water surface temperature, and this may be beneficial for some crops, such as rice.

The reduction of fog at airports by seeding of the water droplets also belongs in this category of man-controlled local changes. In the case of supercooled droplets, injection of suitable freezing nuclei into the fog will cause freezing of some drops, which grow at the expense of the remaining droplets and fall out, thus gradually dissipating the fog. For warm fogs, substances promoting the growth or coalescence of droplets are used. In many cases dispersal of fog or an increase in visual range sufficient to permit flight operations can be achieved. Gratifying though this achievement is for air traffic, it barely qualifies as even a microclimatic change because of the small area and brief time scale involved. Similarly, the changes produced by artificial heating in orchards and vineyards to combat frosts hardly qualify as microclimatic changes.

Finally, a brief note on general weather modification is in order. Most of the past effort in this field has been devoted to attempts to augment rainfall and suppress hail. The results have been equivocal and variously appraised. The technique, in all cases, has been cloud seeding by various agents. This produces undoubted physical results in the cloud, but the procedures are too crude to permit prediction of the outcome. Thus, precipitation at the ground has been both increased and decreased. The most reliable results of attempts to induce rainfall have been achieved through seeding clouds forming in up-slope motions of winds across mountains and cap clouds. Elsewhere targeting of precipitation is difficult, and the effects of seeding downwind from the target area are not well know. No analysis has ever satisfactorily shown whether cloud seeding has actually caused a net increase in precipitation or only a redistribution. In any case, if persistently practiced, cloud seeding could bring about local climatic changes. But an ecological question arises: If we can do it, should we? This point remains controversial.

Attempts to suppress hail by means of cloud seeding are also still in their infancy. Here the seeding is supposed to achieve the production of many small ice particles in the cloud, to prevent any of them from growing to a size large enough to be damaging when they reach the ground. The seeding agent is introduced into the hail-producing zone of cumulonimbus — for example, by ground-fired projectiles. Some successes have been claimed, but much has yet to be learned before one would acclaim seeding as a dependable technology for eliminating this climatic hazard.

Hurricane modification has also been attempted. The objective is reduction of damage caused by wind and storm surges. Seeding of the outer-wall clouds around the eye of the storm is designed to accomplish this. The single controlled experiment that has been performed, albeit successfully in the predicted sense, provides too tenuous a basis for appraising the potential of this technique. Here again we have to raise the warning flag because of the possibility of simultaneous change in the pattern of rainfall accompanying the storm. In many regions tropical storm rain is essential for water supply and agriculture. If storms are diverted or dissipated as a result of modification, the economic losses resulting from altered rainfall patterns may outweigh the advantages gained by wind reduction. As yet such climatic modifications are only glimpses on the horizon.

GENERAL URBAN EFFECTS

By far the most pronounced and locally far-reaching effects of man's activities on microclimate have been in cities. In fact, many of these effects might well be classified as mesoclimatic. Some of them were recognized during the last century in the incipient metropolitan areas. Currently the sharply accelerated trend toward urbanization has led to an accentuation of the effects. The problem first simply intrigued meteorologists, but in recent years some of its aspects have become alarming. Consequently the literature in this field has grown rapidly and includes several reviews summarizing the facts.

We are on the verge of having a satisfactory quantitative physical model of the effect of cities on the climate. It combines two major features introduced by the process of urbanization. They concern the heat and water balance and the turbulence conditions. To take changes in turbulence first, the major contributory change is an increase in surface roughness. This affects the wind field and, in particular, causes a major adjustment in the vertical wind profile so that wind speeds near the surface are reduced. The structural features of cities also increase the number of small-scale eddies and thus affect the turbulence spectrum.

The change in the heat balance is considerably more radical. Here, when we change a rural area to an urban one, we convert an essentially spongy surface of low heat conductivity into an impermeable layer with high capacity for absorbing and conducting heat. Also, the albedo is usually lowered. These radical changes in surface that accompany the change from rural to urban conditions lead to rapid runoff of precipitation and consequently to a reduction in local evaporation. This is, of course, equivalent to a heat gain — one which is amplified by radiative heat gain resulting from the lowering of the albedo. This heat is effectively stored in the stone, concrete, asphalt, and deeper compacted soil layers of the city. In vegetated rural areas usually more incoming radiation is reflected and less is stored than in the city. Therefore structural features alone favor a strongly positive heat balance for the city. To this, local heat production is added. The end result is what has been called the urban heat island, which leads to increased convection over the city and to a city-induced wind field that dominates when weather patterns favor weak general air flow.

Most of the features of the near-the-surface climatic conditions implied by this model have, over the years, been documented by comparisons of measurements made within the confines of cities and in their rural surroundings, mostly at airports. Such comparisons gave reasonably quantitative data on the urban effect, but some doubts remained. These stemmed from the fact that many cities were located in special topographic settings which favored the establishment of a city — such as a river valley, a natural harbor, or an orographic trough. They would by nature have a microclimate different from that of the surroundings. Similarly, airport sites were often chosen for microclimatic features favorable for aviation. Some of the uncertainties can be removed by observing atmospheric changes as a town grows. An experiment along this line was initiated three years ago in the new town of Columbia, Maryland. The results so far support earlier findings and have refined them.

Perhaps of most interest is the fact that a single block of buildings will start the process of heat island formation. This is demonstrated by air and infrared surface temperature measurements. An example is given in Figure 3. The observations represented by the curves of Figure 3 were made in a paved court enclosed by low-level structures which were surrounded by grass and vegetated surfaces. On clear, relatively calm evenings the heat island develops in the court, fed by heat stored in the daytime under the asphalted parking space of the court and the building walls. This slows down the radiative cooling process, relative to cooling from a grass surface, and keeps the air that is in contact with the surface warmer than that over the grass.

The heat island expands and intensifies as a city grows, and stronger and stronger winds are needed to overcome it. And although it is most pronounced on calm, clear nights, the effect is still evident in the long-term mean values. Figure 4 shows the isotherms in the Paris region, which is topographically relatively simple and without appre-

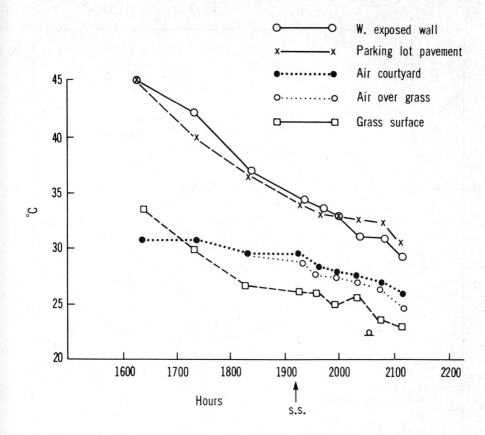

Figure 3. A typical example of microclimatic heat island formation in incipient urbanization. The top two curves show radiative temperatures of wall and parking lot pavement on a clear summer evening (6 August 1968). The two middle curves show air temperatures (at elevation of two meters) in the paved courtyard and over an adjacent grass surface; from sunset (s.s.) onward, the courtyard is warmer than the air over the grass. The bottom curve gives the radiative temperature of grass. The symbol at 2030 hours indicates the start of dew formation.

ciable differences in elevation. A pronounced metropolitan heat island of about 1.6°C in the mean value can be seen. This is typical of major cities. In the early hours of calm, clear nights the city may be 6° to 8°C warmer than its surroundings. The Paris example is noteworthy because it has been demonstrated that the rise in temperature is not confined to the air but also affects the soil. It has been observed in a deep cave under the city, where temperatures have been measured for two centuries. Curiously enough, the cave temperature was once considered so invariant that the cave

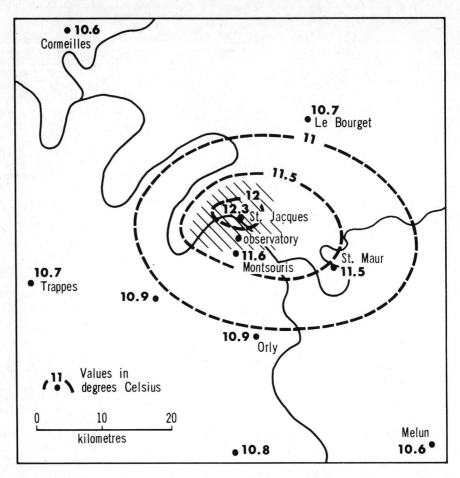

Figure 4. The urban heat island of Paris, shown by mean annual isotherms in degrees Celsius. The region is characterized by minimal orographic complexity.

in question was proposed as one of the fixed points for thermometer scales. This artificially introduced trend in temperatures also plays havoc with the long-term temperature records from cities. They become suspect as guides for gauging the slow, natural climatic fluctuations.

Part of the rise in temperature must be attributed to heat rejection from human and animal metabolism, combustion processes, and air-conditioning units. Energy production of various types certainly accounts for a large part of it. In the urbanized areas the rejected energy has already become a measurable fraction of the energy received from the sun at the surface of the earth. Projection of this energy rejection into the next decades leads to values we should ponder. One estimate indicates that in the year 2000 the Boston-to-Washington megalopolis will have 56 million people living within an area of 30,000 square kilometers. The heat rejection will be about 65 calories per square centimeter per day. In winter this is about 50 percent, and in summer 15 percent, of the heat received by solar radiation on a horizontal surface. The eminent French geophysicist J. Coulomb has discussed the implications of doubling the energy consumption in France every 10 years; this would lead to unbearable temperatures. It is one of a large number of reasons for achieving, as rapidly as possible, a steady state in population and in power needs.

An immediate consequence of the heat island of cities is increased convection over cities, especially in the daytime. That has been beautifully demonstrated by the lift given to constant-volume balloons launched across cities. The updraft leads, together with the large amount of water vapor released by combustion processes and steam power, to increased cloudiness over cities. It is also a potent factor in the increased rainfall reported from cities, discussed below in conjunction with air pollution problems. Even at night the heating from below will counteract the radiative cooling and produce a positive temperature lapse rate, while at the same time inversions form over the undisturbed countryside. This, together with the surface temperature gradient, creates a pressure field which will set a concentric country breeze into motion. A schematic circulation system of this type is shown in Figure 5.

The rapid runoff of rainfall caused by the imperviousness of the surfaces of roads and roofs, as well as by the drainage system, is another major effect of cities. In minor rainfalls this has probably only the limited consequence of reducing the evaporation from the built-up area and thus eliminating much of the heat loss by the vaporization that is common in rural areas. But let there be a major rainstorm and the rapid runoff will immediately lead to a rapid rise of the draining streams and rivers. That can cause flooding and, with the unwise land use of flood plains in urban areas, lead to major damage. The flood height is linearly related to the amount of impervious area. For the 1- to 10-year recurrence intervals, flood heights will be increased by 75 percent for an area that has become 50 percent impervious, a value not at all uncommon in the usual urban setting. Observations in Hempstead, Long Island, have shown, for example, that, for a storm rainfall of 50 millimeters, direct runoff has increased from 3 millimeters in the interval from 1937 to 1943 to 7 millimeters in the interval from 1964 to 1966. This covers the time when the area changed from open fields to an urban community.

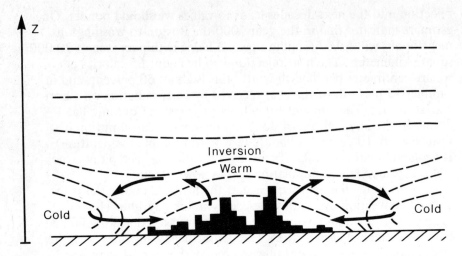

Figure 5. Idealized scheme of nocturnal atmospheric circulation above a city in clear, calm weather. The diagram shows the urban heat island and the radiative ground inversions in rural areas, a situation that causes a "country breeze" with an upper return current. (dashed lines = isotherms; arrows = wind; Z = vertical coordinate)

It is very difficult to document the decrease of wind speed over cities. Long records obtained with unchanged anemometer exposures at representative heights are scarce. Reasonable interpretations of available records suggest a decrease of about 25 percent from the rural equivalents. This is not unreasonable in the light of measurable increases in aerodynamic roughness. These are around 10 to 30 centimeters for meadows and cultivated fields and around 100 centimeters for woodland. There are several estimates for urban areas. I will give here a value calculated from the unique wind measurements on the Eiffel tower at a height of 316 meters, and from other wind records in the Paris region. These data yield values around 500 centimeters. They also suggest a decrease in wind at the top of the Eiffel tower from the interval 1890–1909 to the interval 1951–1960 of 0.4 meter per second, or 5 percent of the mean wind speed. In view of the height of this anemometer, this is quite a notable adjustment of the wind profile to the increase in terrain roughness.

Air Pollution Effects

Most spectacular among the effects of the city upon the atmospheric environment are those caused by air pollution. The catalogue of pollutants put into the air by man is long and has been commented upon in so many contexts that reference to the literature will have to suffice. Nor shall I dwell here on the special interactions of pollutants with the atmosphere in climatically and topographically specialized instances, such as the much investigated case of Los Angeles. I shall concentrate, instead, on the rather universal effects of pollutants on local climates.

Among these is the attenuation of solar radiation by suspended particulates. Although this affects the whole spectrum, it is most pronounced in the short wavelengths. The total direct radiation over most major cities is weakened by about 15 percent, sometimes more in winter and less in summer. The ultraviolet is reduced by 30 percent, on an average, and in winter often no radiation of wavelengths below 390 nanometers is received. The extinction takes place in a very shallow layer, as simultaneous measurements taken at the surface and from a tall steeple have shown.

Horizontally, the particulate haze interferes with visibility in cities. When shallow temperature inversions are present, the accumulation of aerosols can cause 80- or 90-percent reduction of the visual range as compared with the range for the general uncontaminated environment. The haze effect is accentuated by the formation of water droplets around hygroscopic nuclei, even below the saturation point. This is the more noteworthy because relative humidities near the surface are generally lower in cities than in the countryside. This is attributable partially to the higher temperatures and partially to the reduced evaporation. Nonetheless, fog occurs from two to five times as often in the city as in the surroundings. Fortunately, this seems to be a reversible process. Recent clean-up campaigns have shown that, through the use of smokeless fuels, considerable lessening of the concentration of particulates, and hence of fog and of the attenuation of light, can be achieved. In London, for example, with the change in heating practices, winter sunshine has increased by 70 percent in the last decade, and the winter visibilities have improved by a factor of 3 since the improvements were introduced.

I have alluded above to the increase in cloudiness over cities. It is likely that the enormous number of condensation nuclei produced by human activities in and around cities contributes to this phenomenon. Every set of measurements made has confirmed early assessments that these constituents are more numerous by one or two orders of magnitude in urbanized regions than in the country. Every domestic or industrial combustion process, principally motor vehicle exhaust, contributes to this part of the particulate. Independent evidence suggests that there is more rainfall over cities than over the surrounding countryside. But the evidence that pollutants are involved is tenuous. There is little doubt that the convection induced by the heat island can induce or intensify showers. This has been demonstrated for London, where apparently thundershowers yield 30 percent more rain than in the surrounding area. Orographic conditions would lead one to expect more showers in hilly terrain. This is not the case. Although this buoyancy effect is certainly at work, it does not stand alone: in some towns there are observations of precipitation increases from supercooled winter stratus clouds over urban areas.Some well-documented isolated cases of snow over highly industrialized towns suggest a cloud-seeding effect by some pollutants that may act as freezing nuclei. Also the rather startling variation of urban precipitation in accordance with the pattern of the human work week argues for at least a residual effect of nucleating agents produced in cities. The week is such an arbitrary subdivision of time that artificial forces must be at work. Observations over various intervals and in various regions indicate increased precipitation for the days from Monday through Friday as compared with values for Saturday and Sunday. These increases usually parallel the increase in industrialization, and, again, there is evidence for a more pronounced effect in the cool season.

   Although most studies indicate that the increase in precipitation in urban areas is around 10 percent — that is, close to the limit of what could still be in the realm of sampling errors — some analyses have shown considerably larger increases in isolated cases. These instances have not yet been lifted out of the umbra of scientific controversy. But we should note here that some industrial activities and internal combustion engines produce nuclei that can have nucleating effects, at least on supercooled cloud particles. In the State of Washington in some regions that have become industrialized there is evidence of a 30-percent increase in precipitation in areas near the pulp mills over an interval of four decades. There are also incontrovertible observations of cloud banks forming for tens of kilometers in the plumes of power plants and industrial stacks. This is not necessarily associated with increased precipitation but raises the question of how far downwind man's activities have caused atmospheric modifications.

   In the absence of systematic three-dimensional observations. we have to rely on surface data. A recent study by Band throws some light on the conditions. He found that, for a heat island 3°C warmer than its surroundings, a small but measurable temperature effect was still notable 3 kilometers to leeward of the town. Similarly, a substantial increase in the number of condensation nuclei was noted 3 kilometers downwind from a small town. In the case of a major traffic artery, an increased concentration of nuclei was measurable to 10 kilometers downwind. For a major city, radiation measurements have suggested that the smoke pall affects an area 50 times that of the built-up region. These values, which are probably conservative, definitely indicate that man's urbanized complexes are beginning to modify the meso-climate.

As yet it is very difficult to demonstrate that any far-reaching climatic effects are the results of man's activities. If man-made effects on this scale already exist or are likely to exist in the future, they will probably be a result of the vast numbers of anthropogenic condensation and freezing nuclei. Among the latter are effective nucleating agents resulting from lead particles in automobile exhaust. These particles have become ubiquitous, and if they combine with iodine or bromine they are apt to act as freezing nuclei. Schaefer and others have pointed out that this could have effects on precipitation far downwind. These inadvertent results would lead either to local increases in precipitation or to a redistribution of natural precipitation patterns. They are, however, among the reversible man-made influences. As soon as lead is no longer used as a gasoline additive — which, hopefully, will be soon — the supply of these nucleating agents will stop and the influence, whatever its importance, should vanish promptly because of the relatively short lifetime of these nuclei.

Perhaps more serious, and much more difficult to combat, is the oversupply of condensation nuclei. Gunn and Phillips pointed out years ago that, if too many hygroscopic particles compete for the available moisture, cloud droplets will be small and the coalescence processes will become inhibited. This could lead to decreases in precipitation, a view that has recently been confirmed.

There remains one final area of concern: pollution caused by jet aircraft. These aircraft often leave persistent condensation trails. According to one school of thought, these artificial clouds might increase the earth's albedo and thus cause cooling. Although on satellite pictures one can occasionally see cloud tracks that might have originated from these vapor trails, they seem to be sufficiently confined, with respect to space and time, to constitute a very minute fraction of the earth's cloud cover. The other view of the effect of these vapor trails, which change into cirriform clouds, is that ice crystals falling from them may nucleate other cloud systems below them and cause precipitation. Any actual evidence of such events is lacking. And then we have the vivid speculations concerning weather modifications by the prospective supersonic transport planes. For some time military planes have operated at the altitudes projected for the supersonic transports. The

ozone layer has not been destroyed, and no exceptional cloud formations have been reported. The water vapor added by any probable
commercial fleet would be less than 10^{-9} of the atmospheric water
vapor; thus, no direct influence on the earth's heat budget can be expected. At any rate, it seems that the sonic boom is a much more direct
and immediate effect of the supersonic transport than any possible
impact it may have on climate.

There is little need to comment on the multitude of schemes
that have been proposed to "ameliorate" the earth's climate. Most of
them are either technologically or economically unfeasible. All of them
would have side effects that the originators did not consider. The new
trend toward thinking in ecological terms would lead us to require that
much more thoroughgoing analyses of the implications of these schemes
be made than have been made so far before any steps are taken toward
their implementation.

Summary

Natural climatic fluctuations, even those of recent years,
cover a considerable range. They can be characterized as a "noise"
spectrum which masks possible global effects of man-caused increases
of atmospheric CO_2 and particulates. Local modifications, either
deliberate or inadvertent, measurably affect the microclimate. Some
artificial alterations of the microclimate are beneficial in agriculture.
Among the unplanned effects, those produced by urbanization on
local temperature and on wind field are quite pronounced. The influences on rainfall are still somewhat controversial, but effects may
extend considerably beyond the confines of metropolitan areas. They
are the result of water vapor released by human activity and of the
influence of condensation and freezing nuclei produced in overabundance by motor vehicles and other combustion processes. Therefore
it appears that on the local scale man-made influences on climate are
substantial but that on the global scale natural forces still prevail.
Obviously this should not lead to complacency. The potential for
anthropogenic changes of climate on a larger and even a global scale
is real. At this stage activation of an adequate worldwide monitoring
system to permit early assessment of these changes is urgent. This
statement applies particularly to the surveillance of atmospheric
composition and radiation balance at sites remote from concentrations
of population, which is now entirely inadequate. In my opinion, man-
made aerosols, because of their optical properties and possible influences
on cloud and precipitation processes, constitute a more acute problem
than CO_2. Many of their effects are promptly reversible; hence, one

should strive for elimination at the source. Over longer intervals, energy added to the atmosphere by heat rejection and CO_2 absorption remain matters of concern.

SUGGESTED READINGS

Bryson, R. A. "All Other Factors Being Constant — A Reconciliation of Several Theories of Climatic Change." *Weatherwise* 21 (1968): 55 – 61.

Lamb, H. H. *The Changing Climate.* London: Methuen, 1966.

Meteorological Monographs 8, No. 30 (1968).

Namias, J. "Climatic Anomaly over the United States During the 1960s." *Science* 170 (1970): 741 – 743.

Peterson, J. T. *The Climate of Cities: A Survey of Recent Literature.* National Air Pollution Control Administration, Publication AP – 59. 1969.

Plass, G. N. "Carbon Dioxide and Climate." *Scientific American* 201 (1959): 41 – 47.

Rasool, S. I. "Evolution of the Earth's Atmosphere." *Science* 157 (1956): 1466 – 1467.

Sewell, W. R. D., ed. *Human Dimensions of Weather Modification.* Chicago: University of Chicago, Department of Geography Research Paper No. 105, 1966.

Stern, A. C. *Air Pollution.* 3 vols. New York: Academic Press, 1968.

Thornthwaite, C. W. "The Modification of Rural Microclimates." In *Man's Role in Changing the Face of the Earth,* edited by W. L. Thomas, Jr., pp. 567 – 583. Chicago: University of Chicago Press, 1956.

United States, Council on Environmental Quality. "Man's Inadvertent Modification of Weather and Climate." In *Environmental Quality: The First Annual Report of the Council on Environmental Quality,* pp. 93 – 104. Washington: U. S. Government Printing Office, 1970.

Urban Climates. Technical Note No. 108. Geneva: World Meteorological Organization, 1970.

CHAPTER 4

The Integrating Flows of Water
Introduction

For all of us, water is probably the most familiar subsystem of the natural environment. We drink it, we bathe in it, we swim in it, we water our lawns and gardens with it, we use it for disposing of our waste products. It is a simple chemical compound of only two elements, hydrogen and oxygen. The water subsystem, as manifest in oceans, rivers, lakes, or ponds is immediately recognizable, and it seems simple enough on first view. The fact that water occurs freely in liquid, solid, and gas form at ordinary temperatures may reinforce the notion that the water subsystem is relatively simple.

But such is not the 'case. As a chemical compound, water has many unique properties. Just to mention a few; it is an extraordinary solvent; it has the greatest specific heat (ability to store heat energy for a given increase in temperature) known among liquids; it has a high latent heat of vaporization (that is, much energy is needed to change it from liquid to gas). The chemistry and physics of water are indeed complex.

Everyone knows something about the hydrologic cycle. Water is heated and it evaporates into gas form, it is cooled and condenses into liquid again, it falls as rain and flows back to the sea. Less well-known but equally important is the fact that much of the life-sustaining and work-achieving energy received from the sun is transmitted to the other subsystems through water. Water provides the energy that shapes landforms. Water plays a role in soil formation; it dissolves minerals, moves particles about, and provides nutrients in solution for plant roots. And in biotic systems, water is an essential compound in photosynthesis and in all other growth processes. Water serves as raw matter, as a transporter of matter, as a cooling agent, as a provider of energy. Hence our use of the term "integrating flows of water."

All the water we see on the land comprises less than 1 percent of the total global supply. Just as less than 1 percent of the incoming solar radiation is used by plants for photosynthesis, so too less than 1 percent of the water available on earth is responsible for all the effects of water that we see in our landscapes.

The hydrologic cycle operates according to well understood physical laws of evaporation and condensation. But the flow pathways and their characteristics are often incredibly complex. On the global scale, the hydrologic cycle operates continuously, using both direct and transformed inputs of solar energy and the energy of gravity. In terms of its own matter supply, it is virtually a closed system in a steady state condition, since global evaporation balances global precipitation. The supply of water is constant on a global scale, and storage in the oceans doesn't vary measurably.

But the quantities and spatial pattern of water storage on land and its flow pathways in the air, land, soil and biota vary continuously. Regional and local water systems are open systems receiving inputs from their external environment; their long-run trajectory may be up, down or constant.

At the most general resolution level, hydrologists study exchanges of matter and energy between the water subsystem and the air, land, soil, and biota subsystems. At an intermediate resolution level, four components of storage and flow are usually recognized: surface water, soil water, ground water, and the water in the stream network. At a more specific (local) resolution level, three component subsystems of storage and flow are of primary concern: surface runoff (direct storm response), soil moisture flows, and ground water flows.

In actual practice, the hydrologic engineer deals mainly with the direct storm response and the flood flows associated with it. The unit hydrograph technique depicting the flow response over time for a given input of water into a given river system is used to predict the flood flow of the stream. Even though the processes operating in the system are not understood, reasonably accurate predictions can be made if known physical laws are operating and if inputs and outputs have been measured sufficiently often over a long enough period of time.

Measuring balances between inputs and outputs and the related concept of budgets are practical approaches. Such measurements can provide useful predictive information. It is usually possible to measure flows in and out of a system long before the scientific work is done which will make the system's internal processes understandable. The type of information needed to allow us to better understand the internal workings of a lake ecosystem is illustrated in Crippen and Pavelka's article on Lake Tahoe.

Given the complexity of most natural systems, we still have much to learn about their internal workings. Nace's article stresses the fact that our knowledge of the global water system is still hopelessly incomplete. Adequate hydrological flow data are lacking for two-thirds of the land area and nearly all the water area of the earth. Our knowledge of water systems is probably most complete at the regional scale, as illustrated by the article on Lake Tahoe. At this scale meaningful data are often available on the weather-climate, landforms, soils and vegetation which provide inputs to the water subsystem. And at this resolution level, the effect of inputs from the external environment are more noticeable.

While the systems of individual lakes and rivers are linked to all subsystems of the natural environment, they are directly dependent on inputs from their regional weather-climate system. Water enters from land surface flows, by direct fall on the water surface, and (in limited amounts) through soil and ground water seepage. Moisture flows across the land-water-air interfaces emphasize the importance of air mass movement to the hydrologic cycle. Various studies show that only 10–15 percent of the precipitation falling on the land of a given region is accounted for by water evaporated from the land of that region. The remainder is brought in by air masses flowing across the region. Tremendous amounts of water vapor flow into, through, and out of the atmosphere over each continent from ocean sources.

Three systems principles are important in relating water movement and storage to practices of management of lake or stream watersheds. First, an open system in nature tends toward a steady state equilibrium. Thus, there will be a balance of constructive and destructive forces involving the natural processes operating in the particular system itself and in its external environment. This is the principle noted previously by Odum: we cannot maximize both efficiency and stability. Trade-offs must be carefully considered for wise management of our natural systems. Second, the smaller and simpler the watershed system, the more easily can man modify it. In a small watershed local vegetation, soil, and stream characteristics more directly affect the watershed, and are easily accessible to man's interference. At the larger regional scale, climatic factors almost completely beyond man's control dominate the characteristic patterns of the water flows. Third, if the processes operating in the watershed are understood, then small actions or inputs by man can have large and anticipated effects. Efficient watershed management demands use of these three systems principles.

Hynes's article demonstrates an integrating ecosystem approach to managing streams which is based on all three principles. Hynes points out that while large-scale projects on streams have attracted much attention, small actions can trigger sizeable reactions from the organisms living in streams. For example, releasing water from the bottom of the reservoir behind a dam can prevent warm water fish from breeding. Hynes presents many other examples. We should particularly note the role played by standing and running water in cycling nutrients, as leaves and other organic debris are trapped by the water. Flowing water is familiar to all of us. But how many of us appreciate the many system processes that it accomplishes?

Water Resources: A Global Problem With Local Roots

Raymond L. Nace
Water Resources Division, United States Geological Survey
Department of the Interior

Reprinted with some deletions and modifications by permission of the author and
the publisher from *Environmental Science and Technology* 1 (1967), pp. 550–560.
Copyright 1967 by the American Chemical Society.

After 8000 years of historic and prehistoric management and
use of water, man has yet to come of age in his relations with water and
other aspects of the earth environment. Maturity in these relations will
depend on improved understanding of the environment, in which water
is a crucial factor. Water is rather well understood as a substance, but
the behavior of this substance in the global phenomenon known as the
hydrological cycle is but poorly understood. Intensive and extensive
needs and plans for water management, including transcontinental
diversions and distribution, will usher in a new era in history and a new
order of magnitude in environmental impacts and problems.

In order to cope with these problems, nations of the world must
cooperate to study water on national, international, continental, and
global scales. The International Hydrological Decade (IHD) from 1964
to 1974 in which 100 nations participated, provided the framework
for such cooperation. . . .

WATER AND CIVILIZATION

In the pre-dawn of the first morning of civilization, a man with
a wooden hoe labored somewhere on the Mesopotamian plain, digging a
long trench from his sown field toward the silt-laden River Euphrates,
or perhaps the Tigris. A final stroke of the hoe removed the last clump
of earth separating trench from river; the trench became a canal and the
field became an irrigated farm. The trickle of water in the irrigation
ditch has been heavenly music to men throughout the ensuing 8000
years.

The unknown farmer had planted more than the seed of grain
in his field. The seed of civilization quickened there. A one-farm irrigation system requires nothing but one-man initiative. But irrigation in
Mesopotamia spread within a few centuries through many hundreds of
thousands of acres, based on a complicated, well-engineered system
of river diversions and sluice gates, hundreds of miles of feeder canals
and ditches, systematic hand dredging of silted-up canals, and mainte-

nance of levees. Such a system required central administration and control for maintenance, allocation of water rights, and regulation of production. The first Chief of State may have been a river master.

A food supply assured by irrigation farming permitted the first permanent villages and in Mesopotamia it led to the first city-states and kingdoms. The subsequent spread of irrigation and ancient civilization in the Middle East, in Egypt, in India, and in China is a long story. Even longer is the story of the evolution of civilization as a whole and of its close ties to water for irrigation, navigation, sanitation, industrial and public supply, and waste disposal. During most of this 8000-year period, men simply used water where they found it, without understanding how fresh water happens to be where it is, or how it got there. As my colleague Walter B. Langbein expresses it, human water economy remained in the hunting and gathering stage during most of history and is still in that stage in the use of ground water. Many non-industrial countries are still in the hunting and gathering stage of water use.

A Rude Awakening

Around the middle of the present century hydrologists suddenly realized that hydrology had never found a place in the water-development industry comparable, for example, to the role of chemistry in industry. Hydrologists had been so engrossed in measuring the flow of rivers, the levels of ground water in wells, and the vagaries of precipitation that few of them had gotten into the market place and made hydrological facts and variables an integral part of water planning. They lacked even a common language for communication with economists, policy makers, and sociologists.

Awakened social consciousness among scientists is a phenomenon largely of the twenty years or so just past. This awakening contributed to the realization among hydrologists that, just as water development and planning go beyond the local area or individual river basin, so must hydrology go beyond these. Nor can it stop with multiple-basin regions or even the continents. The total amount of fresh water on the continents is only a minute percentage of all the world's water, most of which is brine or ice. Hence the flow of water in the Amazon River, for example, is important to North Americans, for a given molecule of water cannot be present in the Amazon and the Colorado at the same time.

The water cycle is a global phenomenon. Therefore, water resources are a global problem with local roots. The occurrence and movement of water in one part of the world are consequences of its occurrence and movement in all other parts of the world. At present this cycle can be described only in crudely quantitative terms which

are of little help in prediction, but prediction is essential for rational
water management. Controlled systematic modification of phenomena
such as precipitation requires vastly improved knowledge and understanding of the water cycle on a global scale. Hydrological data are
either lacking or totally inadequate for two thirds of the land area and
nearly all of the water area of the world. Among the nearly blank areas
are the great weather factories: polar areas, tropical areas, and major
oceans. Not even the United States is rich enough or sufficiently well
supplied with technical manpower to undertake studies of all the data-
deficient areas of the world. How, then, can knowledge and understanding be achieved? The International Hydrological Decade was an
attempt to answer this question. . . .

WORLD WATER BALANCE

Study of the world water balance consists of an inventory of
the total amount of water in the Earth system and its movement
through the global hydrological cycle (see Table 1). About 97 percent
of all water in the system is in the world ocean. Most of the remainder
is frozen assets in icecaps and glaciers. Much less than 1 percent is
present at any given time as liquid fresh water in rivers, lakes, and
aquifers. The average amount of water vapor continually present in the
atmosphere is a vanishingly small percentage of total water. Rivers
annually discharge about 9000 cubic miles of water into the seas, but
this value is merely a rough approximation because less than 5000 cubic
miles of discharge is actually measured.

The amount of water in land areas is such a small part of total
earth water (326,000,000 cubic miles) that it is virtually lost in the
system. An explorer from space who wished to tell the home office
about that curious substance, water, which covers most of the earth,
probably would ignore continental water, because the amount is far less
than the margin of error in estimates of the oceans and icecaps. Nevertheless, earthlings must pay increasing attention to the relatively negligible continental part of Earth's water system. This entails many
problems because the water is constantly moving and means for measuring it outside the laboratory are relatively crude.

For water planning, development, and management, continuous
measurement of river stages is necessary in order to calculate daily,
seasonal, annual, and long-term yield. Under good conditions the flow
of an ordinary river of moderate size can be calculated from measurements of depth and velocity of water with an accuracy of 95 percent or

Table 1. World water budget is tiny though important portion of world water supply

Water Item	Volume (cubic kilometers)	Percent of Total Water
Supply		
Water in land areas:		
Fresh-water lakes	125,000	0.009
Saline lakes and inland seas	104,000	.008
Rivers (average instantaneous volume)	1,250	.0001
Soil moisture and vadose water	67,000	.005
Ground water to depth of 4,000 m.	8,350,000	.61
Icecaps and glaciers	29,200,000	2.14
Total in land area	37,800,000	2.8
Atmosphere	13,000	.001
World ocean	1,320,000,000	97.3
Total, all items	1,360,000,000	100
Budget		
Annual evaporation:[a]		
From world ocean	350,000	0.026
From land areas	70,000	.005
Total	420,000	0.031
Annual precipitation:		
On world ocean	320,000	0.024
On land areas	100,000	.007
Total	420,000	0.031
Annual runoff to oceans from rivers and icecaps	38,000	0.003
Ground-water outflow to oceans[b]	1,600	.0001
Total	39,600	0.0031

[a] Evaporation (420,000 km.^{3}) is a measure of total water participating annually in the hydrological cycle.
[b] Arbitrarily set equal to about 5 percent of surface runoff.
Note: Values in the table are approximations based on data compiled from many sources. They should not be construed to mean that any of the values is precise.

even better. But a large flood cannot be directly measured at all by any means now available. A river as large as the Amazon near its mouth requires an expedition and an ocean-going ship to make a single direct measurement of normal flow.

Ground water presents even greater difficulties than surface water because it is out of sight, its movement cannot be measured directly, and its total quantity is unknown except in a few local areas

that have been studied intensively. From general geological and hydrological information, it is evident that unused ground water is available
in many areas. Development of ground water has the advantage that
wells can be drilled quickly for irrigation, domestic supply, public
supply, and industry. Where adequate ground water is available, wells
can be drilled singly or by the hundreds without awaiting construction
of multimillion-dollar dams and canal systems. Thus thousands of wells
have been drilled in the Gangetic Plain of India and the ground-water
supply is adequate for thousands more. Ground-water is available even
in some desert areas which have no other source of water. The vast
Sahara Desert (nearly as large as the conterminous United States) is
underlain by great thicknesses of geological formations which are
abundantly water-bearing at some places. Further exploration may
disclose that the Sahara contains an extensive system of aquifers that
can be exploited. This, however, will require vastly more scientific
knowledge about the area than is available now because groundwater
management is by no means simple. . . .

Evaporation from oceans and continents and total precipitation
on land and sea are additional hydrological factors for which only crude
or sparse data are available. But enough has been said about other
aspects of the hydrological cycle, to show that it is a very large task
just to inventory the average amounts of water in various environments
to derive a still picture. To go beyond that and to portray the moving
picture of the water cycle in quantitative terms is a vastly greater task
which will require synoptic measurements at many places throughout the world and throughout each year.

Some measurements can be made by remote-sensing, a field in
which technology is advancing rapidly. Techniques include ordinary
and color photography, infrared imagery and scanning, and radar
scanning, to mention only a few. Remote-sensing instruments carried
in airplanes can do part of the job but repetitive wide coverage by that
means would be prohibitively expensive. Prospects are good that much
may be accomplished quickly and economically with instruments in
orbiting satellites. Examples of information that might be obtained
from satellite data are maps of large flooded areas; seasonal variations
in snow cover in remote areas; long-term variations in the boundaries of
icecaps; boundaries and extent of oceanic currents; breakup of pack ice
and shelf ice and distribution of large icebergs; extent of glaciers and
perennial snow in remote areas; and many other possibilities. In addition, communications satellites may permit more efficient use of data
that have been obtained by conventional methods. Stream gauges, for
example, can be equipped to transmit data by radio to a satellite. The

satellite would relay information to a national or regional computer center, which would manipulate the data, print it out and transmit it to data users. . . .

Cold-Storage Lockers

Glaciers and icecaps cover 11 percent of the land area of the world, and most of the ice area has been mapped only crudely or on very small scales. An additional 10 percent of the land areas is locked in permafrost-permanently frozen ground. At any given time, 30 to 50 percent of the world land area is covered with snow, while 25 percent of the ocean is occupied by pack ice and icebergs. Worldwide, 75 percent of all fresh water in existence is stored as ice, chiefly in Antarctica and Greenland, but ice and snow loom large in the water cycle in vast areas that are far more hospitable than polar regions. . . .

Snow and ice studies are part of the world water balance project, but they have much additional significance. . . . Glaciers in the state of Washington alone, covering 135 square miles, store about 42 million acre-feet of water — about equal to the combined storage of the state's reservoirs, lakes, and stream channels. During the dry months of July and August, these glaciers release about 800,000 acre-feet of water to streamflow — about equivalent to total pumpage of ground water in the state during a whole year. The principal source of streamflow in Washington and other Western States is snow and ice above 7000 feet of altitude.

Glaciers and perennial snowfields are, in effect, nonstructural water reservoirs, and the possibilities for their management merit thorough investigation. Possibilities include suppression of evaporation, suppression of melting in wet years, inducement of melting in dry years, and others. The possibilities have more than local significance. Snow, ice, and permafrost dominate the water scene in Alaska and huge areas in Canada, northern Europe, Siberia, and high mountain areas in Asia and South America. Alaska alone contains 20,000 linear miles of glaciers storing perhaps 12 billion acre-feet of water. The extent to which reserves of snow and ice are manageable for water supply is an almost totally unexplored field.

Glaciers are highly sensitive to variations in climate. The weight of evidence seems to indicate that many alpine and valley glaciers have been shrinking appreciably during more than 100 years. However, evidence of growth during the same period is definite for certain glaciers. Whether the major ice sheets are waxing, waning, or in equilibrium is controversial among specialists, which means that not enough data are available to support firm conclusions.

It is important, however, to know current and recent trends, because small changes of world climate can profoundly affect water supplies regionally and locally. It is equally necessary to know what variations occurred during past centuries. If recurrent patterns or cycles have occurred, perhaps future ones can be predicted. Methods are available for study of past variations: ice cores are being studied to compare the water content of successive annual layers; precipitation rates can be estimated from oxygen-isotope ratios in successive layers; individual layers may be correlated from glacier to glacier and even from continent to continent on the basis of volcanic dust falls. Dust from several violent volcanic eruptions during the historical period has spread through the atmosphere of the entire globe. Glaciologists some-day may find the ice-dust layer correlative with the eruption of Thira volcano, which some investigators believe destroyed Minoan Crete and perhaps ancient Troy in about 1400 B. C.

The International Commission of Snow and Ice (a scientific commission of the International Association of Scientific Hydrology) has recommended, and the IHD Council has endorsed, a world-wide network of glacial observation stations. This would include a latitudinal chain of stations extending from northern Europe and the Alps east-ward to the Caucasus and through the mountains of Central Asia and the Himalaya. In North America, Canadians expect to extend one or two chains eastward across their country. A second world chain would be meridional, extending from Alaska through the coastal ranges of British Columbia and western United States and through the Andes of South America to Patagonia. These studies will be coordinated with other investigations, such as expeditions to Antarctica and Greenland and Canada's Axel Heiberg Expedition to her Arctic island of that name. . . .

Research

Studies of the world water balance, including snow and ice, will require specific research to close gaps in understanding of the water cycle. An example of an important topic is the causes of the incidence and spread of continental drought. Other types of IHD research, how-ever, concern specific hydrological processes. An example is studies of representative basins.

Small hydrological basins have been selected for special study in each continent. These are large enough to represent conditions and processes in larger areas, yet small enough to be studied intensively with adequate instrumentation. Six basins have been chosen in the United States. The hydrological characteristics and regimes of these basins will be studied in relation to climate, vegetation, soils, geology, and other factors in an effort to derive general principles. Studies of this kind can be and have been made individually in various countries without benefit of international cooperation. Few of these studies have been broadly or fundamentally definitive because isolated studies may and often do lead to wrong conclusions whose wrongness becomes apparent only when the supposed basic principles fail on application in a different and differing area. . . . The purpose of the international project is to stimulate study in a large number of basins throughout the wide range of physical and ecological conditions from arctic tundra to searing desert, from tropical rain forest to alpine valley, and so on. Participation in this activity extends from countries in Europe and Asia to those of Africa and from North and South America to New Zealand and Australia.

Another example of important long-term research is the establishment of hydrological benchmarks analogous to topographical benchmarks. Locations are chosen in isolated areas that have been disturbed little or not at all by human activity and have a chance of remaining inviolate for many years. These will be observed (runoff, precipitation, water quality, sediment movement, etc.) in an effort to relate hydrological variations with their natural causes. In most areas, man has so disturbed the environment that it is difficult or impossible to determine which hydrological variations are man-induced and which are natural. Benchmarks will aid in differentiation of causes but obviously must be operated far longer than a decade. The importance of this idea has been widely recognized but action has been slow. Undisturbed areas that will remain so are scarce or lacking in most European countries. In addition, many developing countries have not solved the problem of obtaining systematic observations in remote areas.

Water Facts for the Future

People make decisions about water every day, but in many areas hydrologists can contribute little to the soundness of these decisions even when their advice is sought. One of the principal reasons for this is lack of basic data. Officials of the Food and Agriculture Organization of the United Nations have emphasized to the IHD Coordinating Council that, in their agricultural development projects, they commonly have to design projects on the basis of only one to a few years of sparse hydrological data, whereas they need 20 or more years of record. The reason is that rainfall, river flow, ground water levels and other phenomena vary widely. These variations are not just seasonal or annual. Superimposed on the short-term variations are longer ones ranging from decades to hundreds of years. Given a decade or two of streamflow records, hydrologists have methods for synthesizing and predicting probable variations during much longer periods of time.

The uses of data are so many and varied that they cannot even be summarized here. It can be stated only that water facts are crucial for the future. Many countries, therefore, are making strong efforts to improve their data networks and to establish networks where none exist. Countries that have skill in data collection and analysis are assisting less privileged countries by assisting them with network design, selection of instruments, training of personnel, and application of methods for analysis and interpretation of data. . . .

SUGGESTED READINGS

Chorley, R. H., ed. *Water, Earth and Man.* London: Methuen, 1969.

Cram, J. S. *Water: Canadian Needs and Resources.* Montreal: Harvest House, 1969.

Hunt, C. A. and Garrels, R. M. *Water: The Web of Life.* New York: Norton, 1972.

Olson, R. E. *A Geography of Water.* Dubuque, Iowa: Wm. C. Brown, 1970.

Scientific American. *The Ocean.* San Francisco: Freeman, 1969.

Sellers, W. D. *Physical Climatology.* Chicago: University of Chicago Press, 1965.

Tweedie, A. D. *Water and The World.* Rev. ed. Melbourne: Thomas Nelson, 1969.

The Hydrology and Limnology of Lake Tahoe

J. R. Crippen and B. R. Pavelka
United States Geological Survey, Department of the Interior

Reprinted by permission of the authors and the publisher from *The Lake Tahoe Basin, California–Nevada*, Geological Survey Water Supply Paper 1972 (Washington: U.S. Government Printing Office, 1970), pp. 33–47.

Hydrology is the study of the waters of the earth, their occurrence, distribution, and movement. A description of the hydrology of the Lake Tahoe basin is concerned with the water brought to the basin as rain or snow, its movement within the basin, the forces that act upon it, and its manner of leaving the basin.

Hydrology is not as yet an exact science. The study of forces and factors involved in the behavior of water in the environment includes atmospheric physics, hydraulics, chemistry, and biology. The quantities involved are tremendous; a winter storm that brings 2 inches of water to the basin in 2 or 3 days as rain or snow carries more than 70 million tons of moisture. At the same time the destiny of each molecule of water entering the environment is uniquely determined by the physical and chemical interactions to which it is exposed. Obviously, we can only generalize about those quantities and forces. The random variations that exist in nature from place to place and from time to time make precise measurements rather pointless. We can only gather records of data that most directly concern us and use that information to describe what we consider to be the important characteristics of hydrology.

Data that have been gathered in the Lake Tahoe basin (Figure 1) include snow depths and water contents, total precipitation (rainfall plus the water equivalents of snowfall), evaporation of water from a standard 4-foot diameter pan, and temperature. Precipitation, evaporation, and temperature data have been gathered at only a few points, mostly near the lake. The most accurately measured data, however, are the outflows from the lake into Truckee River. These have been measured since 1901, and daily as well as annual flows are known to within a few percent. Records of the level of water in the lake have also been kept, and therefore variations of the amount of water in storage are known.

The tabulation of quantities of inflow of water to a region and of the quantities leaving the region and the routes by which they leave is called a hydrologic budget. Figure 2 is the estimated annual hydrologic budget of the Lake Tahoe basin. The value shown for average

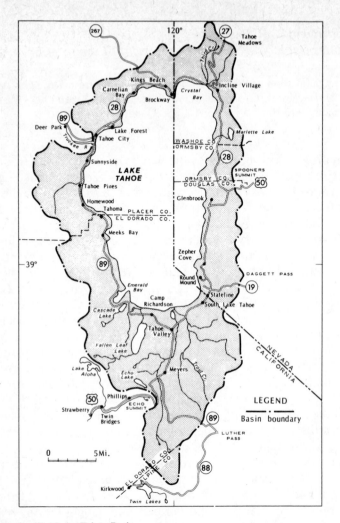

Figure 1. The Lake Tahoe Basin

annual change in storage is really meaningless because a drop of 7 inches in lake level during the 66 years would change storage by 70,000 acre-feet and would be interpreted as an average annual change of 1,000 acre-feet. Changes in storage of more than 70,000 acre-feet during single years are frequent.

The story of Figure 2 is amplified by the information in Table 1, statistics of the annual hydrologic budget of the Lake Tahoe basin. The table shows the mean value (that is, the average of all estimated or

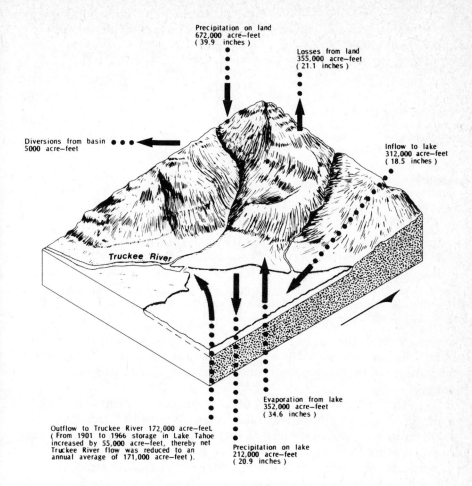

Precipitation on land
672,000 acre—feet
(39.9 inches)

Losses from land
355,000 acre—feet
(21.1 inches)

Diversions from basin
5000 acre—feet

Inflow to lake
312,000 acre—feet
(18.5 inches)

Truckee River

Evaporation from lake
352,000 acre—feet
(34.6 inches)

Outflow to Truckee River 172,000 acre—feet.
(From 1901 to 1966 storage in Lake Tahoe
increased by 55,000 acre—feet, thereby net
Truckee River flow was reduced to an
annual average of 171,000 acre—feet).

Precipitation on lake
212,000 acre—feet
(20.9 inches)

Figure 2. Estimated annual hydrologic budget of the Lake Tahoe basin.

observed annual events), the median (the value between the highest
half and the lowest half of events), the standard deviation (a measure
of scatter; for example, about two-thirds of the years had outflow
of between 52,000 and 290,000 acre-feet), and the greatest and smallest
estimated or observed annual values. Because of the relative ease of
measurement, the values of outflow of water from the lake are much
more accurate than any of the other components of the budget. The
values of average annual precipitation and water loss pertaining to land
and water surfaces may be in error by several percent. The same is
true of the precipitation lines of Figure 3 and of the component values
suggested for individual years in the specific instances that are cited

Table 1. Estimated statistics of the annual hydrologic budget of the Lake Tahoe basin, 1901–66.

Component	Mean	Median	Standard Deviation	Maximum	Minimum
Runoff to lake, after diversion (inches)	18.5	17.0	8.0	41.5	4.6
Precipitation on lake (inches)	20.9	20.5	4.2	35.0	12.8
Evaporation from lake (inches)	34.6	35.2	3.3	39.5	28.2
Net runoff from basin[1] (acre-feet)	172,000	155,000	205,000	767,000	−194,000[2]
Outflow to Truckee River[3] (acre-feet)	171,000	152,000	119,000	657,000	4,700
Range in stage (feet)	2.27	1.97	.94	4.9	.8

[1] Represents outflow to Truckee River if year-end lake level were always the same.
[2] Negative value reflects excess of evaporation from the lake over the sum of inflow and precipitation on the lake.
[3] Outflow as it actually occurred.
Note.—0.3 inch of runoff is diverted from the basin and therefore does not reach the lake. Highest lake stage: 6,231.26 feet, July 1907. Lowest lake stage: 6,221.74 feet, December 1934.

in this report; however, because their integrated residual in the form of changes in storage and outflow are known rather precisely, the relative magnitudes of the components, one to another, cannot be greatly in error.

The annual diversion of 5,000 acre-feet . . . is from Echo Lake, Marlette Lake, and Third Creek. The losses from land of 355,000 acre-feet include evaporation from small lakes and streams, in addition to evaporation from moist soil surfaces, and from transpiration, the process by which plants utilize water. After these losses, probably a little less than half the water that falls on the land reaches the lake in the form of streamflow or underground seepage. The lake also receives precipitation directly on the lake surface. It loses water to the air by evaporation, and the residual flows over the dam and through the gates at Tahoe City into the Truckee River or is retained to increase the amount of water stored in the lake. Losses from the lake by underground flow or seepage are probably very small or non-existent.

As shown in Table 1, the components of the hydrologic budget vary greatly from year to year. The period October 1 to September 30 of the following year is by convention called the water year. It is selected as the period most convenient for hydrologic computation. During the wet water year from October 1, 1906, to September 30, 1907, inflow to the lake from the land was 698,000 acre-feet, and

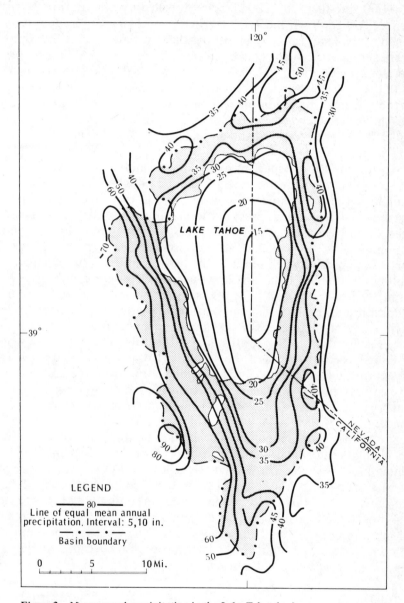

Figure 3.   Mean annual precipitation in the Lake Tahoe basin.

precipitation on the lake was 356,000 acre-feet. Of this input of 1,054,000 acre-feet, 287,000 acre-feet was lost by evaporation, 657,000 acre-feet flowed down the Truckee River, and 110,000 acre-feet remained in the lake. In contrast, during the dry water year 1924, only 78,000 acre-feet reached the lake from the land and 130,000 acre-feet by direct precipitation; 402,000 acre-feet was lost by evaporation and 178,000 acre-feet was released to the Truckee River. Because of the low total inflow, storage in the lake was diminished by 372,000 acre-feet. The extreme changes in lake storage were the decrease just described, in water year 1924, and an increase of 419,000 acre-feet in water year 1938.

An important aspect of hydrology, in addition to quantity, is timing because the growing season is the period when both man and nature have the greatest need for water. The Lake Tahoe basin has the same seasonal variation in precipitation as does the entire region west of the Sierra Nevada; that is, winter precipitation and summer dryness. The timing of inflow to Lake Tahoe is also affected by the fact that much of the precipitation input to the basin is in the form of snow, awaiting release by the melting that occurs in late spring and early summer. Thus, most of the 212,000 acre-feet average inflow from direct precipitation upon the lake comes during the months December to March, while much of the 312,000 acre-feet runoff from the land area is often delayed until the months of April to July. These inflows, when considered as components of the net input to the storage and discharge regimen of the lake, are modified by evaporation from the lake surface. The evaporation loss is relatively small during the damp, cool winter months and is greater during the late spring and summer (the melt period).

August, September, and October are months of little precipitation, negligible snowmelt, and high evaporation. Therefore the 9 remaining months can be considered the inflow period and can in turn be separated into the 5-month winter period, November to March, when most precipitation arrives but when there is little melting of snow and the 4-month melt period, April to July, when there is much less precipitation but more snowmelt and evaporation. The variations in timing and magnitude of net input to the lake can be demonstrated by data from the unusually dry and unusually wet years 1961 and 1965:

1961 net input:	Winter Period	Melt Period
Time	Jan. 24–March 31	Apr. 1–June 13
Percent	29	71
Thousand acre-feet	28	70

1965 net input:

Time	Dec. 19–Mar. 31	Apr. 1–Aug. 17
Percent	60	40
Thousand acre-feet	333	226

Net input is the sum of Truckee River outflow plus increase in storage in Lake Tahoe. The 1961 melt period was rather short, while in 1965 a severe storm in December caused both heavy wintertime runoff into the lake and a prolonged period of snowmelt. Before and after the periods shown, evaporation loss from the lake was generally greater than inflow.

The variation of annual precipitation from place to place is shown by Figure 3. Inflow to the lake generally varies in location in proportion to the quantity of precipitation received by the various contributing streams. Inspection of Figure 3 shows that the south and west parts of the basin, especially the areas draining towards Emerald Bay and Fallen Leaf Lake, receive the most precipitation; that region therefore contributes a large part of the inflow. Of the inflow to Lake Tahoe from land areas, 70 to 90 percent is from California.

The slopes of the Lake Tahoe basin are drained by many streams; by far the greatest flow is from three that enter the south end of the lake. These are, from east to west, Trout Creek, Upper Truckee River, and Taylor Creek. Together they drain about 36 percent of the land area of the basin and yield from 40 to 45 percent of the runoff. These and other selected basins are shown in Figure 4.

Under natural conditions the streams entering Lake Tahoe carry an average of 100 to 250 milligrams per liter (i.e. parts per million) of suspended sediment, as do most streams in the Sierra Nevada. This is equivalent to about 0.13 to 0.34 tons of sediment per acre-foot of inflow, or 40,000 to 100,000 tons per year, on the average. Some of the sediment settles in the lake, and the Truckee River probably carries away not more than 0.06 to 0.13 ton per acre-foot, or 10,000 to 25,000 tons per year. This indicates that perhaps 50,000 tons of sediment are deposited in Lake Tahoe each year, enough to reduce the average depth of the lake by 1 foot in about thirty-two hundred years. The activities of man in the basin probably increase the volume of sediment entering the lake, and some of this material is undoubtedly deposited on the lake bottom. However, our knowledge of the quantities involved and of their trends is not complete enough to justify an estimate of the long-range effect.

Lake Tahoe water contains some 60 to 70 milligrams per liter of minerals in solution. Most streams in the area that have been studied contain similar concentrations of dissolved solids, so it is reasonable to

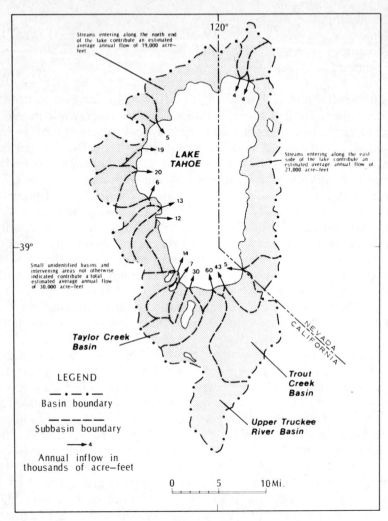

Figure 4. Principal subbasins contributing to Lake Tahoe and their estimated average annual flow.

assume that streamflow entering and leaving the lake has the same characteristic; studies of Truckee River water show about the same concentrations. These values converted to weights show that about 30,000 tons of dissolved solids per year on the average enter the lake in streamflow and about 17,000 tons leave it. Precipitation and fallout of soluble dust from the air can be conservatively estimated to add another 1,000 tons per year of dissolved solids, so that the net increase of minerals in Lake Tahoe is probably about 14,000 tons per year. If all this material remained in solution, concentration of dissolved solids would increase about 10 milligrams per liter in one hundred years; however, there are several physical, chemical, and biological processes that remove solutes from the water, and therefore the actual increase in concentration is considerably slower. The dissolved solids in both the streams and the lake are in the form of ions, mostly bicarbonate, silica, calcium, sodium, sulfate, and chloride.

In addition to suspended sediment and dissolved minerals, flowing water carries organic material derived from the environment through which it passes. This material ranges in size from floating tree trunks, through decaying leaves and bark, down to particles too small to see. If conditions are favorable the organic material eventually decays to form gases and adds to the dissolved mineral content of the water. The processes and products of decay are important to the biology of a stream or lake, and the density and character of aquatic life are dependent upon the physical and chemical characteristics of the water.

Lake Tahoe receives organic material from the streams that feed it. Because of the great volume of water in the lake, the incoming water remains there a very long time, and the processes of decomposition are given the opportunity to operate more completely than in a smaller lake. Also, about 40 percent of the water annually entering the lake comes as precipitation and is almost completely free of organic material. Moreover, in the past there has been a low supply of nutrients to the lake, therefore biological productivity of the lake has been inhibited. For these reasons, under the natural regimen the lake as a whole is almost completely free of the disagreeable side effects that accompany an overabundant supply of organics, such as objectionable odor, taste, or color of the water.

LIMNOLOGY

Limnology is the scientific study of bodies of fresh water, with special reference to plant and animal life. In this section, Lake Tahoe is described as an example of the family of lakes, and its unique characteristics as an individual are examined in terms of lakes in general. Limnology and hydrology are thoroughly intertwined; therefore, this and the preceding section are closely related.

Lakes originate in many ways. Glacial movement sometimes scoops out a trough that may fill with water and become a lake; Fallen

Leaf Lake is an example of such action. Glacial debris, landslides, or volcanic outflows can obstruct valleys and create lakes. The ground surface can subside, either because of the removal of soluble underlying rock by water or because of crustal movements of the earth, and provide a basin that will fill until water finds a point of overflow. Lakes form in the craters of inactive volcanoes and in the oxbow-shaped troughs left behind when a river changes its course. Lake Tahoe has been affected by many of these phenomena. The Tahoe valley itself was formed by the sinking of a massive block of the earth's crust during a period of geological instability. The level of the lake and the location of its outflow have been affected by glacial action, by lava flows from volcanic vents, and undoubtedly by landslides. Because of the predominating influence of crustal sinking in its formation, Lake Tahoe is considered a magnificant example of a graben lake. Many large lakes have been formed in this manner, among them the two deepest known: Baikal in Siberia (greatest known depth about 5,700 feet), and Tanganyika, in Africa (4,800 feet). Pyramid Lake, into which the Truckee River flows, is a graben lake about one-fifth as deep as Lake Tahoe.

Although Lake Tahoe is not among the large lakes of the world in surface area, it is the 14th largest natural fresh-water lake in the United States, excluding the Great Lakes. The combination of area, depth, and altitude, together with the relatively small area of contributing basins, creates a unique situation. The great volume of the lake, about 122 million acre-feet, results in a relatively slow flushing action by the water that flows through. Flushing time, sometimes called self-purging time, must be measured on the basis of outflow from the lake; water losses by evaporation tend to concentrate impurities rather than to remove them. The flushing time of Lake Tahoe computed thus (dividing volume by annual outflow) is roughly 700 years; this compares to some 185 years for Lake Superior, having 97 times the volume of Lake Tahoe; about 10 years for lakes Chelan in Washington, Seneca in New York, and Sebago in Maine; and 2.6 years for Lake Erie, having more than four times Lake Tahoe's volume. Thus the flushing action resulting from the passage of water is much slower in Lake Tahoe than in most lakes, and the time of residence of a given mass of water, together with all the organic and inorganic material carried by the water, is relatively long. This long residence probably has some effect upon the dissolved minerals; it can be very important to the fate of organic materials, and it allows the settling of a large part of the incoming sediment. Because flushing time is dependent upon the complete exchange of water in the lake and because it is unlikely that all the water involved in vertical mixing processes within the lake passes through the inflow-outflow system of the lake at a uniform rate, it is probable that the true flushing time for Lake Tahoe is considerably longer than 700 years.

The clarity of water can be measured in several ways. The most common method that provides a basis for comparison from place to place is by noting the depth to which a Secchi disk can be followed. Results of this method are subject to a rather wide range of error, however, because of differences among observers, differences in the condition of the water surface, and differences in conditions associated with the incoming light at the water surface. The transmission of light through water can be measured more objectively by use of a hydrophotometer, a device that is relatively free of such errors. Hydrophotometer readings taken at Lake Tahoe indicate that, in general, between depths of about 30 to 500 feet, 90 percent of incoming light is extinguished by 120 or 130 feet of water. Hydrophotometer readings and Secchi disk readings in other lakes show that the waters of Lake Tahoe are among the clearest water found in nature anywhere in the world.

Water temperature is an important characteristic of a lake. Its variation from time to time and its role in creating vertical currents are very significant in determining the nature of biological activity. Lake Tahoe, like most lakes, frequently has three strata or layers of water of differing temperature characteristics; the vertical extent of these layers varies with weather conditions, especially wind, and with the amount of heat added to or removed from the water within the lake. The layering fades out of existence as autumn winds and low temperatures cool the surface of the lake, and there may be mixing of water within the upper 500 feet or so of the lake because of density currents arising from temperature differences and agitation by the wind.

The three layers of water are most clearly defined during late summer and early fall. At that time there is an upper layer of relatively warm water, called the epilimnion, in which temperature decreases very slowly with depth. The temperature of the epilimnion in Lake Tahoe may sometimes slightly exceed 70°F, and the layer sometimes extends to depths as great as 75 feet. In shallow protected parts of the lake, water temperatures may be somewhat higher than the prevailing temperature of the epilimnion.

Below the epilimnion, from March or April to November or December, is another layer that varies in vertical thickness as the season advances and sometimes may reach to a depth of 250 feet. This is the region in which temperatures decrease much more rapidly as depth increases, and in a typical late summer period it may exhibit a decrease in water temperature from 65°F at a depth of 35 feet to 45°F at 180 feet. This zone of rapid temperature change is called the thermocline; in shallower lakes the thermocline occupies a much narrower range of depths and the temperature gradient is necessarily much steeper.

Below Lake Tahoe's thermocline lies another layer, the hypolimnion, in which temperature again changes but slowly with depth. The hypolimnion exists as a separate zone only during the summer period when temperatures in the epilimnion are markedly higher than those at greater depths; thus the upper boundary of the hypolimnion corresponds to the lower boundary of the thermocline, and the mutual boundary in Lake Tahoe is very indefinite. The warmest temperatures of this deep layer are probably about 50° F in late summer. Very few readings have been made of water temperatures in Lake Tahoe at depths greater than 500 feet; the few data that are available indicate that, the year around, the temperature of this deep water is very close to 39° F, the temperature at which water has its greatest density. Professor C. R. Goldman, of the University of California at Davis, has conducted studies that include the collection of data from great depths in Lake Tahoe.[1] He concluded that the lake is "monomictic"; that is, the water is mixed completely to the bottom once each year. This conclusion is supported by data of temperature and chemical gradients and by the fact that the water is nearly saturated with oxygen throughout the depth of the lake.

The oxygen content of the water is another factor in establishing the nature of a lake. In general, water in Lake Tahoe contains from 7 to 11 parts per million of dissolved oxygen, existing as molecules intermixed with the molecules of water. This represents a healthy condition because there is great capacity for eliminating organic impurities; low oxygen content is usually reflected by the presence of organic material that is only partially decomposed, a condition resulting in disagreeable color, odor, or taste and in a loss of transparency of the water. The dissolved oxygen in Tahoe seems to range from 90 to 105 percent of saturation throughout the upper 500 feet of the lake and varies in concentration chiefly with temperature and depth.

In water containing the relatively low concentrations of dissolved solids that are present in Lake Tahoe, biological activity depends strongly on the presence of oxygen, the prevalence of favorable temperatures, the clarity of the water which allows light necessary for photosynthesis to penetrate, and the availability of nutrients, especially nitrate and phosphate. Almost all water, including that of Lake Tahoe, contains microscopic organisms called plankton. Plankton includes plants, such as algae, and animals, such as protozoa. The plants thrive on nitrate and phosphate, and when these substances are present in the proper quantity and proportions, algae grow and multiply rapidly, sometimes experiencing bursts of growth called "blooms" that produce clouds of greenish algae. Under some circumstances, live algae growths can cause unpleasant characteristics to appear in water, similar to those associated with partially decomposed organic material.

In the normal regimen of a lake, the algae propagate and then die at a moderate rate, and the dissolved oxygen contained in the lake water is sufficient to support decomposition of the dead algae as well as all the other organic material that is continually entering the lake. If the volume of algae increases beyond some critical point, however, oxygen may be depleted by the decomposition of dead algal cells and other organic material in the water. When this occurs, the water may become colored by the undecomposed material, and the taste and odor of the water may be affected. The entire process — that of enrichment and the chain of events culminating in increased organic content — is called eutrophication.

Eutrophication proceeds most rapidly in shallow lakes that receive large amounts of plant nutrients. Algae grow most bountifully where light is present, and little light reaches the bottom of deep lakes. Lake Erie, which is rather shallow and receives nutrients in great volumes, has reached a high degree of eutrophication while none of the other and deeper Great Lakes shows such advanced signs of enrichment. It is likely then that under natural conditions, eutrophication of Lake Tahoe would be a long-time process. However, it is possible that the phase of eutrophication that is accompanied by the widespread appearance of algal blooms near the surface could be initiated in the near future if phosphate and nitrate, found in great quantity in sewage and fertilizers, continue to be injected into the lake.

From the preceding description of eutrophication, it is obvious that under the natural regimen of Lake Tahoe conditions favorable to small localized algal blooms might exist in some parts of the lake. Such blooms do in fact occur and have been observed in shallow, sheltered coves where organic material has been deposited and the circulation of water from the main body of the lake is restricted. Undoubtedly, such situations arose before man affected the lake. It is probable that, regardless of the true extent of change due to the entry of man, phenomena such as algal blooms now are more quickly detected and more widely publicized because of the widespread attention that has been directed to Lake Tahoe.

There has been much study of the eutrophication of lakes and streams but the process is very complex and involves many chemical and biological interactions so there remains much that is unknown.

Most authorities now believe that accelerated eutrophication might begin in Lake Tahoe with the addition of nitrate and phosphate and that the phosphorus now in the lake is present in concentrations that are almost critical so that an increase in nitrogen could trigger the process.

In terms of geologic time, Lake Tahoe, like all lakes, is doomed to a short life; however, its life expectancy is much longer than that of most other lakes because of its great depth. Lake Tahoe will probably remain as a large body of water long after many other lakes have been emptied by geological processes or have become filled with sediment to form marshes or solid land. It is possible, however, for man to introduce contamination that can make at least some aspects of the lake less pleasing than they have been in the past. The history of our treatment of other lakes and streams gives ample proof that our refuse can defile such beauty quickly and easily and that it probably will do so unless safeguards of some type are adopted.

Fortunately, in the Lake Tahoe basin, there is little evidence of such obvious befouling of the environment as is found in large industrial areas — the great clouds of smoke from factory chimneys, the spreading oozing heaps of slag, the windrows of trash that collect at hedges and fences, and the floating scum and solids that appear in ponds and streams. Probably there never will be smoke clouds or slag heaps in the region; there is little likelihood that heavy industry will find the basin to be an economical site. There are other and more subtle processes of contamination, however, and these are the threats that are feared.

Metropolitan region planners generally consider that on the average each person imposes about 120 gallons of sewage and 4 pounds of rubbish daily on his environment. Sewer lines, treatment facilities, and trash collection systems are usually planned to handle such an output. In the Tahoe basin, however, much of the population is transient and does not use as much water as would the same number of permanent residents, and there is little industry. For these reasons the per capita use of water in the Tahoe basin can be assumed to be somewhat lower, perhaps 90 gallons per day in 1965 and 100 gallons per day by 1990. Thus the quantities of refuse and sewage that were produced in 1965 and may be produced in 1990 in the basin can be summarized by the estimates of Table 2.

Both rubbish and sewage are sources of pollution that can adversely affect Lake Tahoe. In addition to unsightly remains, they introduce minerals and organic substances that may upset the aquatic community that has developed under the natural regimen. Chief among

Table 2. Pollution Inputs.

Period	1965		
	Population[1]	Sewage (millions of gallons)	Rubbish (tons)
Daily, slack season	26,000	2.3	52
Daily, average	53,000	4.8	110
Daily, peak season	170,000	15	340
Annual Total		1,700	40,000

	1990		
	Population[1]	Sewage (millions of gallons)	Rubbish (tons)
Daily, slack season	90,000	9	180
Daily, average	170,000	17	340
Daily, peak season	420,000	42	840
Annual Total	—	6,200	124,000

[1] Middle range of estimates from several sources made during 1960–66.

these harmful substances are phosphate and nitrate, which are abundant in fertilizers; therefore, water that has passed over or percolated through fertilized soil adds to the nutrient load that enters the lake. However, chemical and biochemical processes within the soil tend to decrease the quantity of phosphate and nitrate that are contributed by fertilizers.

Little can be done to reduce the amounts of nutrients that enter Lake Tahoe from the undeveloped parts of the basin. It would probably be harmful to stop that contribution even if it were practicable to do so; the well-balanced cycle of microscopic life that has existed in the lake is necessary to the existence of desirable characteristics. It is an overabundance of activity that is to be avoided, and the greatest potential for creating such an overabundance is in the probable increase in sewage.

Most of the sewage from the larger communities in the basin is now treated before being released, although overloads and breakdowns of equipment have occasionally allowed untreated sewage to enter the lake. Before the influx of visitors and residents that began about 1950, the amount of sewage entering the lake was not believed to pose a serious problem. The only effects of human activity that are clearly defined are an occasional increase in coliform organisms in some popular beach areas, especially at the south end of the lake, and local increases in turbidity when construction activity has introduced sediment into the lake.

Many plans have been proposed for avoiding the contamination of Lake Tahoe by sewage. All plans call for the complete capture and subsequent treatment of all sewage originating within the basin. The degree of treatment differs according to the ultimate disposal of the effluent as envisioned by each plan. Treatment methods are known that, although expensive, will produce an effluent of such high quality that it would meet generally accepted standards for drinking water, but even then the concentrations of nitrate might be unacceptable as inflow to the lake. Distillation of the sewage would leave only pure water, of course, but it would be prohibitively expensive.

The plan that seems most practical, and that has been adopted, is to treat the sewage thoroughly in order to produce an effluent of drinking-water quality and to pump the effluent through pipelines to streams outside the basin. This would involve the export, by 1990, of perhaps 19,000 acre-feet each year and therefore would require that the outflow of the lake be lessened by that amount or that water of acceptable quality be imported to supply the deficiency. The export destinations that are planned are the headwaters of the Carson River, for sewage originating at the south end of the lake, and the Truckee River, for sewage from the northern region. Sewage from regions along the east and west shores of the lake can be routed to one or the other of these export systems. The southern export route might require a total pumping lift of well over 1,000 feet, while the northern route would be almost level and therefore require much less pumping.

The solution by treatment and export is expensive, but not prohibitively so; local, State and Federal groups are agreed on the need for preserving the purity of Lake Tahoe, and there will be cooperation from each of these sources. Probably the greatest difficulties to be surmounted are those created by the tangle of conflicting jurisdictions and by prejudices. Laws, court decisions, and agreements of the past have established attitudes concerning water rights that are not always in accord with the maximum benefits that can be obtained, while even the most complete purification cannot remove from some peoples' minds the stigma sometimes associated with water that has once been sewage. The resolution of these difficulties requires sessions of patient discussion leading to mutual understanding. Some authorities have suggested that the creation of a regional agency with jurisdiction over water-associated matters in the area affecting the Tahoe basin may be the most practical way to bring this about.

Construction activity of almost every nature can affect the lake adversely. In addition to the introduction of sediment, nutrient transport is likely to be accelerated by the disruption of the natural ground cover. Here again, cooperation on a regionally uniform basis is necessary. It may be that guidelines can determine the nature and location of construction and logging activity and perhaps the timing, on the basis of optimum use of the lake and its environs.

Boaters, too, can introduce undesirable contaminants to the lake. Proposals for the reduction of pollution arising from boat use include the sealing of sanitary facilities and periodic inspection to insure that neither human wastes nor grease and oil leakage can reach the lake.

Rubbish and garbage can be removed from the basin by truck to some point of disposal. It is highly probable that, within the next few decades, garbage and the solid residue of sewage treatment plants can be economically converted to serve as fuel, fertilizer, or raw materials for reprocessing. Until such a time, however, some suitable disposal site must be used.

To summarize: Eutrophication is part of the natural evolution of a lake. Geologically speaking, lakes are temporary features of the landscape. In terms of human history, however, they are long lived and can be enjoyed by many generations. If mankind is careless in his treatment of a lake, he can speed up eutrophication to the point that the desirable characteristics of the lake can be adversely affected within decades. In the case of Lake Tahoe, there are indications that rapid and unpleasant changes in the lake may be imminent. The cooperative efforts of all who are associated with the basin of Lake Tahoe can prevent this catastrophe. The means of forestalling that day are obvious and are within our reach: we have only to stop the uncontrolled inflow of everyday waste products into the basin.

REFERENCES

[1] C. R. Goldman and Carter, R. C., "An Investigation by Rapid Carbon-14 Bioassay of Factors Affecting the Cultural Eutrophication of Lake Tahoe, California-Nevada," *Journal of the Water Pollution Control Federation* 37 (July, 1965): 4044–4059.

SUGGESTED READINGS

Black, P. E. "The Watershed in Principle." *Water Resources Bulletin* 6 (1970): 153–161.

Bruce, J. P. and Clark, R. H. *Introduction to Hydrometeorology*. Oxford: Pergamon, 1966.

Dooge, J. C. I. "The Hydrologic System as a Closed System." *Proceedings, International Hydrologic Symposium* 2 (1967): 98–113.

Goldman, C. R. and Carter, R. C. "An Investigation by Rapid Carbon-14 Bioassay of Factors Affecting the Cultural Eutrophication of Lake Tahoe, California-Nevada." *Journal of the Water Pollution Control Federation* 37 (July, 1965): 1044–1059.

Kazmann, R. G. *Modern Hydrology*. 2nd ed. New York: Harper & Row, 1972.

Laycock, A. H., Francisco, M., and Fisher, T., eds. *Water Balance in North America*. Urbana: American Water Resources Association, 1969.

Rasmussen, J. L. "The Atmospheric Water Balance and the Hydrology of Large River Basins." *Water Resources Bulletin* 6 (1970): 631–639.

United States, Environmental Protection Agency, Water Quality Office, *Agricultural Pollution of the Great Lakes Basin*. Washington: U.S. Government Printing Office, 1971.

The Ecology of Flowing Waters in Relation to Management

H. B. N. Hynes
Professor of Biology, University of Waterloo, Waterloo, Ontario

Reprinted with some deletions and modifications by permission of the author and the publisher from *Journal Water Pollution Control Federation* 42 (1970), pp. 418–424, Washington, D.C. 20016.

In this second half of a century in which man probably has done more to alter his environment than in any previous millenium of his history, we are at last coming to appreciate some of the bad consequences of our actions. It is now possible to find words "ecosystem" and "eutrophication" in the popular press, terms which twenty years ago were all but unknown outside the campus or the most esoteric government research laboratory, and it appears that most journalists really know what they mean. This is a great advance, as it has resulted in public awareness of pollution, dust bowls, falling water levels, and other desecrations of the landscape that had previously attracted little, or only passing, attention.

But these are the obvious effects of modern man — his population explosion and his industries. We know how to mitigate many of them, and very often it is merely a question of the money and the will to do something about it. Certainly some big problems remain, such as how to cope with persistent insecticides, how to prevent enrichment of lakes, and worries about the increasing carbon dioxide in the atmosphere and its possible effects on climate. The purpose of this report is to point out that there are also lesser problems that have not hit the headlines. Some of them may be quite important in our efforts to preserve at least some rivers and streams, in something like their original condition, for posterity.

We cannot, in this paper, deal with the whole scope of the ecology of running water. For a more complete treatise on this subject see *The Ecology of Running Water* by Hynes. Herein we choose certain aspects of the subject and show how they may be related by subtle disturbances by man, and how this may have a bearing on management practices.

TEMPERATURE

An unaltered stream in a temperate climate has a definite seasonal temperature regime, but it rarely becomes very warm because it is always shaded by riparian trees. Some streams become very cold in winter, but others, because they are spring-fed or receive large amounts of groundwater, remain relatively warm. Small differences of a few degrees often are important to stream organisms. For instance, in southern Ontario the winter-warm streams never contain winter stoneflies of the genus *Allocapnia*, and our most common species of *Gammarus* is confined to spring-fed streams. At the other end of the scale, the brook trout cannot survive temperatures above 25.3°C, so it also is confined in southern Ontario to cool waters. Probably in pre-settlement times it occurred almost everywhere in the province, but clearing of the land·exposed the streams to the sun, and summer temperatures rose above the brook trout's limit of tolerance. The general public may be indifferent to alterations in distribution of invertebrates, but many of them certainly are concerned about trout, and a biologist wonders if it was really necessary to clear the woods right down to the stream banks quite so universally. The same thing is known to have occurred in the Appalachians, where the trout now occur almost entirely in the high, still forested areas, and the phenomenon is probably general over most of this continent.

There are even more subtle effects of changes in temperature. Most stream animals have definite breeding seasons, and their life-cycles are geared to fit into the annual cycle of temperature change. For winter stoneflies it must be cold, actually very cold, for growth to occur, and trout must have water colder than 14.4°C in order to breed. Blackflies emerge only when the water reaches about 10°C, and many mayflies grow only in cool water. They must therefore have a long spring warm-up period in which to develop; and if the summer temperatures come too soon, before they have escaped as adults to lay heat-resistant eggs, they are killed by the heat.

What appear to be quite minor changes in temperature may have profound biological effects. Merely clearing out the trees and bushes may lengthen the blackfly season or kill off a number of mayfly species, and the warm effluent which raises the temperature by only a few degrees in winter, or even a degree or two in summer, may eliminate the trout as surely, but much less spectacularly, than a dose of poison. Similarly a dam that releases cold water from the deeper levels of the impoundment during the summer will prevent warm-water fishes, such as largemouth bass, from breeding. Cold water does not kill them, they would not survive the winter if it did, but they need the high summer temperatures for successful reproduction.

It follows that many apparently harmless human actions can cause quite dramatic changes, but in so subtle a way that they occur almost unnoticed.

THE SUBSTRATUM

The second point concerns the river bed, which is itself a product of the river and in particular of the regime of discharge. It may be composed of rocks or rubble, gravel or sand, or a mixture of these materials, and it may be clean or silty. Where the discharge increases considerably at times — as it does in most streams because of thaw or storm — the ligher material is swept away, and a particular type of substratum is maintained.

Many species of animal and plant are confined to one or very few types of substratum, either because they need a special surface to which to attach, as do mosses, or because they need to shelter under stones, or burrow down into clean gravel, etc. Rooted plants, the so-called weeds, are of particular interest here because while most of them occur primarily in silt, a few, such as milfoil and water crowfoot, can establish themselves in gravel. Then, as they grow and spread with prostrate stems and adventitious roots, they trap silt and produce little hummocks of stems, roots, and silt on the bed. These are unstable and freshets break them up, so that there is a constant irregular cycle of colonization and breakdown. However, where the discharge is fairly even and freshets do not occur, as below large springs and in lake outflows, great stable areas of weeds develop, and they completely alter the substratum and with it the animal populations. In England, where the many miles of nineteenth century canals are just such rivers, albeit manmade, a great deal of time and money is spent in keeping the waterways open for pleasure craft, which unlike the old-time barges do not keep the weeds down. Similarly below many dams on North American rivers there are great green swards of growth. They may be in no way objectionable, indeed they are often beautiful, but they are not a normal river habitat, and such places do not support the original riverine animals. The Shand Dam on the Grand River in Ontario, which is used for flood control and makeup water during periods of low flow, produces a long stretch of weedy and algal covered substratum because no very high water occurs to sweep the plants away. As a result the benthic fauna is very different from that above the impoundment, and some normal animals, e.g., stoneflies, are absent. The fish fauna also is different, but that is probably because of temperature; cold water is released in summer and several warm-water species have been eliminated.

It is not meant to imply that such results of river management are deleterious, only to point out that they occur, and that we should be aware of them and think about them when we plan. Sometimes a dam results in a marked improvement in the ecosystem, or it may produce conditions that we would regard as desirable. An example of the former is an impoundment on the South African Vaal River, that holds back the scouring sand that elsewhere in the river results in reduced populations of invertebrates, and hence probably of fishes. Examples of the latter are dams which discharge cold water and allow the development of trout fishing in regions that otherwise would be too warm for trout.

We should, however, always be aware that alteration of the substratum may lead to biological problems. Concrete structures in the otherwise sandy, silty-bedded Mississippi have permitted the establishment of net-spinning *Trichoptera* in such numbers that the adults swarm to lights and become a serious nuisance, and it was necessary, during the construction of the Volta Dam in Ghana to prevent the development of large blackfly populations on the apron. Ontario blackflies merely bite and drive people to distraction, but a common and well-named African species, *Simulium damnosum,* carries disease, so a large population caused by the provision of a suitable substratum, can be a real menace to health.

THE SOURCES OF FOOD FOR STREAM ANIMALS

In most ecosystems the primary source of food for the animals is grown more or less where it is eaten. We are accustomed, therefore, to finding large numbers of insects, and of things that feed on them, in places where there is a lot of plant growth, and we do not expect to find many animals in deserts where plants are scarce. Rivers and streams are exceptional in that they nearly always support great numbers of invertebrates and fish, yet comparatively rarely are they well vegetated. Admittedly, large rivers support phytoplankton, as does the open water of lakes, but it is usually strictly seasonal and unstable as it is swept away readily by floods, and in small rivers and streams it is quite unimportant. From where then does the energy come that supports all the animals? The answer appears to be from the land surface in the form of leaves, twigs, and dissolved organic matter, and if one thinks of streams as they must have been before man intervened, this fact is hardly surprising. Valleys are damp places even in a dry climate, so river and stream banks must nearly always have been heavily vegetated. Most small streams were undoubtedly completely canopied over, as were the shallower littoral regions of rivers. Running water was not, therefore, a good habitat for plants, and it is not surprising that not many types evolved that were capable of living in it. On the other hand it was always very well supplied with litter, and certainly more so than the forest floor as the water surface acts as a trap — a leaf that is blown onto it does not blow off again. The whole ecosystem has, therefore, become adapted to using this material, and running water is thus a normal consumer of dead organic matter. That is why we have been able to use it so effectively for disposal of our wastes, until we came to expect too much of it and caused what we term pollution.

In our laboratory we have been studying what happens to the ordinary plant debris that falls into streams; we feel that it is important to know about this in order to understand the fundamental processes of pollution. Some of our results to date are of considerable relevance to water management.

When a dead leaf falls into water, it rapidly loses weight because of the leaching out of soluble material, between 4 and 16 percent of the dry weight according to the species of tree. It then enters upon a long period of decay during which it loses weight more or less rapidly, again according to species, but also according to the quality of the water. If the latter is enriched by nitrate and phosphate the rate of decay is markedly increased; the leaf absorbs nitrate from the water to such an extent that, although its own weight is decreasing, the amount of nitrate in it is actually rising. This nitrate is converted into protein so that the protein content of the leaves does not decline as the leaves decay, and may even rise in some species, providing a continuous supply of good food for secondary consumers. This is almost certainly one of the mechanisms that results in higher production of fish from rich than from poor streams.

Results show that this nutritional enrichment of whole leaves is caused almost entirely by the growth of fungi, most of which are quite ordinary soil-dwelling species. Moreover, these fungi render the leaves attractive to the invertebrates that feed on them, and they definitely select leaves on which the fungi have grown. The rate of decay of leaves is, therefore, a measure of their attractiveness, and leaves such as elm and maple are eaten before those of oak and beech that lose weight more slowly.

Apparently, at this early stage of decay, bacteria play a very minor role, but they may be important in the further decay of the undigested decay material of the first eaters. Perhaps it should be stressed here that most of the animals that chew up rotting leaves also eat detritus, and that this is very largely material that they, or their fellows, have already passed through their systems. Although we still do not know this for certain, detritus also gathers up nitrate and converts it to protein for further use repeatedly, until all the energy in the organic matter is used up.

It will be clear, therefore, that water quality must to a great extent control the rate of use of organic matter in rivers and streams, and that this is quite independent of any plant growth in the water. Even well purified wastewater, or drainage of fertilizers from fields, therefore must have a profound effect on the biota. We do not really know what this is, except that production is increased, but it would appear that it would also tend to shift low altitude animals upstream, e.g., to bring suckers into trout water. In any event we should be aware that we are changing things, and we should study those changes and decide if they are acceptable. They quite certainly are subtle and would not be obvious from the road bridge, but they undoubtedly would be there.

This also raises the question, "What are the consequences of adding just some organic matter, not enough really to alter the Dissolved Oxygen (DO) or even to change the Biological Oxygen Demand (BOD) appreciably?" We are certainly changing the so-called heterotrophic cycle, and this may have far-reaching results.

Actually when we add a little organic matter, such as wastewater or farm or rural industry effluent, much of it is in solution. We saw above that several percent of leaf litter normally dissolves very soon. What becomes of it? Our studies show that, again with much variation according to species of origin and water quality, it becomes particulate. First, particles of about 1 micron diameter appear; they then aggregate into particles of about 10 microns, and these coalesce still further and finally sink to join the detritus on the bottom. This process is only partly biotic as it also occurs under sterile conditions, but in normal stream water the particles are bacterial and fungi. Ten microns is about the size of most of the food particles taken by blackfly larvae, and this may well be the source of most of their food. It has already been shown that these larvae can be reared to maturity on suspensions of bacteria, and there is evidence that pollution has caused them to increase in the Saskatchewan River. Almost certainly therefore a little mild pollution aids these pests. One wonders how many screen-embattled cottagers and enshrouded fishermen in the north country realize this, and whether money spent on insecticides and repellants would not be better spent on better drains.

The Breeding of Fishes

To the general public fishes are probably the most important component of aquatic life and cause millions of dollars to change hands every year.

Adult fish are remarkably tolerant of conditions, and they live and grow well in almost all types of water as long as they are not poisoned, suffocated, starved, or overheated. This is evident from the remarkable circumstances in which many goldfish are kept, and the unlikely looking ponds that are successfully stocked with trout. But many of the fishes of running water are fairly narrowly restricted in their choice of breeding site, and if suitable conditions are not available they simply fail to breed. Some require large stones, some silt-free gravel, some clean sand, and many move out onto flooded land to spawn on terrestrial vegetation and fail to breed well in years in which the river scarcely overflows its banks. Even within these broader categories there are restrictions. Trout, for instance, spawn only where there is actually flow through the gravel that they can detect because of movement of water into or out of the gravel surface, and some chubs can only use sites where the stones are small enough for the male fish to carry them in his mouth and pile up a nest. Moreover, the breeding sites are often not where the adult fishes live, and many species move from pools to riffles, or far upstream into shallower headwaters to breed.

Any human interference with a water course is likely, therefore, to alter breeding sites in such a way as to restrict or encourage the reproduction of certain species, and possibly eliminate some species altogether. The trouble in the last instance is that the extinction occurs quite unnoticed; no mass deaths occur but the species disappears. Some such alteration of breeding site, or of access to it, probably accounts for the disappearance of the Ohio shad. Impoundment for navigation, flood control, or water supply may alter the bed by siltation or the development of vegetation, and thus render it unsuitable for the spawning of some species, and channelization for flood control can remove some types of habitat altogether. It will be apparent also that levees, dykes, and other structures that preserve flood plains from inundation must adversely affect species that spawn on terrestrial plants.

Almost any sort of weir or dam interferes with the upstream movement of breeding migrations, and many of the more sluggish species are readily held back. Even the active *Salmonidea*, which are well-known for their leaping ability, can jump high only from fairly deep water where the standing wave caused by the falling water gives them an upward thrust. A long rocky chute, or a manmade concrete apron at the foot of a dam, therefore, makes an effective barrier, and can seal off miles of breeding site. There is now a large volume of fish-pass lore, but even so, the fish often fail to use the passes provided as they are not stimulated to leap at the right place. It seems that they are attracted to the point of greatest discharge or impact of falling water, and often they try futilely to leap over obstacles that they cannot clear and ignore passes that they could easily negotiate, because the correct stimulus is absent.

However, allowing fishes to reach the breeding site is only part of the problem. The site also must remain suitable, or inadequate breeding occurs. Species that need shallow riffles cannot use channelized reaches, and *Salmonidae* cannot use gravel in which the interstices are blocked by silt. Even quite small amounts of soil erosion, especially in the valleys of streams in which floods are controlled and which never get a thorough wash-out, reduce the subsurface flow to a degree that is fatal to the eggs. Indeed it has been suggested that almost all the trout streams in America will be affected seriously in this way unless steps are taken to reduce sheet erosion. Here we are dealing with a very insidious manmade change.

Now if the adult fishes must go up to breed the young must get downstream to grow, and here also dams may have unexpected effects. Many small fish normally travel downstream near the bottom, and this habit takes them safely over waterfalls and through natural lakes. In the latter the bottom slopes up fairly gently at the downstream end and the little fish are led up to the outflow. But in an impoundment the deep water is usually just upstream of the dam and there is no slope leading up to the outflow. Young fish tend, therefore, to get stuck in the area just upstream of a dam, and there is evidence that many young salmon perish in such places. It seems highly probable that this applies to other species also.

Conclusion

The above points are just a few that have been selected from our present knowledge of the ecology of rivers and streams to illustrate the fact that almost any management practice can result in unexpected changes. Many others that we know about could have been used, and there are doubtless many more of which we are still ignorant.

The message is not that we should not manage waters and that everything that we do in that direction is to be deplored. That sort of Garden-of-Eden approach, which is taken by some biologists and conservationists, is, of course, ridiculous in the modern world. People are important, and our existence in large numbers means that we must have water supply, farms, flood control, navigation, and effluents. But we should understand more thoroughly what we are doing when we manage rivers, and be able to weigh up the results of our actions dispassionately, balancing losses against gains in an objective way.

Watershed managers should be reasonably well versed in running water ecology so that they are aware of the likely consequences of the activities of themselves and others. Decisions should include political, sociological, and aesthetic considerations as well as purely economic ones, and we should plan to preserve at least a few aquatic Gardens of Eden for our successors to enjoy. At present we are in real danger of altering everything just a bit, with little knowledge of the consequences, and one day we may discover that there is no wild river left.

Biologists, chemists, engineers, manufacturers, politicians, sociologists, and waterworks managers should get together more often and more closely than they do. Collectively we know quite a lot and together we can learn more, and make more rational decisions. Our environment on this planet is a precious thing, as our recently acquired knowledge of Mars and Venus has emphasized. We owe it to our species to manage it well, and we have the knowledge to do that if we act together, without greed and with thought for more than just short-term gain.

SUGGESTED READINGS

Chutter, F. M. "Hydrobiological Studies on the Vaal River in The Vereenigung Area." *Hydrobiologia* 21 (1963): 1–65.

Coker, R. E. *Streams Lakes Ponds.* New York: Harper and Row, 1968.

Cordone, A. J. and Kelley, D. W. "The Influence of Inorganic Sediment on the Aquatic Life of Streams." *California Fish and Game* 47 (1961): 189–228.

Hynes, H. B. N. *The Ecology of Running Waters.* Liverpool: Liverpool University Press, 1970.

Leopold, L. B., Wolman, M. G., Miller, J. P. *Fluvial Processes in Geomorphology.* San Francisco: Freeman, 1964.

Mitchell, R., ed. *Water Pollution Microbiology.* New York: Wiley-Interscience, 1972.

Morisawa, M. *Streams: Their Dynamics and Morphology.* New York: McGraw-Hill, 1968.

Owen, O. S. *Natural Resource Conservation: An Ecological Approach.* New York: Macmillan, 1971.

United States, Department of The Interior, Bureau of Reclamation and the American Institute of Biological Sciences. *Water, Man, and Nature.* Washington, D.C.: Government Printing Office, 1972.

United States, Department of the Interior, Federal Water Quality Administration, *Clean Water for The 1970's: A Status Report.* Washington, D.C.: Government Printing Office, 1970.

United States, Environmental Protection Agency, *Studies on Effects of Watershed Practices in Streams.* Water Pollution Control Research Series. Washington, D.C.: Environmental Protection Agency, 1971.

CHAPTER 5

Landforms: Process and Pattern Introduction

      Seventy years ago W. M. Davis laid the foundations for the scientific study of the earth's land surface forms when he formulated his famous dictum: Landforms = structure + process + stage. These three concepts from the 1890s are quite compatible with a systems approach to the study of the earth's scenery in the 1970s. However, until quite recently, geomorphological work consisted primarily of studies probing the long-term evolution of regional-scale landscapes. As a result of this historical orientation, Davis's stage factor was seen as the crucial explanatory variable in landform studies. Today, however, the trend of research in geomorphology is clearly away from the historical approach and toward the dynamic approach, in which the chief goal is to achieve understanding of the precise character of the complex interrelationships between the morphological characteristics of landforms (structure) and the behavior of the formative agencies of landscape development (process) over the short run.

      For two reasons we have limited our choice of articles for this section to examples of work in dynamic geomorphology. First, from a conceptual point of view, the dynamic approach is more or less synonymous with the systems approach. Second, from a practical point of view, the landform parameters studied, the landform changes observed, and the time scales utilized by dynamic geomorphologists are precisely those which are most directly relevant for the everyday life of mankind, and for assessing the role and the impact of the human factor in landscape change.

      The dynamic geomorphologist begins by viewing whatever

type or size of landform feature concerns him as a dynamic open physical system. Such a system is one whose structural components are subject to continuous modification in response to fluctuating inputs and throughputs of energy and matter. Over time, an open system tends toward a steady-state condition, which can be thought of as the end state or goal of the system. In this state outputs of energy and matter from the system balance inputs, while the morphology of the system and the flow of energy and matter through the system are in a situation of mutual adjustment.

A hierarchy of landform systems exists. At the top level come the global-scale, first-order landform features — the continents and the ocean basins. Middle level systems consist of second-order, regional-scale landscape units defined in terms of tectonics. They include such features as the Canadian Shield; the Appalachian Mountains; the Colorado Plateau; or the Great Plains. Alternatively, second-order systems may be defined in terms of climatically determined morpho-genetic regions such as humid tropical, temperate, glacial or arid. Second-order landforms can be subdivided into numerous subsystems or elements that exist at a local scale. For example, in a desert region, third-order elements may include such things as dune fields, pediments, or bolsons. In glaciated country, moraines, spillways, and outwash plains are examples of third-order forms.

The articles selected for this section include two studies on the functioning of landform systems at global and regional scales. The third article, a study done at a local scale, assesses the effects of man's activities on fluvial geomorphological processes in urbanizing areas.

At the global level, planetary surface form is a function of the interplay between two sets of opposing forces. Forces of construction, fueled by energy from within the earth, are continuously at work adding to and redistributing the stock of geological materials which make up the continental land masses. At the same time, forces of destruction, fueled by kinetic energy derived from atmospheric events, and by the potential energy of gravity, continuously work to reduce the bulk of the continents. These two sets of forces represent the two major links of a global lithological cycle in which materials removed from the land and deposited in the ocean may eventually be reconstituted as continental material through the operation of various geophysical processes associated with mountain building and tectonic uplift. The periodicity of the lithological cycle is, of course, immensely long compared to the time required for one complete circuit of any of the other global cycles analyzed in this book. It is measured in millions of years rather than days or weeks.

The article by Judson summarizes what is known about the functioning of the lithological cycle and offers quantitative estimates of the magnitude and rate of operation of its various linkages (weathering, erosion, deposition, and so on). Perhaps the most significant of Judson's findings is his estimate that at the global scale human activities have had the effect of speeding up the natural forces of continental destruction by a factor of 2½. Clearly, in the space of about one to two million years of residence on this planet, man has become perhaps the single most potent agent of landscape evolution, able to achieve a level of geomorphological work equivalent to any one of the natural agencies, whether it be running water, ocean waves, ice, wind or volcanoes.

Systematic regional variation of macroclimatic conditions around the globe gives rise to an equivalent systematic variation in the nature and intensity of operation of the agents of landscape reduction. In effect, the world's landscapes are evolving under the impact of a mosaic of regional-scale denudation systems, ranging in effectiveness from high energy situations typical of tropical latitudes (particularly in tropical areas of great relief, for example, the Andes, Himalayas), to low energy conditions of polar regions (for example, Tundra Plains of Arctic Canada and the U.S.S.R.). It is river networks which carry out denudation at all scales — global, regional, and local.

Perhaps the best examples of open systems in nature are rivers and river drainage networks. Everywhere, despite widely variant geological and climatic environments, the areal pattern of river systems exhibit a remarkable degree of similarity and of quasi-mathematical order. Indeed, numerous quantitative analyses of drainage basins have established that quite precise correlations exist between parameters such as stream order, number, length, basin area, and others. At the same time, extensive analyses of stream gauging data, gathered in a variety of climatic regions and in locations underlain by many different types of geological materials, have again revealed the presence of quite precise relationships between the form and flow parameters of individual streams and their segments, which can be expressed in simple mathematical equations. All of this suggests that stream channels individually, and drainage nets collectively, function as open systems. Form parameters such as channel cross-section, slope, channel pattern (straight, meandering, braided) and flow parameters such as discharge, velocity, sediment load, and so on, are in a state of continual adjustment, fluctuating around a dynamic equilibrium condition. All of these points are covered in some detail by Leopold's article on the behavior of rivers.

Our third selection is an article by Wolman which shows that the systems approach, in general, and the notion of the steady-state condition, in particular, are of more than only academic value. Steady-state conditions provide us with a point of reference from which we can measure and even predict the kind of changes that are likely to occur in the form and behavior of natural open systems like rivers as a consequence of human interference. Wolman describes what happens when the natural equilibrium of river channel systems is upset by the sequence of land use changes that accompany the urbanization of drainage basins. Specifically, changes in channel form and sediment yield are traced from preurban through construction to fully urban stages of development.

River networks clearly show open systems in operation and illustrate well that in the long run flows create form (structure). The other landform-creating energy agents (ocean waves, wind, ice and volcanoes) could just as well be used in illustration. The particular mix of glacial landforms left in an area reflect the inputs and throughputs of an ice-dominated open system in interaction with the geological structure and atmospheric energy and moisture flows. Thus one area is dominated by landforms representing a decaying, retreating glacial system, for example, kame terraces, eskers, irregular outwash forms, while another area is represented by forms from a growing, advancing system, such as till moraines, large spillways. Similar illustrations can be provided for coastal landforms, desert landforms or volcanic landforms. Everywhere the pattern of landforms reflects the processes using energy and matter flows as inputs and throughputs.

Erosion of the Land, or
What's Happening to Our Continents?

Sheldon Judson

Reprinted with some deletions and modifications by permission of the author and the publisher from *American Scientist* 56 (1968), pp. 356–374.

Not quite two centuries ago James Hutton, Scottish medical man, agriculturalist, and natural scientist — now enshrined as the founder of modern geology — and Jean André de Luc, Swiss emigré, scientist, and reader to England's Queen Charlotte, carried on a spirited discussion concerning the nature and extent of erosion of the natural landscape. De Luc believed that once vegetation had spread its protective cloak across the land, erosion ceased. Not so, in Hutton's opinion. He argued:

> According to the doctrine of this author (de Luc) our mountains of Tweed-dale and Teviotdale, being all covered with vegetation, are arrived at the period in the course of times when they should be permanent. But is it really so? Do they never waste? Look at rivers in a flood — if these run clear, this philosopher has reasoned right, and I have lost my argument. [But] our clearest streams run muddy in a flood. The great causes, therefore, for the degradation of mountains never stop as long as there is water to run; although as the heights of mountains diminish, the progress of their diminution may be more and more retarded.[1]

We know today, of course, that vegetation plays an important role in the preparation of material for erosion. We know also that although vegetation may slow the removal of material from a slope it does not stop it completely. Hutton's view is overwhelmingly accepted today. Erosion continues in spite of the plant cover, which in fact is conducive to certain aspects of erosion. The discussion now centers on the factors determining erosion, the nature of the products of this process, how these products are moved from one place to another, and at what rates the products are being produced. Hutton, in his day, had no data upon which to make a quantitative estimate of the rates at which erosion progressed. Today we, unlike Hutton, measure rates of erosion for periods of a fraction of a man's lifetime, as well as for periods of a few hundreds or thousands of years of human history. In addition, radioactive dating and refined techniques of study in field and laboratory allow us to make some quantitative statements about the rates at which our solid lands are wasted and moved particle by particle, ion by ion, to the ocean basins.

This report sets forth some of what we know about these

erosional rates. We will understand that erosion is the process by which earth materials are worn away and moved from one spot to another. As such, the action of water, wind, ice, frost-action, plants and animals, and gravity all play their roles. The destination of material eroded is eventually the great world ocean, although there are pauses in the journey and, as we will see later, the material delivered to the ocean must be in some way reincorporated into the continents.

SOME MODERN RECORDS

Let us now examine some modern records of erosion of various small areas on the earth's crust, essentially determinations of rates at specific points. There is a large amount of information to be gleaned from agricultural, forestry, and conservation studies as well as from some studies by geologists. Data on erosion are expressed in metric tons per square kilometer and as centimeters of lowering either per year or per thousand years. A specific gravity of 2.6 is assumed for material eroded from the land.

Even a casual inspection of our cemeteries demonstrates that some rock goes to pieces at a measurable rate and that rocks have differing resistance to destruction. Four marble headstones inspected in 1968 in the Princeton, New Jersey, cemetery indicate what can happen to marble in the 172 years involved. The marker erected in 1898 was still easily legible 70 years later, but the crisp, sharp outline of the stone carver's chisel was gone. . . . The stone put up in 1796 was completely illegible. In this instance the calcite ($CaCO_3$), which makes up the marble, was attacked by a carbonic acid formed by rain water and the CO_2 of the atmosphere. In general, marble headstones become illegible in the humid northeastern states after 150 to 175 years of exposure.

In contrast to the marble headstones is . . . a stone in the Cambridge, Massachusetts Burying Ground, erected in 1699 and inspected in 1968. It is made of slate, often used as a headstone material in many New England cemeteries until marble became fashionable at the turn of the nineteenth century. Unlike marble it is resistant to chemical erosion. Nearly 270 years after the stone was erected the inscription stands out clearly. Graveyards do most certainly provide examples of the impermanence of rock material as well as of the relative resistance of different rock types. . . . In general, however, a graveyard does not present the best conditions for the accumulation of quantitative data.

More reliable data seem to come from agricultural stations.

Here is an example. A summary of measurements has been made at 17 different stations on plots measuring 6 by 72.6 ft and under differing conditions of rainfall, soil, slope, and vegetative cover. Periods of record in this instance vary between 4 and 11 years. On the average, erosion from plots with continuous grass cover annually lost 75 tons per square kilometer, a lowering of about 3 meters per 1000 years. This is a dramatic demonstration of the role of plants in affecting erosion. In this instance the rate of erosion increased 100 times between grass-covered plots and well-tilled row-crop plots.

Obviously climate will also affect the rate of erosion. For example, recent studies by Washburn in eastern Greenland show that seasonal freeze and thaw in a nearly glacial climate produce erosion rates ranging between 9 and 37 meters per thousand years. This contrasts with the rates in more temperate climates cited previously. In semiarid lands, where vegetation is discontinuous and rainfall low (± 25 cm per year) and unpredictable, the erosion rates are high but not as high as those in the rigorous climate of northeastern Greenland. Studies of bristlecone pines in Utah and California have allowed an estimate of erosion rates on a time base of hundreds and even thousands of years. Thus the pines, which may reach 4000 years in age, betray the amount of erosion during their lifetime by the amount of exposure of their root systems. The depth of exposed roots on living trees is a measure of the amount the land surface has been reduced since the tree began to grow. Rates of lowering in general vary with exposure (greater on north-facing slopes) and with declivity of slopes (greater on steeper slopes). On the average, the rate varies between about 2 cm per 1000 years on slopes of 5 degrees and 10 cm on slopes of 30 degrees. A total of 42 observations indicate a direct relation between the erosion rate and the sine of the slope.

A different sort of study, this one in the rain forest of New Guinea Mountains, has yielded the estimate that between 1 and 2 cm per 1000 years is lost from the area by landslides alone. How much additional material is lost through the agency of other processes is not known.

Archaeological sites may yield information on erosional rates and have, as in the case of the bristlecone pines, a fairly long time base. Data collected in Italy show that for the sites studied the range in rates is 30 to 100 cm per 1000 years. . . .

Rates of erosion are variable when the observation is for a single spot or limited area. Not only are they highly variable but they can hardly be representative of rates of erosion over large areas. It is apparent that the material eroded in one spot may be deposited nearby, at least temporarily, and thus the net loss to an area may be little or nothing. Erosion is more rapid at some spots than others for any one of many different reasons. Material removed from its position at any single spot on the landscape follows a slow, halting, devious course as natural processes transport it from the land to the ocean.

RIVER RECORDS

When we ask now how much material is being lost by the continents to the ocean, the spot measurements such as those reported above are of little help. We need some method of integrating these rates over larger areas. One way to do this is to measure material carried by a stream from its drainage basin at the point where the stream leaves the basin. Alternatively, the amount of sediment deposited in a reservoir or in a natural lake over a specific length of time is indicative of the rate at which the land has been worn away in the basin lying upstream. The mass of sediments accumulated in unit time can be averaged out over the area of the contributing drainage basin to produce an erosion rate. Of course the erosion rate is not uniform over the entire basin, but it is convenient for our purposes here to assume that it is.

If we examine the solid load of a stream carried in suspension past a gauging station we discover that the amount of material per unit area of the drainage basin varies considerably according to a number of factors. But, if we hold the size of the drainage basin relatively constant, we find pronounced correlation between erosion and precipitation. Figure 1 is based on data presented by Langbein and Schumm (1958) from about 100 sediment gauging stations in basins averaging 3900 sq. km. It suggests that a maximum rate of erosion is reached in areas of limited rainfall (± 25 cm per year) and decreases in more arid as well as in more humid lands.

Considering small drainage basins (averaging 78 km²), Langbein and Schumm also show a similar variation in erosion with rainfall, but at rates which are 2 to 3 times as rapid as for the larger basins. In still smaller basins erosion rates increase even more. A small drainage basin in the Loess Hills of Iowa, having an area of 3.4 km² provides an extreme example. Here sediments are being removed at a rate which produces a lowering for the basin of 12.8 m per 1000 years.

We have data based on river records for larger areas. Judson and Ritter have surveyed the regional erosion rates in the United States and have shown that, on the average, erosion is proceeding at about 6 cm per 1000 years. Here too, as shown in Table 1, there are variations.

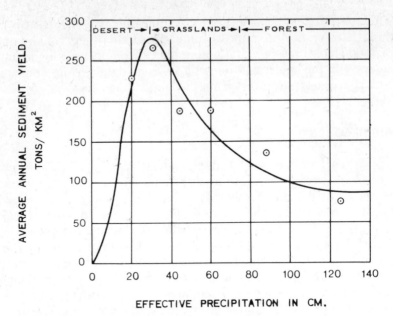

Figure 1. Variation of the yield of sediments with precipitation. Effective precipitation is defined as precipitation necessary to produce a given amount of runoff. (Based on data in W. B. Langbein and S. Schumm, in *Transactions of the American Geophysical Union* 39 (1958): 1076.)

These appear to be related to climate as in the smaller areas already discussed. Greatest erosion occurs in the dry Colorado River basin. In examining the rates of regional erosion we note that although erosion rates increase with decrease in discharge per unit area, they do not increase quite as rapidly as the major component, the detrital load, increases. This is so because the absolute dissolved load decreases with decreasing discharge per unit area. This inverse relation between solid and dissolved load is shown in Figure 2.

These data suggest that on the average the United States is now being eroded at a rate which reduces the land surface by 6 cm each 1000 years. Actually the rate is somewhat less when we consider that the area of the Great Basin, with no discharge to the sea, is not included in these figures — and that for all practical purposes the net loss from this area is presently close to zero.

EFFECT OF MAN

What effect does man's use of the land have on the rate at which it is destroyed by natural forces? Three examples are cited here:

Table 1. Rates of regional erosion in the United States.*

Drainage Region	Drainage[1] Area Km^2 $\times 10^3$	Runoff m^3/sec	Load tons Km^2/yr Dissolved	Solid	Total	Erosion $cm/1000\ yr$	% Area Sampled	Avg. years of record
Colorado	629	0.6	23	417	440	17	56	32
Pacific Slopes, California	303	2.3	36	209	245	9	44	4
Western Gulf	829	1.6	41	101	142	5	9	9
Mississippi	3238	17.5	39	94	133	5	99	12
S. Atlantic & Eastern Gulf	736	9.2	61	48	109	4	19	7
N. Atlantic	383	5.9	57	69	126	5	10	5
Columbia	679	9.8	57	44	101	4	39	<2
Totals/Averages	6797	46.9	43	119	162	6	—	—

[1] Great Basin, St. Lawrence, Hudson Bay drainage not considered.

*Based on data in S. Judson and D. F. Ritter, in *Journal of Geophysical Research* 69 (1964): 3395.

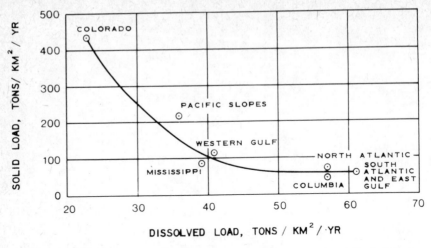

Figure 2. Relation by regions in the United States between solid load and dissolved load in tons/km²/yr. (Based on data in Judson and Ritter, in *Journal of Geophysical Research* 69 (1964): 3395.)

Bonatti and Hutchinson have described cores from a small volcanic crater lake, Lago di Monterosi, 41 km north of Rome. An archaeological survey of the environs of the lake indicate that intense human activity dates from approximately the second century B.C. when the Via Cassia was constructed through the area. At this moment the cores indicate a sudden increase of sedimentation in the lake. The rate varies somewhat but continues high to the present. Extrapolation of the sedimentation rate in the lake to the surrounding watershed shows that prior to intensive occupation by man (that is, prior to the second century B.C.) the erosion rate was 2 to 3 cm per 1000 years. Thereafter it rose abruptly to an average of about 20 cm per 1000 years.

Ursic and Dendy (1965) have studied the annual sediment yields from individual watersheds in northern Mississippi. The results of their data are shown in Figure 3. These indicate that, when the land is intensively cultivated, the rate of sediment production and hence the rate of erosion is three orders of magnitude or more above that experienced from areas with mature forest cover or from pine plantations.

Wolman has described the variation of sediment yield with land use for an area near Washington, D.C. These data show that, under original forest conditions, erosion proceeded at the low rate of about 0.2 cm per 1000 years. With the rapid increase of farmland in the early nineteenth century the rate increased to approximately 10

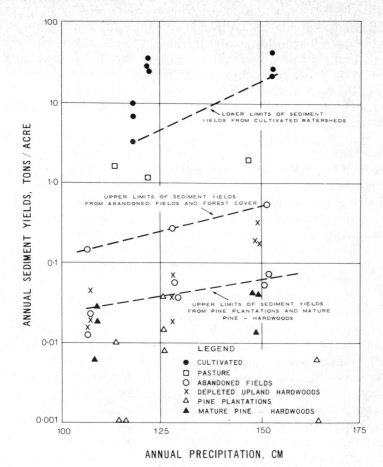

ANNUAL PRECIPITATION, CM

Figure 3. Variation in sediment yields from individual watersheds in northern Mississippi under different types of land use and changing amounts of precipitation. One ton/acre equals 224 tons/km^2. (Based on data in J. Ursic and F. E. Dendy, in *Proceedings of the Federal Inter-Agency Sedimentation Conference,* 1963.)

cm per 1000 years. With the return of some of this land to grazing and forest in the 1940s and 1950s this high rate of erosion was reduced perhaps by one-half. Areas undergoing construction during the 1960s show yields which exceed 100,000 tons per square kilometer for very small areas, which approximate a rate of lowering of 10 m per 1000 years. For completely urban areas the erosion rates are low, less than 1 cm per 1000 years.

There is no question that man's occupancy of the land increases the rate of erosion. Where that occupation is intense and is directed toward the use of land for cultivated crops the difference is one or more orders of magnitude greater than when the land is under a complete natural vegetative cover such as grass or forest. The intervention of man in the geologic processes raises questions when we begin to consider the rates of erosion for the earth as a whole and to apply modern rates to the processes of the past before man was a factor in promoting erosion.

Ian Douglas postulates that man's use of the landscape has so increased the rates of erosion that they far exceed those of the past before man became an important geologic agent. He presents persuasive data and arguments to suggest that any computation of present-day erosion rates on a world-wide basis are unrepresentative of those that pre-date man's tampering with the landscape. So, as we turn to the question of world-wide erosion, we will want to distinguish between present-day rates which are profoundly affected by man's activity and those of the immediate past before man introduced grazing, agriculture, and other activities.

Let us first attempt an estimate of erosion before man began to affect the process. It is estimated that approximately one-fourth of the United States is in cropland. If this area is now undergoing a rate of erosion ten times that of its natural rate then, for the United States as a whole, the increase of rate of erosion because of man's use of the land increases the rate of the removal of solid particles from the earth's crust by a factor of a little over three times. Assuming that this is correct and that the dissolved load does not change appreciably, then, as a first approximation, the present rates of erosion listed in Table 1 for the United States would be decreased to approximately 3 cm per 1000 years, which is about 78 tons per square kilometer per year. This figure would apply then to the area of the United States before the intervention of man with intensive agricultural practices.

RATES FOR ENTIRE EARTH

What can we say now about the rate of erosion for the entire earth? Presented in Table 2 are data for approximately 10 percent of the earth's surface. The table includes erosional data for the drainage basins of the Amazon, the world's largest river; the Congo; and for that part of the United States covered in Table 1. Here, however, the data for the United States have been adjusted to account for the increased rates of erosion presumed to have occurred because of man's cultivation of the land. Neither the Congo nor the Amazon basins are signifi-

Table 2. Rates of erosion for the Amazon River Basin, United States and Congo River Basin.*

Drainage Region	Drainage Area $Km^2 \times 10^6$	Load, tons $\times 10^6$/yr Dissolved	Solid	Total	Tons Km^2/yr	Erosion cm/1000 yr
Amazon River Basin	6.3	232	548	780	124	4.7
United States	6.8	292	248	540	78	3.0
Congo River Basin	2.5	99	34	133	53	2.0
Totals	15.6	623	830	1453	93	3.6

*Sources of original data are provided in the complete article by Judson in *American Scientist* 56 (1968): 356 – 374.

cantly affected by man. For the 15 million square kilometers of these three areas the average rate of erosion is 3.6 cm per 1000 years or 93 tons per square kilometer annually.

Let us accept the figures just given as representative of erosion rates prior to man's intervention in the process and use them to extrapolate to erosion rates for the whole area of the earth. The earth's land surface has approximately 151 million square kilometers, but much of this area has no streams which drain directly to the ocean. For example, a large area of western United States is without direct drainage to the sea, as is a large percentage, about 50 percent, of Australia. Areas of little or no drainage to the sea are estimated to occupy approximately one third of the earth's surface. So for our purposes we estimate that 100 million square kilometers of the earth's surface are contributing sediments directly to the sea by running water. In addition to this there is a certain amount of wind erosion, and part of the materials eroded by the wind are delivered to the sea. It is even more difficult to find data on the amounts of regional erosion by wind than it is by running water. We have some preliminary estimates for the amount of eolian material which has been dumped into the oceans. These lie between 1 and 0.25 mm per 1000 years. Whatever the future, wind erosion of the land is volumetrically unimportant when compared with the amount of material carried by the streams.

We can estimate, then, the amount of sediment carried as solids and as dissolved material from the continents each year to the ocean basins as 9.3×10^9 tons. This figure is based on the assumption that, on the average, 3.6 cm per 1000 years are eroded from the 100 million square kilometers of land which are estimated to drain into the oceans. Further, the figure attempts to eliminate the effect on the erosion rate of man's activity. If we include an estimate for the amount of erosion by wind action then this figure increases by an amount approximating 10^8 tons. Glacier ice may add a similar amount. . . .

Let us now estimate the present rate of erosion. In this the major component is the suspended load carried by rivers. Of the data available, Holeman's appear to be the most inclusive and reliable. Allowing the bed load to be 10 percent of suspended load and adding these two figures to the dissolved load as calculated by Livingstone, then the total material delivered annually to the sea by rivers at the present is 24×10^9 metric tons. This is about two and one half times the rate that we estimated existed before man started tampering with the landscape on a large scale (Table 3).

Returning now to our estimate of the material produced by erosion before the serious intervention by man, we should be able to check our figure by comparing it with the amount of material deposited annually in the oceans. Thus far our only way of determining annual sedimentation rates over large areas is to average them out over the last several thousand years. Because man has only recently become a world-wide influence on erosion, this averaging serves to curtail his impact on the rate of accumulation of the sedimentary record.

What figures do we have on sedimentation in the oceans? Large areas of the ocean floor and the rates at which sedimentation takes place there are but dimly known at the present. We have data from coring of the ocean bottom but our data are scanty at best. In considering the tonnage which settles annually to the ocean floors we should distinguish between the deep oceans and the shallower oceans. As far as sedimentation goes there is probably a difference between those ocean floors lying below 3000 m and those above 3000 m. . . .

Table 3. Mass of material estimated as moved annually by rivers to the ocean before and after the intervention of man.

	10^9 *metric tons*
Before man's intervention	9.3
After man's intervention	24

Table 4 compares the estimate of the amount of material deposited each year in the oceans with the estimate of the amount delivered by various agents annually to the oceans. In both estimates we have tried to eliminate the effect of man.

Whether we use the rate of erosion prevailing before or after man's advent, our figures pose the problem of why our continents have survived. If we accept the rate of sediment production as 10^{10} metric tons per year (the pre-human intervention figure) then the continents are being lowered at the rate of 2.4 cm per 1000 years. At this rate the ocean basins, with a volume of 1.37×10^{18} m^3, would be filled in 340 million years. The geologic record indicates that this has never happened in the past, and there is no reason to believe it will happen in the geologically foreseeable future. Furthermore, at the present rate of erosion, the continents, which now average 875 m in elevation, would be reduced to close to sea level in about 34 million years. But the geologic record shows a continuous sedimentary history, and hence a continuous source of sediments. So we reason that the continents have always been high enough to supply sediments to the oceans.

Geologists long ago concluded that the earth was a dynamic system, being destroyed in some places and renewed in others. Such a state would help resolve the problem of what happens to the sediments and why continents persist. Thus, although the sediments are carried from continents to oceans to form sedimentary rocks, we know that

Table 4. Estimated mass of material deposited annually in the oceans compared with estimated mass of material delivered annually to the oceans by different agents.*

	10^9 metric tons/year
Estimated mass of material deposited in ocean	
Oceans shallower than 3000 meters	5–10
Oceans deeper than 3000 meters	1. 17
Total	6.2–11.2
Estimated mass of material delivered to oceans	
From continents	
By rivers	9.3
By wind	0.06–0.36
By glacier ice	0.1
From extraterrestrial sources	0.00035–0.14
Total	~9.6

*Man's influence on rates of erosion is excluded from estimates.

these rocks may be brought again to the continental surface. There they are in turn eroded and the products of erosion returned to the ocean. These sedimentary rocks may also be subjected to pressures and temperatures which convert them from sedimentary rocks to metamorphic rocks. If this pressure and temperature is great enough, the metamorphic rocks in turn will melt and become the parent material of igneous rock. These relationships are the well known rock cycle which has been going on as long as we can read the earth's rock record. In simplified form it is repeated in Figure 4.

Inasmuch as we have been talking about the sedimentary aspects of the rock cycle, we should ask how much time it takes to complete at least the sedimentary route within the whole cycle. Poldervaart gives the total mass of sediments (including the sedimentary rocks) as 1.7×10^{18} tons. Taking the annual production of sediments as 10^{10}

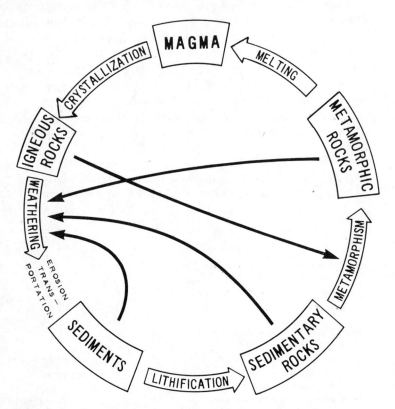

Figure 4. The rock cycle. (From L. D. Leet and S. Judson, *Physical Geology*. Englewood Cliffs, N. J.: Prentice Hall, 1965.)

tons, then one turn in the sedimentary cycle approximates 1.7×10^8 years. At the present rates then we could fit in about 25 such cycles during the 4.5 billion years of earth history.

Accepting Poldervaart's figure of 2.4×10^{19} tons as the mass of the earth's crust then there has been time enough for a mass equivalent to the earth's crust to have moved two times through the sedimentary portion of the cycle.

We began this review with a brief examination of the homely process of erosion. As we continued we found that man has appeared on the scene as an important geologic agent, increasing the rates of erosion by a factor of two or three. We end the review face to face with larger problems. Regardless of the role of man, the reality of continental erosion raises anew the question of the nature and origin of the forces that drive our continents above sea level. In short, we now seek the mechanics of continental survival.

REFERENCES

[1] J. Hutton, *Theory of the Earth,* vol. 2 (Edinburgh: W. Creech, 1795).

SUGGESTED READINGS

Douglas, I. "Man, Vegetation and the Sediment Yield of Rivers." *Nature* 215 (1967): 925 – 928.

Holeman, J. N. "The Sediment Yield of Major Rivers of the World." *Water Resources Research* 4 (1968): 737 – 747.

Hutton, J. *Theory of the Earth.* Vol. 2. Edinburgh: W. Creech, 1795.

Judson, S., "Erosion Rates near Rome, Italy." *Science* 160 (1968): 1444 – 1446.

Judson, S. and Ritter, D. F. "Rates of Regional Denudation in the United States." *Journal of Geophysical Research* 69 (1964): 3395 – 3401.

Langbein, W. B. and Schumm, S. A. "Yield of Sediment in Relation to Mean Annual Precipitation." *Transactions of the American Geophysical Union* 39 (1958): 1076 – 1084.

Livingstone, D. A. *Chemical Composition of Rivers and Lakes.* Professional Paper 440–G. Washington: U.S. Geological Survey, 1963.

Schumm, S. A. *The Disparity Between Present Rates of Denudation and Orogeny.* Professional Paper 454–H, pp. 1 – 13. Washington: U.S. Geological Survey, 1963.

Ursic, S. J. and Dendy, F. E. "Sediment Yields from Small Watersheds

Under Various Land Uses and Forest Covers." *Proceedings of the Federal Inter-Agency Sedimentation Conference, 1963.* United States, Department of Agriculture. Miscellaneous Publications 970, 1965. pp. 47 – 52.

Wolman, M. G. "A Cycle of Sedimentation and Erosion in Urban River Channels." *Geografiska Annaler* 49–A (1967): 385 – 395.

Rivers

Luna B. Leopold
University of California, Berkeley

Reprinted with some deletions and modifications by permission of the author and the publisher from *American Scientist* 50 (1962), pp. 511–537.

Rivers are both the means and the routes by which the products of continental weathering are carried to the oceans of the world. Except in the most arid areas more water falls as precipitation than is lost by evaporation and transpiration from the land surface to the atmosphere. Thus there is an excess of water, which must flow to the ocean. Rivers, then, are the routes by which this excess water flows to the ultimate base level. The excess of precipitation over evaporation and transpiration provides the flow of rivers and springs, recharges ground-water storage, and is the supply from which man draws water for his needs.

The excess of precipitation over evapo transpiration losses to the atmosphere is a surprisingly small percentage of the average precipitation. The average amount of water that falls as precipitation over the United States annually is 30 inches. Of this total fall, 21 inches are returned to the atmosphere in the form of water vapor through processes of evaporation and transpiration from plants. The balance of 9 inches represents that excess which contributes to the flow of rivers.

Interestingly, about 40 percent of the runoff from continental United States is carried by the Mississippi River alone. Deep seepage from ground water to the ocean is not known, but it is believed to be quite small, probably much less than 0.1 inch per year.

It will be noted that for the land area of the continent the water cycle balances: credit, 30 inches of precipitation; debit, 9 inches of runoff plus 21 inches transferred to the atmosphere. However, looking at the atmosphere the budget appears out of balance because 30 inches are delivered to the land as rain and snow but only 21 inches as vapor are received back by evaporation and transpiration. This means that 9 inches of moisture are transported from the oceans to the continent to balance the discharge of rivers to the sea. It is estimated that each year the atmosphere brings about 150 inches from the oceans over the land area of the United States and carries back 141 inches.

A good deal of the water which appears as river flow is not transmitted into the river channels immediately after falling as precipitation. A large percentage of the fall is infiltrated into the ground and flows underground to the river channels. This provides, then, a form of storage or regulation that sustains the flow of streams during non-

storm or dry periods. When one observes water flowing in a creek
or river during periods of bright sunny weather it is obvious that
this discharge represents water that had fallen during previous storm
periods and had been stored in the rocks and in the soil materials of
the drainage basin.

The 9 inches of average annual runoff of rivers of the United
States amounts to a very large amount of water. If it could be visualized
as a uniform flow during the whole year, which in reality it is not, it
would amount to 1.4×10^{11} gallons per day. In fact, runoff is highly
erratic in time and in geographic distribution. For large areas in the
United States an important percentage of the total flow occurs during
the late spring and early summer, the period during which the water
which had been accumulating during the winter as snow appears as
melt-water runoff.

Though the amount of water carried off the continent to the
oceans each year is large, so also is the total length of stream channels.
The writer has estimated that the total length of river channel in the
United States, including all the minor creeks and draws, amounts to
about 3,000,000 miles. Table 1 shows the estimated gross length of
channels of various sizes in the United States, as well as the number
of such channels and their average lengths.

The table presents estimates based on geometric relations among
river system factors. The figures shown are derived from samples ex-
trapolated to cover the whole United States and account for about 97
percent of the continental area of the country. . . .

The three million miles of stream channels in the United States
vary widely in size and occur in a wide variety of topographic and
geologic circumstances. Included in this figure of total length are those
high mountain streams epitomizing wilderness beauty, the dirty and
trashfilled channels too often coursing through our cities, and the
majestic but turbid large rivers flowing in wide valleys of central United
States and the flat expanses of the coastal plain.

One might suppose then, from the variety of geographic and
geologic environments through which these channels are carved, that
there would exist such a variety of river types that but little could be
said about river characteristics in general. Each geographic situation
might be supposed to have its own special kind of river and each would
be a law unto itself. As a matter of fact, the subtle but pervasive unity
that exists, despite the tremendous diversity, is probably the most
important characteristic of river systems.

There is not only unity displayed by important similarities
between rivers in different settings, but also an amazing organization

Table 1. Number and length of river channels of various sizes in the United States. (Excluding tributaries of smaller order.)

Order*	Number	Average Length (Miles)	Total Length (Miles)	Mean Drainage Area, Including Tributaries (Square Miles)	River Representative of Each Size
1†	1,570,000	1	1,570,000	1	
2	350,000	2.3	810,000	4.7	
3	80,000	5.3	420,000	23	
4	18,000	12	220,000	109	
5	4,200	28	116,000	518	
6	950	64	61,000	2,460	
7	200	147	30,000	11,700	Allegheny R.
8	41	338	14,000	55,600	Gila R.
9	8	777	6,200	264,000	Columbia R.
10	1	1,800	1,800	1,250,000	Mississippi R.

*The definition is that of Strahler: Order 1 is channel without tributaries; order 2 is channel with only order 1 tributaries, but includes only the length segment between junction upstream of order 1 channels and junction downstream with another order 2 channel.

†The size of the order 1 channel depends on scale of maps used; these order numbers are based on the determination of the smallest order using maps of scale 1 : 62,500.

of river systems. This in part results from a delicate balance between the forces of erosion and the forces of resistance.

The characteristics of river systems which can be used to demonstrate the unity among forms fall under three general categories, the river channel, the river valley, and the drainage net — the term applied to the system of branching channels ramifying to the smallest tributaries.

The first and most important aspect of the river channel is that it is self-formed and self-maintained. The flowing water carves the groove in which it flows. The water fashions the depth, the cross section, the areal configuration, and the longitudinal profile.

Existing river channels have had a history in many respects analogous to the history of a species in the biological world. An existing river is inherited from an earlier one, which in turn was derived from a still earlier progenitor. The sequence extends backward to that time when the continental area now being drained by the river was once under the ocean.

Thus the river channel usually cannot be spoken of as having been formed, in that no particular time or place of origin of a given river can be specified. Rather, it is best to think that a river has evolved through geologic time, and that the processes of change that may be observed at present are indeed the same processes by which this evolution took place. The changes during the river history in geologic time were brought about by changes in the external conditions, such as a change in climate (including glaciation), a change in elevation of the continental mass and the concomitant changes in vegetation, in rates and types of weathering, and in the amounts and kinds of materials flowing under the influence of gravity toward base-level — the ocean.

The forces involved in shaping and maintaining the channel are related to the fluid flow. The flow of the fluid exerts a shear on both bed and bank and it is this shear which causes particles comprising the bed and bank to be moved along in traction by the water, that is, by pushing, rolling, and skipping. This portion of the debris in transport is referred to as the bedload. The same shear creates the turbulent eddies in the flowing fluid which entrains some particles of matter and throws them up into the main mass of the fluid, thus carrying them as the suspended load.

The transport of sediment debris by rivers to the oceans is a phenomenon known to everyone. It is far less well known that the quantity of dissolved materials carried by rivers to the ocean is also very large. Because the transport process is not visually evident, nor are deposits of dissolved materials obvious, it is hard to visualize that slightly more than half of all the materials carried by river water from continent to ocean is carried as dissolved load. This fact was quantitatively verified in results recently published by Durum, Heidel, and Tison, describing an international project designed to sample the dissolved load of the great rivers of the world.

Fluid shear shapes the river channel. It can be visualized in a general way that if a channel were very deep and very narrow there would be far more shearing action on the channel sides than on the channel bed. It seems logical that, as a result, there would be a tendency in such a channel for erosion to take place along the banks, whereas along the bed there would be a tendency for insufficient shear to carry along the eroded material. Such a channel would widen and become shallower.

An opposite extreme can be visualized, in which a channel was very wide and shallow. The great expanse of bed exposed to the shearing action of the flow would tend to erode and thus degrade the bed, establishing in time a channel of more modest breadth but greater depth. Indeed, some such action does take place, for the width-depth ratios of rivers of comparable size have a great consistency.

If the shearing force on the channel banks is sufficient to overcome the cohesion of the bank materials, erosion takes place, and the eroded particles are swept away from their original position and become a part of the bed materials, there either to be moved or temporarily lodged. On the stream bed, scour takes place when the shear exceeds some critical value, and this occurs during relatively high flow. At low flow it is usual for the shearing forces on the bed to be sufficiently small that the bed materials do not move. Scour, then, occurs primarily during high discharges. The relatively long time periods represented by modest and low flow are periods of but little movement of bed material.

A river increases downstream in size owing to the increase of drainage area as tributaries enter. This increase in size is manifested not only in the amount of water (discharge) but also by an increase in channel width and depth. To accommodate an increase in discharge resulting from tributary entrance, the channel may enlarge in width or in depth, or the increased flow could be achieved by an increase in flow velocity. Because discharge (cubic feet per second) is the product of cross-sectional area times velocity

$$Q = av$$

and area is the width times depth

$$Q = wdv$$

an increase in discharge may be accommodated by an increase in any of these three factors, or by some combination of them.

In actuality, the increase is nearly always divided among these three parameters in the same way. Figure 1 presents data for a number of sample river systems for which there are plotted against discharge increasing downstream, values of mean depth, mean width, and mean velocity. The parallelism of lines in each of the plots shows that the rates of increase with discharge are similar among the various rivers.

Width increases downstream faster than depth, and depth faster than velocity, the latter being very nearly constant along the river length. The increase in width-to-depth ratio can be seen in Figure 2, in which cross sections of five channels are drawn with no exaggeration in vertical scale but at different scales so that the widths appear equal on the printed page. In actuality the creek represented in the upper sketch has a width of only 24 feet whereas the river in the lower sketch is a large river having a width of 1153 feet.

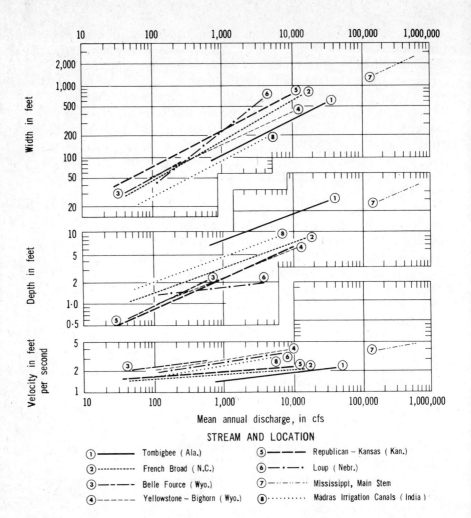

Figure 1. Width, depth, and velocity in relation to mean annual discharge, as discharge increases downstream in various river systems.

It had long been supposed that the speed of water in a river decreased downstream. This supposition was based on the fact that river slope decreases downstream and, generally speaking, the size of bed material also decreases from boulders or cobbles in the headwaters to sand, silt, or clay in the downstream portions of large rivers. It had long been argued, without reference to measurement data, that the supposed downstream decrease in water velocity was causally related to the inability of a river to carry coarse material at the flat

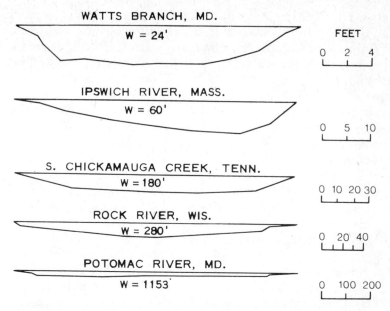

Figure 2. Cross sections of five rivers of different size; no vertical exaggeration, but scaled so that width is equal on printed page.

gradient existing in downstream reaches. Mountain creeks appear to flow more swiftly than the deep water of large rivers, but the appearance of flowing water is a test rather of kineticity than of flow speed. When my colleagues and I showed by measurement data that, in fact, velocity tends to increase or remain constant downstream in most rivers, a new rationale was needed to explain the observed relationships.

It now appears that the constancy or slight increase of velocity downstream results from the fact that river depth increases faster than river slope decreases. But this still does not explain how the requisite changes are divided among the pertinent parameters, nor why this division is so nearly the same in all rivers regardless of size or physiographic setting. This division turns out to be that which most nearly causes entropy to increase equally in each unit of length along the river as will be mentioned later.

That river channels should display such unity as exists is even more surprising as one inquires into the many changes that occur between low flow and high or flood flow. Channel scour during high discharge is an example. Though not universal, it is usual for the bed of a river channel to erode or temporarily to scour during floods, and as the flood recedes, to redeposit an approximately equal amount of

material. The depth of bed scour may in some channels be as much
as half the value of the increase in the elevation of the water surface.
Thus if the water surface elevation increases, say 10 feet, above the
level at low flow, the water depth at that high stage may well be increased not merely 10 feet but 15 feet. Figure 3 is an example. The
passage of the high flow during the spring snow melt of 1956 past the
measurement station on the Colorado River at Lees Ferry resulted
at peak flow in an increase in water surface elevation of 8.2 feet but
a concomitant scour of 4.8 feet. The bed elevation at the end of the
high flow was within 0.5 foot of that existing before the event.

This return to a condition so nearly identical to that existing
before the passage of the high flow implies a tendency for the maintenance, on the average, of a condition of dynamic equilibrium of an
extremely sensitive nature. Scour tends to be balanced by fill on the
average. Such a dynamic equilibrium between erosion and deposition depends on the operation of checks and balances the elucidation
of which is essential to the understanding of river behavior.

The basic mechanics of scour and fill, as exemplified in Figure 3,
are still only imperfectly understood. One of the most important
concepts, recently developed by Bagnold, may elucidate the point.

Many rivers flow over deep deposits of relatively uniform
material. Recognizing that the fluid shear on the granular bed material
tends to increase with increased discharge, a threshold shear may be
postulated at which the bed material will begin to move. When this
threshold is reached a layer of grains at the surface of the streambed is
peeled off and put into motion downstream. Owing to the fact that
there is a considerable depth of similar granular material in the bed,
it might be supposed that the shear capable of peeling off the top
layer of grains would be similarly capable of peeling off the next layer
of identical grains, and the next, ad infinitum. In reality, this does
not happen, and for any given value of shear only a finite thickness
of grains is set in motion. Continued application of the same shear
does not result in further erosion and, instead, a temporary quasi-
equilibrium exists. The transport of grains actually changes the forces
within the fluid in such a manner that continued erosion of the bed
becomes impossible.

Bagnold's 1956 research has shown, first theoretically and
then by experiment, that grains in traction create a downward-acting
stress which actually tends to hold the exposed grains on the stream
bed and thus prevent their erosion. This downward force results from
grain collision during transport. Collisions between grains tend to
knock an individual grain in a direction that may be forward, up,

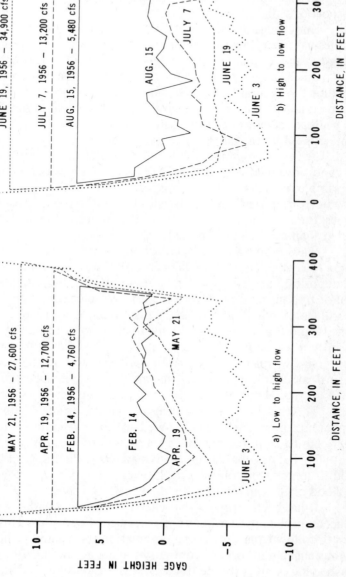

COLORADO RIVER AT LEES FERRY, ARIZONA
WATER INTERVAL 1956

JUNE 3, 1956 — 62,700 cfs

JUNE 19, 1956 — 34,900 cfs

JULY 7, 1956 — 13,200 cfs

AUG. 15, 1956 — 5,480 cfs

AUG. 15

JULY 7

JUNE 19

JUNE 3

b) High to low flow

DISTANCE, IN FEET

JUNE 3, 1956 — 62,700 cfs

MAY 21, 1956 — 27,600 cfs

APR. 19, 1956 — 12,700 cfs

FEB. 14, 1956 — 4,760 cfs

MAY 21

FEB. 14

APR. 19

JUNE 3

a) Low to high flow

DISTANCE, IN FEET

GAGE HEIGHT IN FEET

15   10   5   0   -5   -10

Figure 3. Scour followed by fill during the passage of flood during snowmelt season.

or down. There will be enough grains directed downward against the bed actually to create a downward stress which tends to prevent further erosion of bed grains.

Until Bagnold's work, it had not been recognized that hydraulic relations developed for clear water would not apply directly to water carrying a debris load. The forces within a fluid are altered by the transport of sediment debris.

Knowledge of sediment transport and its relation to river hydraulics has been slow to develop, both in theory and in practice, owing to the fact that it is still impossible to make consistent and accurate measurements of the amounts of debris being transported as bedload in natural rivers. Instruments have long been in use that measured adequately the sediment being transported in suspension, but bedload, being concentrated in a thin zone near the stream bottom, is interrupted by the insertion of any obstacle, no matter how streamlined. The insertion of a sampling device at the stream bed changes the conditions of transport locally in such a manner that a representative sample of the bedload in transport is impossible. Though rates of bedload transport can be successfully measured in experimental flumes, the conditions represented in the laboratory are much more limited than those extant in the field.

Water discharge in a river fluctuates widely from year to year, season to season, and day to day. Thus the forces governing erosion and deposition are highly variable. The channel flows at shallow depth most of the time and is filled to the top of the banks relatively seldom. On still less frequent occasions, the discharge exceeds the channel capacity and flows overbank. An overbank flow is a flood by definition. Recently it was shown that the frequency of the bankfull condition is surprisingly uniform among rivers in diverse settings and among rivers of widely different size. The bankfull stage may be expected on the average about once a year to once in two years.

To state this in another way so that the practical application is apparent, the river channel is large enough to accommodate all the water coming from the drainage area only in the relatively frequent event. The flat area bordering most channels — the flood plain — must flood to some extent on the average every other year. To overflow the flood plain is an inherent characteristic of a river.

It has been surmised that channel formation and maintenance are accomplished primarily during periods of flood flow. This would seem to follow from the general observation that many of the most obvious changes in form or configuration are accomplished by the catastrophic event — by the flood of large magnitude. To the extent this were true, it would be inferred that the events most worthy of study in attempting to isolate the general controlling principles would be extraordinary occurrences.

As recently as 1960, Wolman and Miller introduced another concept that has had an impact on thinking about rivers and, indeed, alters the view of the action of geomorphic processes in general. The principal work in fashioning landscape forms is not done during the frequent event or the predominant condition because the processes acting are incompetent to have any significant effect. Nor is the principal work accomplished by the very effective but very rare event — the catastrophic incident. Rather, it appears that the landscape is fashioned primarily by the event of intermediate frequency and effectiveness.

For example, the total sediment load transported by a river past a given point over a period of time is the sum of the amount transported during a variety of flow events; that is, during many days of low flow, a modest number of days of intermediate flows, and a decreasing number of increasingly great floods. The data indicate that the intermediate flows have a cumulative significance far greater than those of either greater or small magnitude, because the product of effectiveness times frequency is greatest. This concept is a fundamental contribution to thinking about landscape moulding processes.

There are other attributes of river channels which also demonstrate the unity that exists among channels, even channels widely different in size. Nearly all natural channels are sinuous to some extent. Indeed, natural channels are rarely straight for a distance greater than ten channel widths. Not only do channels exhibit a more or less regular aspect of sinuosity, but also the size of the curves assumed by a channel bear a constant relationship to the channel itself. Small channels wind in small curves and large channels in large curves.

Measurement data show that there is quite a constant relationship between channel width and the radius of the curves which the channel exhibits. Also, the meander length or wave length is generally proportional to channel width. These characteristics can be seen on Figure 4, where the meander length is plotted separately against channel width and against the mean radius of curvature. It can be seen that there is essentially a linear relationship between the wave length of the channel curves, channel width, and the radius of curvature. This linear relation occurs not only in most natural rivers but also to meltwater channels developed on the surface of a glacier and in the flow path of the Gulf Stream which is not confined by channel banks.

The consistency of the relation of radius of curvature to channel width is indicated by the following measurement data. In a sample of

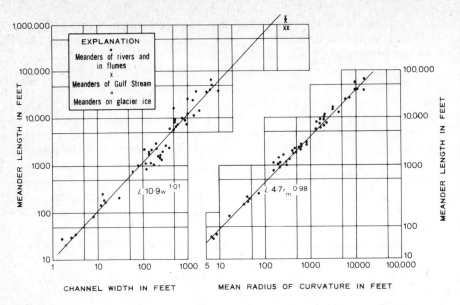

Figure 4. Relations between meander length and channel width (left diagram) and mean radius of curvature (right diagram).

50 rivers of various sizes the median value of the ratio of curvature divided by width was 2.7, the mean 3.1, and two-thirds of the cases occurred between the values of 1.5 and 4.3. The tendency for a constant ratio of radius to width makes all rivers look quite similar on planimetric maps, as is suggested by Figure 5. In fact, when one inspects a planimetric map of a river without first glancing at the map scale, it is not immediately obvious whether the river is large or small owing to this tendency for a similar ratio of radius to width.

When the sinuous bends of a river are relatively symmetrical the channel is said to be meandering. Such a large variation in degree of sinuosity exists in natural channels that the definition of a meandering stream — in contrast with one which is merely sinuous — becomes a matter of arbitrary definition. There is represented in nature, then, an unbroken continuum between slightly wavy channels and well developed meanders which can assume the form of horseshoe loops. Owing to the fact that the meandering character of river channels has long been considered to be associated in basic mechanics with the movement of sediment, the observation that sediment-free channels carved by meltwater on the surface of a glacier can also meander is of considerable interest. Tentatively, the mechanical principles resulting in the meandering form of meltwater channels in the absence of sediment load and

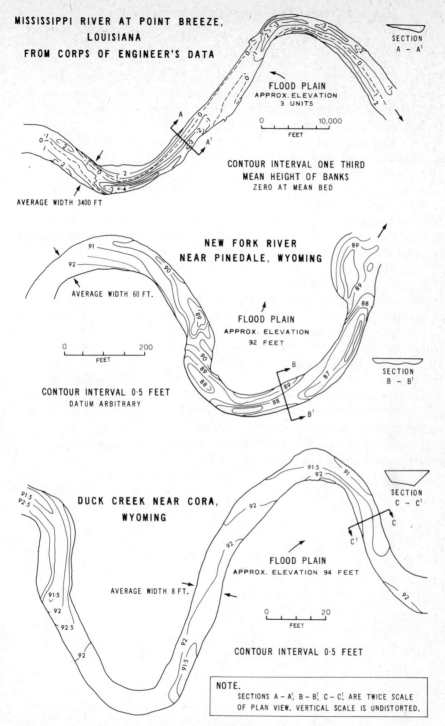

Figure 5. Planimetric map of a meander bend on each of three rivers varying greatly in size; scaled so that meander length is equal on printed page.

those causing the meandering of rivers are probably the same. The similarity in channel form implies that the basic cause is essentially hydrodynamic, rather than a direct result of bank erosion and the lateral transfer of sediment across the channel. . . .

The manner in which a channel moves across the valley floor, eroding one bank and building a nearly flat flood plain on the other, all the while maintaining a cross section similar in shape and size, is another aspect of the dynamic equilibrium that appears to characterize many channel systems.

Another aspect of the unity exhibited by stream systems is exemplified in the branching network of tributaries comprising what is called the drainage net. In 1945, Robert E. Horton showed that the size of a given stream is related to the number of streams of that size, their average length, and average slope. There is a very constant quantitative relationship between these factors which can best be demonstrated by some actual data. Figure 6 is a sketch to define stream order, a measure of stream size. Horton defined order in the following manner. The smallest unbranched tributary in the head-waters is, by convention, designated order 1; a stream which has only tributaries of order 1 size is called second order; a third-order stream is one in which all tributaries are of second order or smaller, etc. Figure 7 shows that there is a logarithmic relation between stream order and length of streams of a given order and between stream order and numbers of streams. After this logarithmic relation within the drainage network was pointed out by Horton, it has been tested by

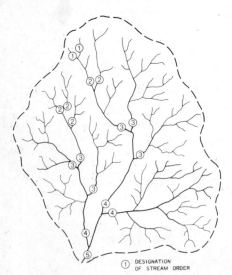

DESIGNATION
OF STREAM ORDER

Figure 6. A typical drainage net on which stream order, an indication of size, is shown by the numerals.

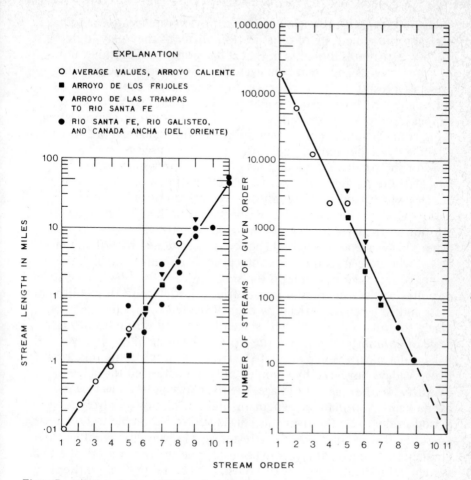

Figure 7. Relation of stream length and number of streams to stream order in basins of eleventh order near Santa Fe, New Mexico.

many workers and found applicable, essentially without exception, to drainage basins of all sizes, including the very smallest rills and large river basins.

One of the basic problems in the study of rivers is the identification of a general law or principle which provides a rationale in physical terms for the different types of unity exhibited by river channels and the networks which they comprise. It is only too easy to speak of the results of the dynamic action of rivers in anthropomorphic terms for, indeed, rivers seem to have an inherent tendency to display many of the characteristics of an organism. There is first an organization of the various parts. All river systems appear to have basically the same type of organization, differ as they may in detail. The river system is dynamic in that it has portions that move and can cause events and create changes. We often read in the popular press, as a result, that the river went on a rampage, overflowing its banks and wreaking havoc on man and his structures. Thus one tends to speak about the river as if it had a will of its own. It is interesting, then, from the philosophic standpoint, to consider some of the aspects of these dynamic characteristics that have been used to express portions or the totality of the actions of the system which appear to have definite tendencies toward a direction of development, or tendencies which tend to maintain the average conditions observed.

One way in which this has been approached has been a description of the river system as having developmental stages through time. This was one of the basic concepts introduced by William Morris Davis, who described the geographical cycle as consisting of three principal stages comparable to the stages in the life of man. The stage of youth was considered by him to follow initial uplift of a continental mass and to be characterized by deep V-shaped valleys having a tendency to downcut rapidly. The stage of maturity was described as a stage of equilibrium in which the work to be done in erosion was balanced against the capacity of the river sytem for doing this work. Broad valleys bordered by rounded hills characterized the stage of maturity. In the stage of old age, the river was pictured as flowing over a nearly flat plain or peneplain, and during this relatively long period in the cycle the river was considered to be unable to do large amounts of work in erosion as a result of relatively low relief and flat gradients. Similarly, at any one point in time the headwaters of a river system could be in the stage of youth, the central portion in the stage of maturity, and the downstream portion in the stage of old age. This characterization of a river system was extremely useful for teaching purposes, but from a quantitative standpoint many aspects are difficult to particularize.

There followed, then, more detailed consideration of the concept of equilibrium, or grade, which Davis had thought of as characteristic of the stage of maturity. A graded stream was described by J. Hoover Mackin as one "in which, over a period of years, slope is delicately adjusted to provide, with available discharge and with prevailing channel characteristics, just the velocity required for the transportation of the load supplied from the drainage basin. The graded stream is a system in equilibrium; its diagnostic characteristic is that any change in any of the controlling factors will cause a displacement of the equilibrium in a direction that will tend to absorb the effect of the change."[1]

Wolman extended this concept and pointed out that the concept of grade had two aspects, involving adjustability and stability. In one respect, the quasi-equilibrium of a graded stream is, as Mackin pointed out, characterized primarily by its ability to adjust to changes in external conditions. Wolman believed that a concept of quasi-equilibrium may be characterized by the stability of the system, but that adjustability perhaps was no less important a criterion.

Another aspect which, under certain circumstances, had been used to describe the underlying tendency for a river toward a quasi-equilibrium condition was what might be called the principle of least work. There are certain characteristics, particularly hydraulic ones, which point to the tendency for minimization of work in a system.

Recently, Langbein and I considered the various factors governing the direction of river work and reasoned as follows. Inspecting the physical principles which recur most often in analyses of different aspects of river morphology, the basic equations which are most prominent are the equation of conservation and the equation of continuity. These laws are so obviously general that they characterize each element or reach in any fluvial system. They must also characterize each unit of any path and at each instant in time. However necessary these equations might be, they are insufficient to explain the paths of particles moving in the river systems, or the relation between one part of the path to another. Therefore, they can alone tell us nothing about the surface form of the landscape, nor can they treat completely the progressive development or change of form with time.

There must, therefore, be some other law of equal generality which would deal with energy distributions and their relation to changes of land forms in space and time. We proposed that implications of the second law of thermodynamics satisfy these requirements.

The development of landscape involves not only the total available energy but also its distribution. The latter may be described by the concept of entropy, adapting that term from the comparable concept in thermodynamics. The essential idea is that the entropy of the system is a function of the distribution or availability of energy within the system and not a function of the total energy within it. Thus, entropy has come to concern order and disorder, an aspect of the conception which has been utilized in physical chemistry and information theory. The degree of order or disorder in a system may be described in terms of the probability or improbability of any observed state.

An increase in entropy is, then, a measure of the decrease in availability of the energy in the sense that a certain amount of energy is no longer available for conversion to mechanical work. The distribution of energy may be stated in terms of the probability of the given distribution occurring relative to alternative distributions possible.

The statistical conception of entropy is that aspect which appears to have application to geomorphic systems. The distribution of energy in a geomorphic system is one way of expressing the relative elevation of particles of water and of sediment which gradually will, in the process of landscape evolution, move downhill toward base level. The longitudinal profile of the river, for example, is a statement of the spatial distribution of stream-bed materials with regard to their elevation and, thus, with regard to their potential energy.

In thermodynamics, heat energy is referred to absolute temperature as a base. The absolute temperature defines an absolute limit or base datum, the situation in which molecular motion becomes zero. It is, then, the base level, or the datum, against which the energy content of a thermal system can be measured. Systems in geomorphology also have a base datum with regard to the distribution of energy. This base datum is the datum of elevation, in most cases represented by mean sea level. But the classical treatment of entropy in thermodynamics deals with closed systems in which entropy continuously increases to a maximum stationary level at equilibrium. In closed systems there is no loss or addition of energy.

Geomorphic processes operate, on the other hand, in open systems in which energy is being added in some places while in other places energy is being degraded to heat and is thus lost insofar as further mechanical work is concerned. A river system, then, we consider to be an example of an open system, defining the system as the water and the debris in the river channel. As the water flows down the channel it gives up potential energy which is converted first to kinetic energy of the flowing water and which in the process of flow is dissipated into heat along the channel margins. Precipitation brings increments of energy into the system because water enters at various elevations and thus with various amounts of potential energy. Heat is lost by convection, conduction, or radiation, yet the channel may be considered in dynamic equilibrium.

The steady state possible in open systems differs from the steady state of static equilibrium of closed systems. We equate, therefore, the term steady state with dynamic equilibrium in geomorphology as defined early in the century by Gilbert and, more recently, by Hack. In an open system in dynamic equilibrium the rate of increase of entropy in the system is zero. The continuity of entropy then takes the form that the rate of outflow of entropy equals the rate of internal generation of entropy. In a river system in equilibrium, the rate of outflow of entropy is the rate of dissipation of energy as heat. This is equated to the rate of generation of entropy represented by the energy gradient toward base level. The stationary state of an open system is characterized by the conditions in which the rate of production of entropy per unit volume of flow is a minimum compatible with the conditions imposed on the system. Hence a stable system corresponds to one of least work, a conception we were able to demonstrate in mathematical terms for certain conceptual models.

The argument was developed that, with respect to the longitudinal profile of the river, the probability of the particular combination of values of energy in various unit distances along the course of the open system of the river could be described as proportional to the negative exponential of its ratio to the total energy of all possible states. This led to the conclusion that the most probable sequence of energy losses in successive units of river lengths corresponds to a uniform increase in entropy in each unit length along the river system. When this specification is fulfilled without constraint on river length the longitudinal profile of the river tends to become exponential in form, a result in agreement with many actual river profiles. . . .

In this brief résumé some of the relatively recent developments in thinking about rivers and river morphology have been mentioned. The contributions in the past decade have been centered around the mathematical analysis of river processes and of channel and drainage net characteristics. This work, contributed by a variety of scientists in different disciplines, has resulted in a quantitative description of many of the physical characteristics of rivers and, at least to some extent, a description of some processes in basic physical terms.

The most immediate general problems still facing the geomorphologist are centered around three types of questions. The first concerns the mechanics of sediment transportation, particularly related to the movement of bedload, which at present still cannot be measured satisfactorily in real rivers under field conditions. The second general area seems to center in the question of the location and mode of energy dissipation in rivers and the effect of the energy utilization on erosion and deposition. This particular area, therefore, involves the relation of hydraulic factors to soil or lithologic factors. Among the latter is the erodibility of different types of materials particularly in relation to their stratigraphy and sedimentational characteristics.

The third general area concerns the mode of transport of materials from slopes into the river channel. To a great extent, recent work in river morphology has been more concerned with river channels than with the hillslopes shedding debris toward the channels. Thus slope development, slope processes, and the relationship of slopes to the channels to which they are tributary remain an integral part of the study of rivers. These subjects encompass an area of nearly unlimited scope for research by engineers, geologists, soil scientists, botanists, physical chemists, and those possessing a variety of other skills.

REFERENCES

[1] J. H. Mackin, "Concept of the Graded River," *Bulletin, Geological Society of America* 59 (1948): 463–512.

SUGGESTED READINGS

Bagnold, R. A. "The Flow of Cohesionless Grains in Fluids." *Philosophical Transactions of The Royal Society* 249A (1956): 235–297.

Chorley, R. J., Dunn, A. J. and Beckinsale, R. V. *The History of The Study of Landforms or the Development of Geomorphology.* vol. 2. The Life and Work of William Morris Davis. London: Methuen, 1973.

Hack, J. T. "Interpretation of Erosional Topography in Humid Temperate Regions." *American Journal of Science* Bradley Volume 258-A (1960): 80–97.

Horton, R. E. "Erosional Development of Streams and Their Drainage Basins." *Bulletin, Geological Society of America* 56 (1945): 275–370.

Leopold, L. B. and Langbein, W. B. *The Concept of Entropy in Landscape Evolution.* Professional Paper 500A. Washington: U.S. Geological Survey, 1962.

Leopold, L. B. and Maddock, T. *The Hydraulic Geometry of Stream Channels and Some Physiographic Implications.* Professional Paper 252. Washington: U.S. Geological Survey, 1953.

Mackin, J. H. "Concept of the Graded River." *Bulletin, Geological Society of America* 59 (1948): 463–512.

Slaymaker, H. D. "Patterns of Present Sub-Aerial Erosion and Landforms in Mid-Wales." *Transactions, Institute of British Geographers* 55 (March, 1972): 47–68.

Wolman, M. G. and Miller, J. P. "Magnitude and Frequency of Forces in Geomorphic Processes." *Journal of Geology* 68 (1960): 54–74.

A Cycle of Sedimentation and Erosion in Urban River Channels

M. Gordon Wolman
Professor of Geography and Environmental Engineering
Johns Hopkins University

Reprinted with some deletions and modifications by permission of the author and the publisher from *Geografiska Annaler* 49A (1967), pp. 385–395.

Equilibrium and a Cycle of Change

Students of geomorphology have long debated the meaning and value of concepts such as grade and equilibrium applied to the behavior of stream channels. These and similar phrases generally denote a condition of balance, stability, or both in the characteristics and behavior of a river channel. However, logical and semantic difficulties demand that phrases associated with the concept of equilibrium must be used with care and circumscribed by qualifications. Thus, progressive degradation over geologic time is inconsistent with a too rigid definition of equilibrium which implies stability in elevation, gradient, and channel form. At the same time, over somewhat shorter periods of time, slow but progressive degradation may yet be associated with near constancy or stability of channel form. With only small changes in inflow of water and sediment, channel form and even channel gradients may remain relatively stable.

While a universally applicable concept of equilibrium may be difficult to formulate because of the problems posed by varying time scales and rates of change of channel gradients and channel forms, the concept of equilibrium can be useful in dealing with the response of channel systems to significant changes in the values of the independent variables such as discharge and sediment load over shorter intervals of time. Under these conditions a reasonable working hypothesis, perhaps paraphrasing Mackin, might be that over a period of years channel slope and form are adjusted to the quantity of water and to the quantity and characteristics of the sediment load provided by the drainage basin. Each of the independent variables, water and sediment, are in turn related to the soil, lithology, vegetation, and climate of the region. This statement of adjustment allows for momentary scour and fill and for short-term trends, measured in years, in channel behavior associated with high water or drought.

If a set of river channels are in equilibrium with prevailing conditions in a drainage basin, it follows that major disturbances on the drainage basin will result in changes in channel form and behavior. The process of urbanization of the landscape constitutes a major interruption of "prevailing" conditions on a watershed. If prior to urban development, a kind of equilibrium prevailed in which channel gradient and form were related to water and sediment derived from the watershed, then the sequential changes which occur as urban development takes place on the watershed can be expected to alter markedly the equilibrium forms and may result in the eventual establishment of new conditions of equilibrium. At the present time the disturbance of equilibrium can be documented, but as the data here will show, it is currently difficult to determine whether a new equilibrium will be established or whether instead a condition of disequilibrium will persist.

The process or cycle of urbanization on the watershed that is reflected in the river channels of a region consists of three stages; 1) an initial stable or equilibrium condition in which the landscape may either be primarily agricultural or dominated by forests, 2) a period of construction during which bare land is exposed to erosion, and 3) a final stage consisting of a new urban landscape dominated by streets, rooftops, gutters, and sewers. This theoretical cycle is sketched in Figure 1 along with estimates of the quantity of sediment derived from the watershed, the presumed channel behavior, and the sequence of land use. The data are based upon experience in the Middle Atlantic region of the United States. The conditions outlined in Figure 1 are described in the following paragraphs. These serve both as an outline and as a summary of the data presented and evaluated in the body of the paper.

In accord with the historical evidence, Figure 1 shows a modest yield of sediment prior to the farming era given here as beginning around 1700 A.D., and a significant increase in sediment yield during the farming period to an average value of about 600 tons per square mile. A decline in yields to a value of perhaps 300 tons per square mile is shown for the period immediately preceding construction based on the observation that in the environs of some of the major urban centers much farmland may be put in grass or allowed to return to brush and forest while awaiting development. With the onset of clearing for construction sediment yields rise to perhaps several thousand or more tons per square mile during a short interval of perhaps one to three years. The interval is short, of course, only where a single or isolated unit of land and channel is considered since progressive development of a large drainage area will affect downstream reaches of channel for a longer period. Following construction, if the entire area has been developed, sediment yields should be expected to decline to values as low as or lower than those experienced prior to the farming era. This condition is shown by a dashed line on Figure 1.

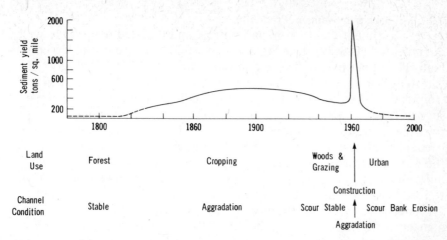

Figure 1. The cycle of land use changes, sediment yield, and channel behavior in a Piedmont region beginning prior to the advent of extensive farming and continuing through a period of construction and subsequent urban landscape.

Changes in the watershed are accompanied by changes in channel characteristics. During the farming era historical evidence indicates considerable accumulation of sediment within channels. Subsequently, in areas returned to brush and forest, much of the fine-grained sediment appears to have been removed returning the channels to a condition in which the channel bed was composed of gravel with lesser amounts of silts and sands. With the onset of construction large quantities of sand are delivered to channel systems and new sandbars and dunes may blanket the bed of the channel. If vegetation becomes established on the bars, channels are constricted, or locally banks may erode, accompanied by an increase in flooding at the channel constrictions. Upon completion of streets and sewerage systems sediment derived from the watershed decreases while the rapidity of runoff is increased. Channel bars and vegetation may be removed by flows of clear water. At the same time the absence of a fresh supply of sediment may result in progressive channel erosion without concomitant deposition.

While this general configuration of the process of urbanization and its effect on channel systems is reasonable, it is the purpose of this paper to review, add to, and evaluate the evidence for successive stages in the cycle. Because the economic consequences of these changes in the natural landscape are significant, it is hoped that a better understanding of the processes may be helpful in evaluating alternative methods of managing the land surface as well as the channel and riverine bottom lands.

Changes in Sediment Production

Sediment yields from agricultural and forested regions are well documented (U.S. Dept. of Agriculture, 1964) and are not repeated here. The upper part of Table 1 shows sediment yields for wholly forested regions as well as for areas of mixed farming and forests. Data from large areas wholly in forest are quite limited but current estimates suggest that yields may be less than 100 tons per square mile. In contrast the figure for the Gunpowder Falls at two successive intervals is of particular interest. From 1914 to 1943, a period of intense farming on the watershed, sediment yield was approximately 800 tons per square mile. During a later period when much land was returned to grazing and to forest in the immediate vicinity of the city of Baltimore, sediment yield declined to approximately 200 tons per square mile or one-quarter of the earlier figure. The dip in the curve in Figure 1 is based upon this observation.

Sediment yields from areas undergoing construction may exceed by several hundred-fold the yields from lands in forests and grazing, or by several fold areas in agriculture. As the selected values in Table 1 show, yields may exceed 100,000 tons per square mile over very small areas. On larger drainage basins in which the entire area is not undergoing construction, yields may still exceed several thousand tons per square mile.

Comparison of sediment rating curves also indicates that for a given discharge or frequency of flow, sediment concentrations may be twice or more than those from similar areas not subject to construction (Figure 2). Keller reports sediment loads 3 to 5 times as high. As one would expect, the quantity of sediment derived from the areas undergoing construction is a function of gradient, quantity and intensity of precipitation, characteristics of the soil, and topographic discontinuities at the construction site. However, even in the absence of precipitation, large quantities of suspended sediment may result from construction activities where heavy machinery operates directly in the stream channels. . . .

The yield of sediment from urban areas following completion of construction is less well documented. In most large cities where measurements have been made construction has continued at successive locations on the drainage area above the measuring site. However, some data are available for streams in the Baltimore area.

Periodic spot observations in three streams in the Baltimore area suggest the order of magnitude of average sediment yields and concentrations in urban areas (Figure 3). The drainage basins of both Western Run and Chinquapin Run are underlain by crystalline rocks of

Table 1. Sediment yield from drainage basins under diverse conditions.

River and Location	Drainage Area (Square Miles)	Sediment Yield (Tons/Sq. Mile/Yr.)	Land Use
Broad Ford Run, Md.	7.4	11	Forested: Entire Area
Helton Branch, Ky.	0.85	15	Same
Fishing Creek, Md.	7.3	5	Same
Gunpowder Falls, Md.	303	808	Rural – Agricultural, 1914–1943, Farmland in County 325,000 to 240,000 acres.
Same		233	Rural – Agricultural, 1943 – 1961, Farmland in County 240,000 to 150,000 acres.
Seneca Creek, Md.	101	320	Same
Building-site, Baltimore, Md.	0.0025	140,000	Construction: Entire area exposed
Little Falls Branch, Md.	4.1	2,320	Construction: Small part of area exposed
Stony Run, Md.	2.47	54	Urban: Entire area

the Piedmont while Moores Run is primarily in the Coastal Plain (Figure 4). None of these samples was collected during storms, and hence concentrations are probably somewhat too low. Nevertheless the values are low and average sediment yields from these urban areas appear to be small.

More detailed observations on both low and storm flow in streams in the Baltimore area show similarly low concentrations of suspended sediment. During a summer storm with a peak flow of 17 cubic feet per second from a drainage area of 2.5 square miles (a flow equaled or exceeded about one percent of the time) the peak concentration of suspended solids was only 439 ppm (Figure 5). A maximum concentration of 793 ppm was observed for a flood flow with a recurrence interval of approximately 1.5 years. . . .

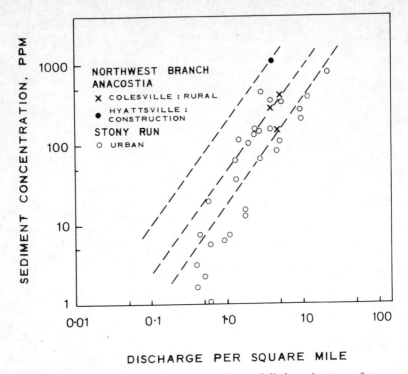

Figure 2. Curves relating sediment concentration and discharge in streams from three drainage areas differing in land use. The drainage area of the Northwest Branch of the Anacostia River above Colesville (21.3 square miles) is rural, between Colesville and Hyattsville (45.2 square miles) considerable land is exposed to construction, while Stony Run (2.5 square miles) lies within the city of Baltimore. Curves suggest highest concentrations from areas undergoing construction with successively lower values for rural and urban watersheds.

A rough estimate indicated that the average fallout of dry solids on the watershed, measured by the city nearby, or 58.7 tons per month in summer and 117 tons per month in winter exceeded the quantity of material removed in solution and suspension. For the storm shown in Figure 5 suspended solids amounted to about 77 percent of the dissolved load. Preliminary estimates indicate that the amount of sediment removed from the basin may be considerably less than the dry fallout but available data is not sufficiently accurate to warrant detailed comparison. However, concentrations are low even in storm periods and a crude computation suggests that average annual clastic load is on the order of 50 tons per square mile.

Evidence of the reduction of sediment supply from urban

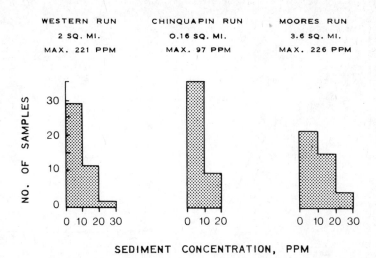

Figure 3. Histograms showing concentrations of suspended solids in three streams in the Baltimore Metropolitan Area. Location of these streams is shown in the map in Figure 4.

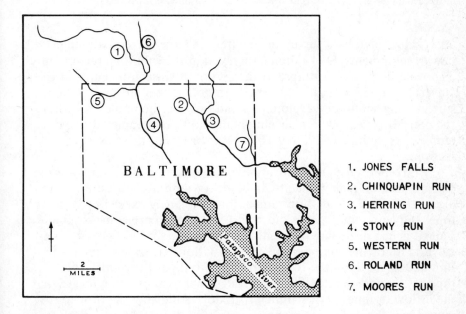

Figure 4. Map showing streams in the Baltimore Metropolitan region referred to in the text.

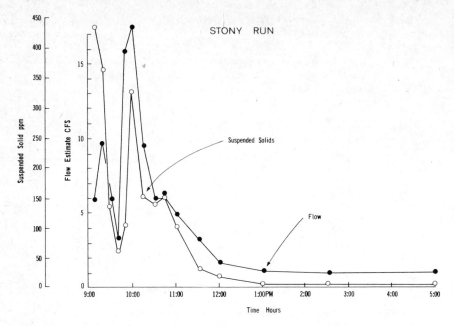

Figure 5. Hydrograph showing variations in flow and in concentrations of suspended solids in Stony Run during a storm on July 29, 1964. Peak discharge represents a flow equaled or exceeded on the order of 1 percent of the time or about three days per year.

areas is provided by a survey of sediment in large culverts draining new developments. Of 14 drains surveyed in the suburban region, only 3 showed 20 percent or more of the end or cross-sectional area of the culvert occupied by sediment. Furthermore, at two of these three, the surrounding suburban development had only been completed within the preceding year. Where development had been completed five or more years, sediment covered 10 percent or less of the culvert cross-section.

To permit rapid removal of runoff, storm drainage culverts are often placed on high gradients. In addition, a number of estimates indicate that peak runoff from impervious areas may exceed by 2 to 6 times the peak runoff from the same area prior to urban development. Thus it is not surprising that sediment is progressively removed from culverts following completion of construction. The rate of removal should depend upon the timing and magnitude of the runoff, the capacity and gradient of the drain. These observations all indicate that the inflow or renewal of sediment is reduced allowing the flow to remove from the drains sediment accumulated during the period of construction.

Data representing the full transition from "natural" or agricultural conditions, through construction, to a completely urbanized watershed at a single location were not available to the author. Therefore curves relating suspended sediment concentration to discharge for three locations on two different streams are compared. The watershed of Stony Run lies within Baltimore City (drainage area 2.5 square miles) and contained no area exposed to construction. In contrast most of the area on the Northwest Branch of the Anacostia above Colesville (drainage area 21.3 square miles) is rural and agricultural while extensive areas are undergoing construction in the intervening region between Colesville and Hyattsville (drainage area 45.2 square miles). . . . As Keller pointed out initially, the curves indicate that for a given flow, concentrations from the areas undergoing construction may be five times greater than from the rural areas. In addition, the curve added here for the completely urban watershed appears to lie below that of the rural area. Eighty-five percent of the points for the "urban river" fall below the Colesville or "rural" curve (Figure 2).

In summary, the data appear adequate to support the contention that sediment yields during construction exceed yields not only from forests but from agricultural lands as well. Less well documented but suggestive is the evidence that sediment yield several years after completion of urban development is very low, perhaps as low as or lower than sediment yields from completely forested areas.

Channel Behavior

In forested regions where sediment yields are low, stream channels in the crystalline Piedmont flow on beds of cobble gravel interspersed with finer grained deposits and occasional bedrock outcrops and within banks generally composed of silty or sandy loam. An influx of sediment laden water derived from construction on the watershed can be expected to result in extensive deposition of sand bars and dune sand generally coarser than the finer sediments carried in suspension prior to the advent of construction. Such a generalization would not be true, of course, if the inflow of sediment was small relative to the transporting capacity of the receiving channel, i.e., 100 acres of exposed land contributing sediment directly to the Mississippi River is unlikely to create new channel forms within the Mississippi. Virtually every large metropolitan center in the region, however, contains a myriad of small streams which may be affected. In metropolitan Baltimore the formation of deltas at the confluence of two channels, of sand bars, and banks of sand dunes over preexisting gravel beds have been observed. Less clear is the progression of channel changes following completion of construction.

Comparison of photographs of the channel of Jones Falls at the time of completion of a super-highway, which involved massive earthmoving, with the same reach three years later shows little or no change in the size of bars. The reach is 100 to 200 yards downstream from the highway construction. Upstream from the reach the area is primarily rural. Further downstream, however, within the urban area, comparison of photographs taken four years apart indicates that some bars may have been removed from mid-channel and from the outside of bends, but in general the channel continues to contain extensive sand deposits, particularly where piles of debris and bridge piers encourage deposition. Photographs of nearby Roland Run, taken 3½ years apart, indicated that with lessening of suburban development on the watershed, some sand and gravel deposits have been scoured from an upstream reach. In a reach 300 yards downstream deposition appears to have increased upstream from a small bridge opening. The intervening steeper channel contains little or no fresh deposits of gravel and sand.

Colby has shown that at a depth of one foot and a velocity of 2 feet per second the rate of sand transport will be about 5 tons per day per foot of width. In an urban channel at a drainage area of 2 square miles these conditions are reached on the order of one percent of the time. Assuming a deposit of sand 0.5 foot thick over a reach ¼ mile long and a unit weight of 100 pounds per cubic foot, without additional inflow of sand, removal of the deposit would require about two years. This figure is of course hypothetical but observation of streams in the Baltimore area suggest that the period will be considerably longer. . . . Observations indicate that channel curvature, local flattening of slope, establishment of vegetation, and particularly trash and debris may inhibit removal of sediment for even longer periods.

Both the expected increase in runoff from urban areas and the absence of sediment should contribute to an increase in channel erosion and to an increase in channel width. An increase in the number of peak flows particularly would tend to increase the amount of bank erosion. With a decrease in the available sediment, deposition would not keep pace with erosion, as it might under "normal" conditions of flood-plain formation, thus promoting progressive widening of the channel.

Exposure of raw banks in miles of urban river channels suggests bank erosion. As Hadley and Schumm have observed, however, raw banks are not prima facie evidence of high rates of bank erosion. Detailed observations of 7200 feet of the channel of Western Run in northwest Baltimore indicate that active bank erosion is occurring along a distance of about 580 feet of the total length of 14,400 feet of channel bank. The channel was straightened and deepened beginning about ten years ago to an average gradient of 1 percent. Maximum observed erosion was about 2.2 feet on the outside of an aligned curve constructed 3½ years ago. With the exception of irregularities at tree roots, at points adjacent to gravel bars, and at junctions of concrete culverts, average erosion is probably less than 1 foot per year. Some slumping can be seen near the top of the higher banks but the result appears to be a gentler side slope not yet attacked by the shallow flow at the base.

Photographs of Chinquapin Run show little or no vertical buildup of point bars is taking place in the urban channels. Similar conditions were observed on Western Run. Locust trees and grass have become established adjacent to and on the low bar along the left margin of the channel. Lateral deposition to a height of 1.5 feet or less is also evident. The right bank is steeper in 1967 than in 1960 and has receded about 3 feet in the 7-year period. Comparison of photographs over the same time interval indicates that the channel has widened particularly in the bend by removal of the sands on the point bar and by erosion downstream from the point bar along the left bank. A locust tree about 3 years old has become established adjacent to the left or concave bank suggesting some stability at that point. Nearby some slump is also evident along the concave bank. One hundred yards downstream from the reach photographed on the outside of a bend, highwater (estimated frequency once or twice per year) on January 26, 1967, undermined a tree 18 inches in diameter resulting in local lateral erosion of about 1 foot. These observations establish the fact that erosion is taking place albeit at a relatively slow pace. However, because such erosion is progressive and unaccompanied by comparable accretion, a net widening appears to be taking place above the elevation of the coarse cobble bed. Because continued widening will reduce the depth of flow for a given discharge, the rate of lateral erosion should be expected to decline. Nevertheless, in the absence of an equivalent inflow of sediment, a new equilibrium in transport will not be established.

Because of the great variability of natural channels, it is difficult to make statistically adequate comparison of channel shape and size before and after urbanization. Figure 6 is an attempt at such a comparison and the data suggest that the width of channels in urban areas may be somewhat larger than in comparable channels in "natural" or agricultural areas.

The erosion and flood characteristics of the urban river may be

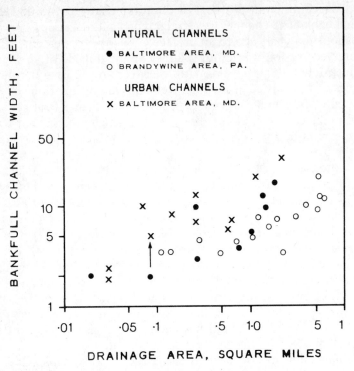

Figure 6. Comparisons of drainage area and channel width for streams in the Piedmont region under rural and urban conditions. Data indicate that at least some of the urban channels show an expected increase in width.

better demonstrated by the visual, subjective, impression of the channel than by any current objective or measurable parameters. The combination of raw banks, exposed cobble bars, and debris including flotsam strewn about the floodplain and channel margins all convey the impression of frequent flooding and the transient character of the alluvial features. Thus, comparative photographs show two aspects of the results of flooding in two completely different environments. Photographs were taken immediately after the record hurricane flood of August, 1955, in Connecticut. They show the abrupt channel widening which commonly results from the deposition of coarse cobble bars and the characteristic flotsam and debris deposited on the channel margins by the floodwaters. Other photographs show precisely the same erosion features and ubiquitous debris in several urban rivers in the Baltimore metropolitan region. Similar exposed banks coupled with tangles of debris on the margins of the channel can be seen

over many miles of urban river channel. While attempts have been
made to quantify this evidence, no readily mappable parameters
have described these conditions as well as the overall visual impact. . . .

Flood debris, eroding banks, scour holes and exposed bars
all appear to suggest the development of an erosive regimen in the
urban river channel following completion of development on the
watershed. These effects may be attributed to the combined action
of an increase in the magnitude and number of peak flows as well
as to a decrease in the availability of sediment derived from the
watershed.

Social Response to Changing Channel Behavior

Recognizing the potential value of river bottom lands for
recreational use, a number of metropolitan areas in the United States
have been moving toward reservation of flood-plain lands for parks
and open spaces. Where such use is contemplated an effort has also
been made to avoid canalizing stream channels with concrete or
other materials in order to preserve a more natural environment.

Accompanying this trend toward reservation of open spaces
in a natural condition, however, has been a public demand for maintenance of urban stream channels against the ravages of erosion
and the accumulation of rat-infested debris. One rather common response to this demand, and in the eyes of some a response completely
at odds with preservation of the natural scene is the canalization of
extensive reaches of channel in concrete. Several assets of such concrete
channels are assumed to be rapid dispersal of storm drainage, an increased potential for self-cleaning, and low maintenance costs. Aside
from aesthetic considerations it is important to recognize that deposition and erosion may be subject to the same controls in floodways as
in the preexisting alluvial channels. Abrupt flattening of gradients in
broad floodways and the accumulation of debris may induce deposition
at precisely those locations where such deposition previously occurred.
Careful and sometimes expensive designs may mitigate such problems,
but in many cases it is likely that removal of sediment and debris and
continuous channel maintenance will be required regardless of design.

Because the urban river poses both opportunities for recreational land use as well as problems in control and maintenance, it is important that alternative plans for control and use of these rivers be
developed in accord with some understanding of the principles of their
behavior. The evidence suggests that even in the relatively restricted
field of erosion and sedimentation in alluvial channels there are significant physical consequences resulting from urban development of entire watersheds. Recognition of these consequences, while it solves no

problems, can perhaps serve a purpose in demonstrating the need for forethought in planning for the appropriate use of the riverine environment. As always, the appropriate combination of aesthetics, economics, and physical limitations is not a constant but must vary from city to city and from river to river.

SUGGESTED READINGS

Carter, R. W. *Magnitude and Frequency of Floods in Suburban Areas.* Geological Survey Professional Paper, 424-B. Washington: U.S. Geological Survey, 1961.

Colby, B. R. "Practical Computations of Bedmaterial Discharge." *Journal of Hydraulics Division, American Society of Civil Engineers* 90 (1964): 217–246.

Dury, G. H. *Perspectives on Geomorphic Processes.* Commission on College Geography Resource Paper No. 3. Washington: Association of American Geographers, 1969.

Gottschalk, L. C. "Effects of Soil Erosion on Navigation in Chesapeake Bay." *Geographical Review* 35 (1945): 219–237.

Hadley, R. F. and Schumm, S. A. *Sediment Sources and Drainage Basin Characteristics in Upper Cheyenne River Basin.* Geological Survey Water Supply Paper 1531B. Washington: U.S. Geological Survey, 1961.

Keller, F. J. *Effect of Urban Growth on Sediment Discharge, Northwest Branch Anacostia River Basin, Maryland.* Geological Survey Professional Paper 450-C. Washington: U.S. Geological Survey, 1962.

Leopold, L. B. *Hydrology for Urban Land Planning — A Guidebook on the Hydrologic Effects of Urban Landuse.* Geological Survey Circular 554. Washington: U.S. Geological Survey, 1968.

Mackin, J. H. "Concept of the Graded River." *Bulletin, Geological Society of America* 59 (1948): 463–512.

Rayner, J. N. *Conservation, Equilibrium, and Feedback Applied to Atmospheric and Fluvial Processes.* Commission on College Geography Resource Paper No. 15. Washington: Association of American Geographers, 1972.

United States, Department of Agriculture. *Summary of Reservoir Sediment Deposition Surveys Made in the United States through 1960.* Misc. Publ. 964. Washington: U.S. Dept. of Agriculture, 1964.

Vice, R. B., Guy, H. P., and Ferguson, G. E. *Sediment Movement in an Area of Suburban Highway Construction, Scott Run Basin, Fairfax County, Virginia, 1961–64.* Geological Survey Water Supply Paper 1591-E. Washington: U.S. Geological Survey, 1969.

Wolman, M. G. and Schick, A. P. "Effects of Construction on Fluvial Sediment; Urban and Suburban Areas of Maryland." *Water Resources Research* 3 (1967): 451–464.

CHAPTER 6

Soils: The Biotic-Abiotic Systems Link Introduction

Soils are the link between the abiotic and the biotic subsystems of the environment in three major ways. First, soils provide the medium in which plants are physically supported so that their green parts can grow toward sunlight and thus obtain the energy and matter needed to drive their photosynthetic processes. Second, through their clay-humus complex, soils provide the liquid solution from which plants obtain all their necessary water and mineral nutrients. Third, soils provide the land habitat for the many plants, animals, and microorganisms that are essential elements in the decomposition processes permitting the continued recycling of matter.

A "typical" productive soil contains on a volume basis 25 percent air, 25 percent water, 45 percent mineral (inorganic) matter, and 5 percent organic matter. In structure as well as function soils are the biotic-abiotic systems link, the critical interface system for life on earth.

Soils are open systems trending toward steady-state equilibrium. Soils are always in a dynamic equilibrium condition, reflecting system responses to inputs of energy and matter which act on existing parent material and organic matter. Entropy is usually counteracted by the capture of organic matter over time and by the cycling of nutrients. During growing seasons, energy, water, gases, and nutrients are continually flowing through and being transformed for use by organisms living in the soil — be they viruses or trees. Continuous adjustments occur within the system. Even in mature soils approximating steady-state conditions, processing and storage of organic and inorganic matter fluctuate in response to rhythms in the input of solar radiation and to daily and weekly fluctuations in moisture inputs. While seemingly inert, the soil skin of landforms is a truly dynamic open system continually in a state of becoming.

Soil development depends on three main processes. Chemical weathering provides inputs of mineral nutrients; biological activities recycle existing stocks of nutrients; soil profile morphogenesis is produced by the interaction of chemical and biological processes with flows of water, gases and energy. These processes produce a particular type of soil.

Despite the multitudinous combinations of possible energy and matter inputs, there are definite patterns of both soil development and distribution. For instance, a combination of subarctic weather and climate, a sufficient water supply, glacial landforms, and coniferous forests interact in a process known as podsolization to produce soils characterized by well-differentiated soil profile features, a distinct upper layer from which clay, iron, and aluminum compounds are removed, and a lower layer in which they are deposited.

On a global scale, there are broad zonal patterns of soils which are determined by global climatic patterns. At the regional and local resolution levels, the diverse inputs from the other subsystems are identifiable in the occurrence of the various soil types. Studied at the general resolution level (global scale), the Great Plains of the United States are characterized by soils of the Mollisol and Alfisol orders. They are medium to high in organic content and in the base minerals of calcium, magnesium, potassium, and sodium — a reflection of the interaction of climatic inputs of moisture with grassland vegetation. At the intermediate resolution level (regional scale), we can identify three broad bands of soils in the Great Plains. The three zones are differentiated by their annual soil temperatures of 49°, 57°, and 72°F., respectively, which reflect seasonal balances of solar radiation input. The dividing lines of the three zones are located approximately through South Dakota and near the Kansas-Oklahoma border. At the local scale we will find patches of Entisols (soils without pedogenic horizons) dominated by particular landform systems and materials. Most pronounced of these local soil types are the psamments (psamm = sand) of the sand hills of west central Nebraska.

Three articles written by soil scientists are used to illustrate how energy, moisture, and nutrient flows interact with organisms, man's activities and parent materials (geologic structure) to produce the many

identifiable soil types. In the currently used United States soil classification soils are identified as they are found, that is, as individual
subsystems. Once the classifying units (pedons) are identified in the
field according to mineral, organic, temperature, and moisture criteria,
the soils are placed in a hierarchical classification system. From most
specific to most general the classification categories are: series, families,
subgroups, great groups, suborders, orders. At the most general resolution level, only six orders are necessary; at the intermediate levels
sixteen suborders and forty-one great groups occur; at the most specific
level several hundred series occur.

In the opening article Paul and Stewart consistently point out
that the soil is an open ecosystem. The functional role of the biological
communities of the soil and their many interactions with the physical
environment is emphasized. They note the very important balancing
interactions between the biological community and the physical environment which help maintain the steady-state condition of a given soil
ecosystem. They discuss some of the processes involved in recycling
three essential nutrients of life: nitrogen, carbon and phosphorus.
Such recycling of matter is a basic function of soil systems.

Simonson's article on soil genesis is a classic statement on soils.
His views underpin the comprehensive United States soil classification
system used today. In this article on soil genesis, Simonson views all
soils as the result of balances between additions, transformations,
transfers, and removals of the organic and non-organic elements which
compose them. As a consequence of this open system approach to
soils, he sees the major soil-forming processes not as drastically different actions, but as different states of balance. Thus, he provides a
simple explanatory framework for all soils and all soil processes.

In the final article a systems approach is used in dealing with
man's impact on soils. Bidwell and Hole take the five commonly
accepted factors of soil formation — parent materials, topography,
climate, organisms, time — and note ways in which man's actions
relate to each of these factors. Specifically, they show that man's
actions must be viewed as potentially beneficial or detrimental. Whether
they will be helpful or harmful will depend on the efforts made by
man to determine the effects of his actions. This can best be done by
viewing our actions in a systems context. Effects and countereffects
must be considered simultaneously. Emphasis on balances resulting
from counteracting forces and processes is essential to systems thinking. Balances are also an essential concept in explaining soil development
and the soils present in any area.

The Living Soil

E. A. Paul and J. W. B. Stewart
Department of Soil Science, University of Saskatchewan

Soil is central to many of man's activities. Definitions of this material therefore often vary with its use. Engineers regard it as the uppermost portion of the earth's surface upon which they construct buildings for roads; geologists call it unconsolidated surface rock. The biologist and soil scientist (pedologist) define soils as a natural body related to the five factors responsible for its formation: climate, organisms, topography, parent material and time.

Figure 1 illustrates how the soil system (pedosphere) is related to the atmosphere, hydrosphere, biosphere and lithosphere. Geological deposits covering the earth's surface are continually subjected to weathering and physical breakdown as a result of the erosion and sedimentation processes. The introduction of plant and animal life into these inert deposits marks the start of their transformation into soil. The establishment of growing plants and organisms is followed by their death and breakdown by the action of the soil fauna and

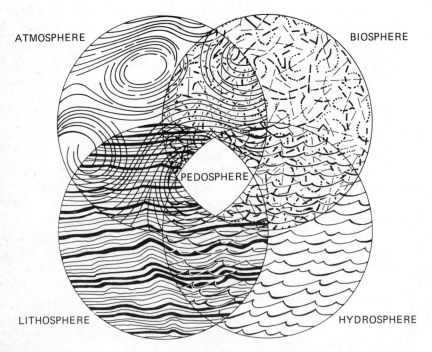

Figure 1. Soil or pedosphere and its place in nature. (From Pauli, *Soil Fertility, a Biodynamical Approach*. London: Adam Hilger, 1967.)

microorganisms. Climate interacts and largely controls the above processes. The end product, soil, consists of various sizes and shapes of mineral particles, living and dead plant roots, organic matter in various states of decomposition (humus), the living soil population, water, dissolved minerals and soil gases. On a volume basis, a productive soil contains an average of 5 percent organic matter, 45 percent mineral matter, 25 percent air and 25 percent water.

Man has influenced and disrupted many of the normal soil processes. This has happened both in agriculture and in industry. For example, management of the soil to increase its fertility has led to larger food crops and has been one of the major factors in the increase in our standard of living. Man can also indirectly bring about some undesirable effects such as erosion and pollution. Proper management of the soil resource requires an understanding of its biotic and abiotic components. The following sections will deal with the soil itself and its biological properties. An example of the interplay of biological and non-biological components is then presented in the discussion of the phosphorus cycle.

The Soil as a Biological Habitat

To understand what is happening within a soil one must be able to visualize some of the dimensions, spatial arrangements and populations involved. Generally speaking, the proportion of the various fractions of sand, silt and clay depends upon the nature of the parent material. The formation of complexes of clay and organic matter and the stabilization of the sand and silt particles into aggregates is the dominant structural feature of most soils. This establishes the soil porosity which regulates its permeability to water, gases, plant roots, and soil organisms.

The different soil pores and the interior and exterior surfaces of the aggregates produce microsites of activity between, on and within the soil aggregates. These can all have different physical environments. This is demonstrated in Figure 2, where aggregates are composed of larger sized quartz (sand) particles in close association with organic matter and clays. The microorganisms in position A would have great difficulty in attacking the organic matter in the lower portion of the aggregate (near position B) as long as this aggregate is not disturbed. This is one of the explanations why much organic material persists in a soil for lengthy periods. Observation of the pore space (A) further illustrates the microsite concept. Microbial respiration could readily make this site oxygen-deficient if the water film surrounding the aggregate was large enough to fill the pore space between the upper quartz particles and the clay domain. This would make site A

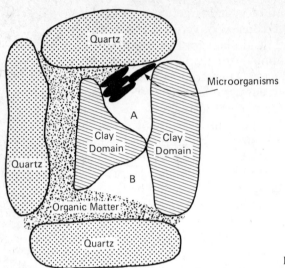

Figure 2.   Model of soil aggregate.

anaerobic in an otherwise aerobic environment. The conditions in
different microsites can be quite different in relation to other soil
characteristics such as pH, nutrient content and even temperature.

Soil is composed of a series of microenvironments in equilibrium.
It can thus withstand a large number of external stress factors. Clay
and organic matter combine to hold water and nutrient elements. This
prevents the immediate loss of nutrients by surface runoff and seepage
or leaching to underground reservoirs. At the same time, plant residues
and organic matter slowly decay at the sites where organic residues
accumulate and where the abiotic conditions are favorable. This decay
completes the carbon cycle and releases the nutrients for further plant
use. The carbon cycle and nutrient mineralization by the soil organisms
are discussed in a later section.

Soil Types

The nature of the soils forming in any given habitat is dependent
on the parent material and on the climatic conditions. The climate
in turn controls the vegetation and the soil population. The soils
formed under moist conditions, where there is enough precipitation
to support trees, will differ in characteristics depending on the tree
type growing there. In evergreen forests, for example, needles containing low amounts of calcium tend to accumulate as an organic surface
mat. The podzolic soils which result, tend to be acidic in nature and
leached of essential plant nutrients. Under many deciduous forests,

where the leaves contain more calcium and where soil animals cause mixing of the mineral and organic debris, the soil maintains a higher base status and supports a greater number and variety of soil organisms.

Grassland soils such as the Chernozemic soils of the Great Plains of North America develop under low rainfall conditions. They are influenced by the extensive root system of the grasses and the relatively dry climate which allows for the buildup of an extensive concentration of organic matter and an accumulation of calcium and oxides of iron and aluminum in the surface layers. These soils usually support a large soil population and the humus is rich in plant nutrient elements.

Under tropical conditions, where rainfall is adequate, the high temperature and rainfall lead to rapid decomposition of organic debris and the development of soils low in organic matter but high in weathered parent materials. A good example of this process is found in the latosolic soils.

The Soil Population

The organisms in the soil are usually classified either as fauna (soil animals) or as microorganisms. This classification disregards the largest living component of soil, the plant roots. These act as a living heterotrophic organism, in that they depend on photosynthetic products brought into the soil from above, utilize water and oxygen and produce carbon dioxide. Through their exudates and upon death, the roots also act as a large carbon source for the other members of the soil population.

Soil Animals

The larger members of the soil fauna, that is, the mammals, are readily recognized. However, they do not constitute the largest proportion of animals in the soil. Those animals not normally observed by the casual observer usually make up the largest biomass and have the greatest activity.

The types of soil animals normally found are pictorially shown in Figure 3. The numbers of organisms shown do not necessarily indicate the biomass present because of the differences in size of the animals. Amongst these animals, the earthworms, where they occur, are usually the dominant group. A considerable portion of the surface soil passes through the alimentary tract of these animals. The worms, in conjunction with bacteria living within them, digest much of the organic material passing through them. They are of importance where organic materials are abundant and accumulate at the surface due to a

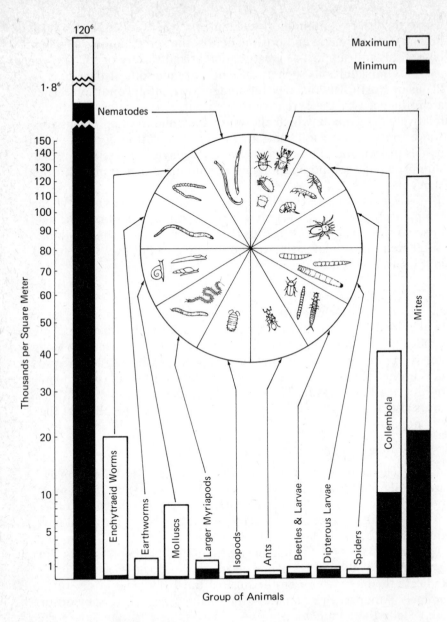

Figure 3. Numbers of animals per square meter in soil of a European grassland plotted on a logarithmic scale. (From Kevan, in *Ecology of Soil-Borne Plant Pathogens.* Berkeley: University of California Press, 1965.)

lack of physical mixing. This occurs in pastures and calcareous forest
soils. It has been found that earthworms in New Zealand pastures are
so abundant that they can equal the weight of sheep grazing on the
pasture. They drag the surface litter down into the soil and mix it
with the mineral materials in the formation of a stable structure.

Earthworms do not always improve soils and there is a danger
in moving them from one type of ecosystem to another. For instance,
in the lacustrine clay soils of Western Canada, earthworms are normally
absent. If they are introduced, as in gardens, they can cause the formation of an undesirable soil structure when they decompose organic
materials and move around when the soil is very wet. This results in a
puddling and cementation of the soil into a massive structure.

Many of the important animals belong in the *phylum Arthro-
poda* (with jointed feet). This includes the myriopods (centipedes and
millipedes), the spiders, mites and insects. These organisms can feed
on living or dead plants and animal residues. They also can be predators
of other small animals or of fungi, algae and bacteria. Many of the soil
microarthropods feed on soil microorganisms as do numerous nematodes. At the same time, there are nematode-trapping fungi in the soil
indicating that there are a wide variety of animal-microbial interactions
in the soil system.

Soil Microorganisms

Microorganisms are usually defined by their size relationships,
for they are too small to be seen by the naked eye. They can be separated on the basis of cell structure into two types of cells, eucaryotic
and procaryotic. The cells of all higher organisms, both plant and
animal, are eucaryotic, in that they have true nuclei and intracellular
organelles. Among the microorganisms, the fungi, protozoa and most
of the algae are eucaryotic. The bacteria, blue-green algae and actinomycetes, however, are said to be procaryotic because of their
simpler cell structure.

The fungi are generally characterized by the filamentous nature
of their vegetative forms. The fruiting bodies of some groups, such as
the basidiomycetes, are familiar to us in the form of mushrooms.
Fungi develop vigorously in forest conditions where they can withstand the acidic pH. They produce a great number of spores in the
soil and generally are fast growing. The fungi, like the heterotrophic
bacteria and actinomycetes, contain no chlorophyll and must obtain
their energy and carbon from preformed organic compounds. Therefore,
these versatile heterotrophic organisms are generally important in the
degradation of cellulose, starch, gums and lignins produced by plant

tissue. The cells of the fungi as well as many other microorganisms, are too small to contain all the enzymes for the vast variety of decomposition reactions they can carry out. They, however, carry the genetic material which controls the production of these enzymes such that they can be produced in the presence of a specific substrate.

The single-celled structures shown in Figure 4 indicate that there is not much structural diversity among the non-filamentous microorganisms. Except for size and the presence of flagella, responsible for motility, in certain organisms one can see very few differences under the microscope. The bacteria exist either in the rod-like forms, such as shown in Figure 4(b), or in the small coccoid form as seen in Figure 4(e). The smaller forms tend to predominate in soil. What the bacteria lack in diversity of form, they make up for in their biochemical reactions. Consider the enzymatic complexity of a simple coccoid bacteria such as the one shown in Figure 4(e). This could be one of the photosynthetic bacteria belonging to the order *Pseudomonadales.* In a single cell so small that it takes 10^{12} to make one cubic centimeter, this organism contains the enzymes required for the production of the essential amino acids and vitamins. In addition, it can fix CO_2 and N_2. Most other bacteria do not contain this much biosynthetic versatility but many of them can produce a variety of enzymes capable of degrading the host of carbon structures found in nature.

A filamentous form of the bacteria, the actinomycetes, are often classified as a separate entity. These organisms have the typical bacterial cell composition and generally act in the degradation of plant components. They have a number of interesting characteristics as they produce many of the antibiotics used by modern medicine. Another by-product of their growth is geosmin, the compound responsible for the typical fresh earth odor. A third attribute of this group

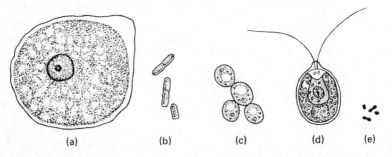

| (a) | (b) | (c) | (d) | (e) |

Figure 4. Drawings of several unicellular microorganisms on the same relative scale. (a) amoeba; (b) large bacterium; (c) a yeast; (d) a flagellate alga; (e) small bacterium ($\times$ 1000).

is the ability to break down hydrocarbons. Thus they act in the degradation of oil spills.

The filamentous nature of the actinomycetes can readily be
seen in Figure 5. This electroscan microscope picture also shows the
relationship of this organism to the soil structure. As this figure shows,
the pore spaces within the soil aggregate are readily visible. The ever-
changing contours on a microscale are also discernible. Bacteria if
present would be growing as a film on the soil surfaces or within the
pore, and usually are not seen when soil microhabitats are observed
with this technique.

Activities of Microorganisms

Microorganisms are often best known for their action as agents
of plant and animal diseases. However, these represent only a very
small portion of the total population. The microorganisms in nature
are essentially responsible for the degradation of organic waste products (including pollutants and pesticides). They play a major role in

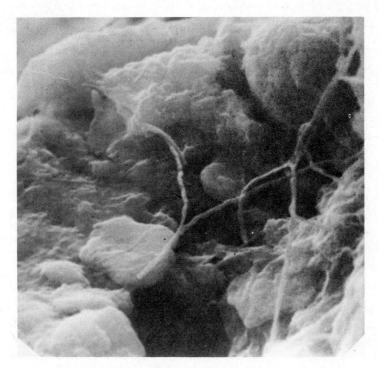

Figure 5. Stereoscan microscope picture of actinomycete hyphae on
soil aggregate (X 1000). (Photo from S. T. Williams).

the carbon cycle, in the mineralization of nutrient elements, and in the oxidation and reduction of a number of biologically important elements such as nitrogen, sulphur, iron and manganese. Transformations of nitrogen include such reactions as:

1. nitrogen fixation: atmospheric N_2 to $NH_4^+ \rightarrow$ proteins $\rightarrow$ microbial cells
2. ammonification: proteins $\rightarrow$ peptides $\rightarrow NH_4^+$.
3. nitrification: $NH_4^+ \rightarrow NO_2^- \rightarrow NO_3^-$.
4. denitrification: $NO_3^- \rightarrow N_2$.

The above reactions can be called portions of the nitrogen cycle, for if carried to completion, atmospheric N_2 is transformed to proteins. Under the proper conditions, further reactions involving ammonification, nitrification and denitrification can lead to the return of N_2 to the atmosphere.

The nitrification process is of special importance because the oxidation of NO_2^- to NO_3^- is one of the few, microbially-mediated soil reactions carried out by a single group of organisms (*Nitrobacter*). These organisms, which are sensitive to pesticides, are indirectly the cause of many of agriculture's problems in nitrogen losses through denitrification and leaching, and are indirectly responsible for some of our nitrogen pollution problems. The oxidation of ammonia, which is held by the soil clay complex, to nitrate by these organisms makes the nitrogen susceptible to losses through leaching. This removes the nutrient from the plant root zone, and can cause pollution of ground waters, lakes, and streams. At the same time nitrification is a preliminary step in the return of nitrogen to the atmosphere as N_2 through the denitrification process. This completes the cycle of nitrogen.

It can generally be said that the soil organisms, because of their small size and their dispersion in microsites throughout the soil system, are more resistant to toxic materials than higher plants and animals. The problem of pollution of the general environment, rather than the specific effects on the microorganisms, usually is the limiting factor in pesticide application.

Effect of the Soil Population on Carbon and Nutrient Cycling

The need for such essential nutrients as carbon, nitrogen and phosphorus by both plants and animals ensures that these elements are moved through an ecosystem. A study of the ecosystem shows that nutrient elements are not homogeneously distributed through the system, but exist in trophic levels in widely differing amounts. Therefore, a knowledge of the rates of transfer of materials between components of the ecosystem is of primary importance in understanding the whole system. Soil fauna and microorganisms play an important role in each step of the process.

The difference in chemical form and properties of the essential elements makes it impossible to consider them together in anything but very general terms. Discussion of the effect of soil fauna and microorganisms on nutrients will be limited to: (1) a discussion of the mineralization of carbon, which is a prerequisite to all mineralization reactions, and (2) a discussion of the cycling of phosphorus which illustrates how non-biotic effects influence the transfer of an essential element.

Carbon and Energy Cycle

The diagram of carbon movement through a native grassland system (Figure 6), shows carbon dioxide being taken up by the plant during the photosynthesis process. Some of the carbohydrates, produced in the leaves, are translocated to the roots. Here a portion is used

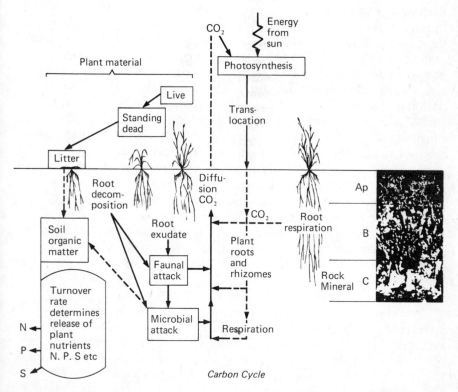

Figure 6.   Transfer of carbon through the soil plant system by plants and microorganisms.

for the production of more plant material. The rest will be respired to provide energy. This releases carbon dioxide. The carbon dioxide in the soil normally will diffuse to the soil surface via the pores. It can also be trapped by soil water in the pores causing anaerobic conditions. The reaction which predominates will depend on the soil's physical and chemical characteristics.

Some organic material will be released as exudates from the roots and will be a source of food, and energy, for numerous fauna and microorganisms in the rhizosphere. This again will result in a release of carbon dioxide. Figure 6 also depicts the gradual senescence of the plant with time: the green living material is shown changing to standing dead material. This in turn becomes litter on the surface. When the moisture and temperature conditions are suitable, the litter will be attacked. In the degradation process, carbon dioxide is evolved and NH_4^+, $H_2PO_4^-$ and $SO_4^=$, and so on, may be released into the soil solution.

During the attack on the organic substrate, microbial cytoplasmic and cell wall constitutents are formed. These can be stabilized in the soil for some periods of time, especially if the soil is high in inorganic colloids. At the same time, a small amount of resistant humic materials are formed. The formation of new humic material is accompanied by the degradation of organic materials already present in the soil, resulting in equilibrium conditions. The relative rates of the degradation and accumulation processes are related to environmental factors such as soil temperature and soil moisture and to the availability of nutrients. They also are affected by man's activities. In grassland soils, humus can accumulate over a period of centuries until very large amounts are present. Cultivation causes a decline in the humus content followed by a stabilization at a new level.

Under forest conditions, the standing crop of trees usually accounts for a greater weight of carbon than the soil humus, even though litter layers accumulate. Complete removal of trees in a forest system, either by cutting or by fire, therefore, usually exerts a greater stress on the soil ecosystem than harvesting of a grass plant cover.

The Phosphorus Cycle

Phosphorus is a major plant nutrient and its deficiency in a terrestrial or aquatic system often limits plant growth. In terrestrial systems, man, other animals and microorganisms have developed methods of harvesting and degrading excess organic production. Actually, man often increases production by adding phosphorus to the soil. In the aquatic system, plants also respond to additional levels of phosphorus by showing greatly increased growth. The organic materials produced by the additions of phosphorus or other nutrients cannot easily be removed either by man or the organisms in the water and sediments. This results in eutrophication problems.

The phosphorus cycle through a native grassland ecosystem such as that found at the Matador International Biological Programme site in Canada is depicted in Figure 7. This shows the amount of phosphorus (in grams per square meter to a depth of 30 centimeters) in each component of the grassland system. The arrows indicate the direction of nutrient flow. Water-soluble phosphorus is taken up by the plant roots and transferred to green, living tissue above ground. From there it may be moved down into the storage tissue in the roots and rhizomes or it may become part of the standing-dead material upon senescence of the plant. The standing-dead material would eventually return to the surface of the soil through the action of rain and wind. This litter then would be incorporated into the soil through the action of fauna, fungi and bacteria.

The degradation of plant material and of the microorganisms themselves means that phosphate compounds will eventually be released in a water soluble form (as the anion $H_2PO_4^-$). Some phosphate also will find its way into the organic phosphate fraction of humus. An alternative route is that depicted when the green or standing dead material is eaten by a variety of above ground animals with the return of waste material to the soil where it will be acted upon by

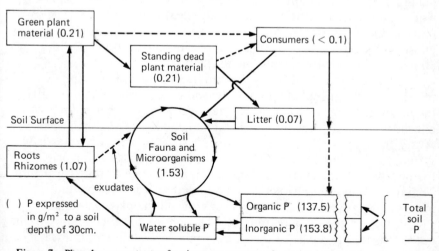

Figure 7. Phosphorus contents of various components of a native grassland.

the soil population. In this particular study, the amount of phosphate in the consumer (animal) population of the ungrazed native grassland and the amount in the above ground plant material are small when compared to the extremely large amount tied up in two large reserves, the organic phosphate fraction of humus and the inorganic phosphate fraction of the soil. If these reserves cycle at a normal rate, plant and microorganisms should experience little difficulty in obtaining enough phosphorus for their needs.

It would appear from the amount of solution-phosphate (Figure 7) that the large reserves of phosphates in the soil are relatively unavailable. An examination of the inorganic and organic phosphorus reserves in the soil helps clarify this picture. Inorganic phosphates in the soils are composed of a variety of compounds that can be loosely grouped into calcium- , aluminium- , and iron-bound phosphates. The ability of these compounds to release phosphate to the soil solutions will depend on their solubility products, and on the reaction conditions within the soil. Phosphate solubility will be markedly affected by changes in pH and by the concentration of cations in the soil solution. Most of the calcium- , iron- and aluminum-bound phosphates are relatively insoluble and therefore the phosphorus concentration in the soil solution will be kept at a low level.

In the particular system described in Figure 7, the soils are calcareous and have a pH of 7.9 in the upper 30 cm. As a result, the inorganic phosphate fraction is dominated by the calcium phosphate, which is largely insoluble. This focuses attention on the organic phosphate fraction which constitutes one-half of the total soil phosphorus. Not all this material had been positively identified, but nucleic acids, phospholipids, inositol phosphates, nucleo proteins, and metabolic phosphate products such as sugar phosphates can account for 40 to 50 percent of the organic phosphate fraction.

In cultivated fields, the contribution of organic phosphates to the available phosphate pool in the soil is not high enough to satisfy the needs of the growing crop. Farmers measure the available phosphorus in the soil at seeding time and add enough extra fertilizer to satisfy the crop needs during the growing season. In a native grassland system the organic phosphate turnover often supplies the majority of the phosphate for the growing plant. It is interesting to note (in Figure 7) that the fungal and bacterial cell populations together contain more phosphate than that required to grow all the plant material.

One of the main reasons why phosphorous is such an important nutrient is that it is part of the energy transfer system within plants. Most grasses need phosphate in quantity in the early growth stages. This makes it essential that phosphate be available in the spring of the year in sufficient quantities for the growing crop. The only two sources of supply are plant-stored phosphorus or phosphorus in solution. At the same time, the microbial population is multiplying and will require phosphate for growth. Mineralization of organic phosphorus in the litter, in dead roots and in the soil organic matter must occur. Microbial activity will also result in the solution of some inorganic phosphate. These activities which complete the phosphorus cycle are in turn dependent on the abiotic environment of the soil. Soil is a dynamic but buffered system in which the various physical, chemical and biological characteristics are closely intertwined.

Summary

The soil has been shown to be a dynamic subsystem of the total ecosystem. This subsystem is dependent on its living population for activity. At the same time, the physical parameters such as climate, structure and parent materials and the chemical characteristics, such as pH and nutrient content, greatly influence the activity of the soil population.

The population of soil animals and microorganisms is characterized by its diversity. In addition, the variety of microsites makes possible the presence of a number of different habitats at any one time. Since the activity of the total soil population is a sum of the activities of all the inhabitants in the various habitats, the population tends to resist changes and is fairly resistant to mismanagement.

The driving force behind the microorganisms' activity was shown to be their never ending quest for the energy tied up in the carbonaceous material. This degradation of organic material makes possible the completion of the carbon cycle and releases the other nutrient elements through the process of mineralization.

The phosphorus cycle is an excellent example of a reaction dependent on both the soil biotic and abiotic conditions. The large amount of phosphate that is contained in the soil as inorganic phosphate is largely unavailable. The rate at which it becomes available will depend directly on the soil characteristics. The organic phosphate in the soil must be mineralized before use. Phosphate released by microbial enzymes is initially tied up in the bodies of microorganisms. This material will be released to the plant via the soil solution upon death and mineralization of the microbial cytoplasm. This means that the rate determining step under the grassland ecosystem discussed is the rate of release of the anion $H_2PO_4^-$ to the soil solution from microbial cells and the ability of the plant to remove this ion in competition with other processes.

SUGGESTED READINGS

Brock, T. D. *Biology of Microorganisms.* Englewood Cliffs, N. J.:
    Prentice-Hall, 1970.
Buckman, H. O. and Brady, N. C. *The Nature and Properties of Soils.* 7th
    ed. New York: Macmillan, 1969.
Burges, A. and Raw, R. *Soil Biology.* New York: Academic Press, 1967.
Gray, T. R. G. and Parkinson, D. *The Ecology of Soil Bacteria.* Toronto:
    University of Toronto Press, 1968.
Kevan, D. K. "The Soil Fauna — its Nature and Biology." In *Ecology
    of Soil-Borne Plant Pathogens,* edited by K. F. Baker and W. C.
    Snyder, pp. 31–51. Berkeley: University of California Press, 1965.
McLaren, A. D. and Peterson, G. H. *Soil Biochemistry.* New York:
    Marcel Dekker, 1967.
Pauli, F. W. *Soil Fertility, a Biodynamical Approach.* London: Adam
    Hilger, 1967.
Tisdale, S. L. and Nelson, W. L. *Soil Fertility and Fertilizers.* 2nd ed.
    New York: Macmillan, 1966.
Stanier, R. Y.; Doudoroff, M.; and Adelberg, E. A. *The Microbial World.*
    3rd ed. Englewood Cliffs, N. J.: Prentice-Hall, 1970.
Stolzy, L. H. and Van Gundy, S. D. "The Soil as an Environment for
    Microflora and Microfauna." *Phytopathology* 58 (1968): 889–899.

Outline of a Generalized Theory of Soil Genesis

Roy W. Simonson
Director, Soil Classification and Correlation, Soil Conservation Service

Reprinted with some deletions and modifications by permission of the author and the publisher from *Soil Society of America Proceedings* 23 (1959), pp. 152–156.

Theories of soil genesis reflect the state of knowledge in the soil science of their day. This state of knowledge includes the extent to which soil properties are known and understood. It includes the relative prominence given to various soils in the classification system in use. It includes the very concept of soil itself. As knowledge of soils has grown over the years, there have been a number of changes in concept of soil. These have been followed in turn by changes in theories of genesis. Review of a few theories widely held in the past will bear out these observations. Furthermore, changes in theories of genesis are part of a continuing process which will not stop in our time. Concepts in soil genesis need continuing scrutiny and modification. This paper is an effort to sketch the outlines of a theory of soil genesis consistent with a concept of soil widely held at the present time.

PAST CONCEPTS OF SOIL

Most scientists concerned with soil a century ago, and even a half century ago, thought of it as disintegrated rock mixed with some decaying organic matter. . . . If soil is considered to be disintegrated rock, weathering alone provides an adequate explanation for its formation. Nothing further is necessary to provide a satisfactory theory of soil genesis.

This early concept was replaced first in Russia and later in other countries by the idea that soils were more than weathered rock and that they had profiles consisting of genetically related horizons. After this concept was developed, weathering alone was no longer an adequate theory of soil formation. A modified theory was required to explain the evolution of the profile with its related horizons. As a consequence, soil genesis was considered to be a combination of weathering and certain additional changes due to interactions between living organisms and weathered rock. In the early Russian studies, much stress was placed on climate and vegetation as factors of soil formation though parent materials, relief, and time were also considered.

221

Functional relationships between soils and their environment were recognized in these studies.

The studies of Dokuchaev and his colleagues were centered on soils with marked horizonation, such as the Chernozems and Podzols. These and parallel groups have continued to receive much attention in soil science. In this country, processes of soil formation have been related directly to prominent great soil groups by names such as podzolization, laterization, and solonization. These processes have been thought to differ from one another in a number of essentials. In fact, some pairs of processes such as podzolization and laterization have been considered to be opposites in large measure.

A number of shifts in theories of soil genesis have occurred since attention was first focused on the profile and on multiple factors of soil formation in Russia some 75 years ago. One point of view developed in that country holds soil evolution to be a continuous process. According to this view, all kinds of soils existing on the earth at any given time are temporary stages. Each kind represents one stage which may disappear, recur, disappear and recur again. Each stage is succeeded by some other stage in the process of continuing evolution. Thus, the patterns of distribution of soils can change over the face of the earth even though, collectively, the kinds of soils remain the same.

PRESENT CONCEPT OF SOIL

A concept of soil widely held in this country at the present time is a further modification of earlier ones. According to this concept, soils are natural bodies formed on the land surface, occupying space, and having unique morphology. The character of the soil profile remains important though it must share place with other features of the soil. Looking upon soils as geographic bodies entails certain consequences which do not follow as long as attention is focused exclusively on the profile.

First of all, each body of soil occupies volume or space. It is an entity with three dimensions; namely, length, breadth, and depth. Each soil body has a distinct upper boundary where it meets the atmosphere. Each has a less distinct perimeter where it meets other soils. Each has an indefinite lower boundary where it grades into weathered rock. This idea is illustrated diagramatically in Figure 1, which also shows the relationship of the soil profile to the soil body.

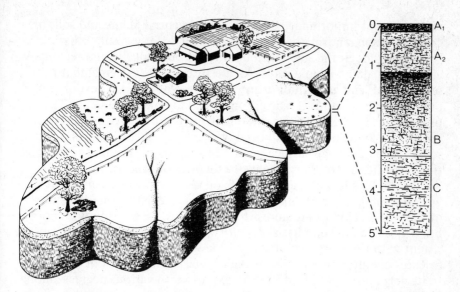

Figure 1. Sketch to illustrate a single body of soil as it occurs together with a diagrammatic soil profile. This body would be shown as one delineation on a detailed map.

Individual bodies of soils are seldom set apart from their neighbors by sharp boundaries. Adjacent bodies commonly grade into one another. The normal gradation between adjacent soil bodies is well known to every man who has helped make a soil survey. Thus, the soils of the world form a continuum or a continuous mantle over most of the land surface.

Every soil type comprises a number of separate geographic bodies or segments of the soil continuum. For the most part, the individual bodies are small so that several occur within a limited area, such as 10 acres. For example, bodies of Fullerton, Dewey, and Emory soils occur in a single small field in east Tennessee. Comparable illustrations can be drawn from any other section of the country. The pattern of small individual soil bodies thus introduces local differences into the soil continuum.

Every soil type has a characteristic region of occurrence. It occurs as a number of separate bodies or segments of the continuum within a certain geographic region or regions. Most soil types commonly occupy characteristic positions in a given landscape. The occurrence of specific soil types in definite geographic regions is reflected in regional differences in the soil mantle of the earth. Thus, there are differences of importance between soils of central Maine and soils of central Arizona, normally greater than local differences in either place.

Although the soil continuum varies both locally and regionally, all soils are alike in some ways. All are three-phase systems; that is, solid, liquid, and gas. All or nearly all consist of the same major components; that is, mineral matter, organic matter, water and air. The proportions of these major components vary widely. All soils have profiles of some kind, and all occupy space. In other words, all form small segments of the surface mantle of the earth. Common to all soils, these features are of consequence to theories of genesis.

To be adequate, a theory of soil genesis must be consistent with the similarities and differences known to exist among the soils of the world. This seems almost too obvious to be worthy of mention but it does deserve emphasis. A theory of soil genesis should be consistent with the existence of soils of the world as a continuum, of features common to all soils, of the normal gradations from one soil to its neighbors, and of differences expressed to various degrees among soils.

STEPS AND PROCESSES IN SOIL GENESIS

Soil genesis can be viewed as consisting of two steps; (1) the accumulation of parent materials, and (2) the differentiation of horizons in the profile. It is not suggested that these steps are clear-cut and distinct or that they lead only in one direction. The two merge and overlap so that it is impossible to tell where one begins and the other ends. . . .

Subsequent discussions in this paper are focused on horizon differentiation. This is not intended to imply that the accumulation of parent material is unimportant. The nature of the regolith in which horizon differentiation proceeds does affect the rate and direction of changes immensely. Lack of space, however, precludes full discussion of either of the two steps. Furthermore, the theory of soil genesis outlined in this paper is more directly concerned with the second step.

Horizon differentiation in soils is considered due to four basic kinds of changes. These are additions, removals, transfers and transformations in the soil system. These four kinds of changes cover a wide range of processes. In his lectures 30 years ago, Marbut observed that processes of soil development did a "good many things" in making soils from parent materials. His examples included decomposition of minerals, accumulation and assimilation of organic matter, removal of substances, translocations of substances, and development of structure.

Each of the four kinds of changes affects many substances comprising soil. For example, there may be additions, removals, transfers, or transformations of organic matter, soluble salts, carbonates, sesquioxides, or silicate clay minerals. Organic matter is added to the soil in the form of fresh residues. It is transformed and lost through decay. It may be transferred from one horizon to another. Rapid and continuing changes thus affect the organic matter in soils, accompanied by much slower alterations of the mineral fraction. Soluble salts may be lost from the profile or moved from one part to another. Silicate clay minerals may be formed by the transformation of primary minerals, or they may be lost by weathering. They may also be moved from the upper to the lower horizons. Transfers of substances from one horizon to another operate in many soils. Transformations of substances from one form to another proceed in all horizons. In the soil as a whole, all of these changes, and others, may contribute to differentiation of horizons.

The additions, removals, transfers and transformations in soils do not necessarily promote horizon differentiation. Some tend to offset or retard it. For example, the materials transferred from one horizon to another by animal activity or by the cracking and churning of certain clays may retard or offset the differentiation of horizons. Similarly, the mixing of soil by windthrow in the northeastern United States also retards the evolution of horizons in a profile. The uptake of nutrient elements from the deeper profile by growing plants is another example of transfer which does not necessarily contribute to horizon differentiation. Thus, the additions, removals, transfers, and transformations may act to promote or retard the development of horizons. Some changes operate in one direction and some in the other. The various processes operating at the same time in the same profile may be in conflict to some degree.

Role of Organic Matter

Additions, removals, transfers, and transformations in organic matter during horizon differentiation are discussed briefly in this section of the paper. The purpose is to illustrate the kinds of changes that do occur. Organic matter has been chosen for the discussion as one example of a major constituent, not necessarily the most important. Parallel discussions would be possible for silicate clays, sesquioxides, silica, or soluble salts and carbonates. It should, therefore, be stressed

that the discussion of organic matter is simply meant to illustrate
what can happen through gains, losses, transfers, and transformations.
Lack of space precludes discussion of other substances rather than any
lack of importance in soil genesis. The discussion in this section is
focused mainly on mineral soils. Organic matter regimes in soils have
been considered at length by Jenny in his discussion of the functions
of living organisms in soil formation.

Additions of organic matter are an early step in horizon differentiation in most soils. The additions of organic matter to the upper
part of the regolith commonly exceed the rate of decay for a time
after soil development begins. For example, a borrow pit used in the
construction of a railroad in North Dakota about fifty years ago is
now marked by a darkened A_1 horizon approximately 6 inches thick.
Crocker and Dickson found appreciable accumulation of organic
matter in soils being formed from fresh glacial drift in Alaska within
a matter of decades. After a period estimated to be 150 years, soils
on this glacial drift were as high in organic matter as are most of those
in the eastern part of the United States. Thus, gains in organic matter
seem to be greater than losses for a time after horizon differentiation
begins.

For most soils, the balance between gains and losses in organic
matter seems to shift as horizon differentiation moves out of the
earliest stages. The rates of loss through decay and transfer increase
until they equal those of gain from plant and animal residues. Under
a given set of conditions, the gains and losses tend to become equal
after a time. Thus, the quantity of organic matter in a soil stabilizes
and remains fairly constant even though additions continue.

The nature and amount of organic matter in each horizon of
a soil depends upon the additions, transformations, and transfers in
the past and present. These are in turn governed by climate, the nature
of flora and fauna, the age of the soil, and the like. For example, the
additions of organic matter are small in desert soils. So are losses. The
rates of additions and decay are both higher in Chernozems. They are
still higher in many Latosols. The points of balance between additions
and losses differ among these three groups of soils. Quantities of organic
matter are low in Desert soils and relatively high in Chernozems and
many Latosols.

Gains in organic matter have been of special importance in
the differentiation of horizons in the soils of grasslands in temperate
zones. The prominent A_1 horizons of Chernozems, Brunizems, Chestnut soils, and Humic-Gley soils are due largely to additions of organic
matter in the past. Other changes have also occurred but the additions

of organic matter have been of special importance in setting apart the prominent A_1 horizons.

Relatively rapid turnover in organic matter is the rule in most soils. The soil is simply a way-station for organic matter moving in a larger cycle. Additions of fresh residues are made periodically. Transformations of organic matter through decay proceed all the while. Losses through decay and transfers also continue. The bulk of the organic matter added as fresh residues during a single growing season decays and disappears before the next arrives. . . .

Transfers of organic matter within the profile contribute to horizon differentiation in many soils. Such transfers may be due to downward moving water, as in Podzols and solodized-Solonetz, or they may be due to the activities of animals.

Evidence of downward transfer of organic matter by water seems clear in Podzols. Narrow moving fronts which appear to be humus can sometimes be observed as water moves downward through the A_2 horizons of Podzol profiles. The marked accumulation of humus in the B_2 horizons of many Podzols is almost certainly due to downward transfer. This is indicated by position of the humus B horizon in relation to the water table in Ground-Water Podzols in Florida and Holland. The depth at which the humus B horizon occurs may vary widely, depending upon the position of the water table. Downward movement is also indicated by the nature of organic matter in certain Podzol profiles in Michigan. . . .

Downward movement of humus by water is also indicated in the profiles of solodized-Solonetz and Planosols. The faces of prisms or columns in B_2 horizons of many solodized-Solonetz profiles have dark coatings. These have been found to be higher in organic matter than the interiors or caps of the prisms or columns. The distribution of the coatings on the vertical faces of the peds and their association with clay films indicate that the humus was transferred downward into the B horizon.

The transfer of organic matter from the A to the B horizon also seems to have occurred in a number of Planosols. For example, the distribution curve for organic matter against depth has two maxima in a profile of Edina silt loam from Lucas County, Iowa. The first and most important is the A_1 horizon (4.41 percent) and the second smaller one is the B_2 horizon (1.47 percent). The A_2 horizon has the first minimum of 0.90 percent and the C horizon the second minimum of 0.32 percent. These differences in amounts of organic matter are not large, but they suggest transfers of organic matter.

Losses of organic matter are apparent in the deeper A horizons of Brunizems which have been occupied by forest and are gradually being changed to Gray-Brown Podzolic soils. The appearance and gradual expansion of light-colored A_2 horizons in the profile are accompanied by parallel decreases in organic matter. Dark coatings on the peds in the underlying B horizons also suggest that organic matter is being transferred downward from the A horizons.

Organic matter is transferred by animals from one horizon to another in many soils. Burrowing animals move soil materials low in organic matter from the deeper horizons to the surface and vice versa in many places. For example, the author has observed as many as four crotovinas per square foot of horizontal cross-section in the upper C horizon of Webster profiles in north central Iowa. [Crotovinas are former animal burrows in one soil horizon filled with organic matter from another soil horizon.] That number is unusual but 1 per square foot is common. Earthworms mix organic matter with the mineral fraction and move it in many soils. In soils such as Oak Lake silt loam in Brookings County, South Dakota, earthworms have completely mixed upper horizons to a depth of 2 feet or more, transferring organic matter down in the process. Earthworms transfer organic matter downward and mix it with the mineral fraction in profiles of Brown Forest soils in New York. These are a few examples which indicate transfers of organic matter by animals from one horizon to another. Collectively, for all soils, the magnitude of such transfer is substantial.

For the most part, the evidence of transfer of organic matter is not clear cut. It seems probable, nevertheless, that there is some transfer of organic matter from upper horizons to deeper ones in most soils, if not in all of them. The relative importance in horizon differentiation of such transfers may be either large or small.

The preceding discussion of organic matter is meant to illustrate the kinds of changes which affect one major soil constituent as horizons are developed. As emphasized in the first part of this section, parallel discussions could be prepared for other substances. Other illustrations could also be drawn of additions, removals, transfers, and transformations. Though not complete, the discussion still suggests the variety and complexity of changes that affect a single major constituent. The discussion also suggests differences in relative importance among the several basic kinds of processes from one soil to another.

Combinations of Processes

It is postulated that additions, removals, transfers, and transformations of the same constituents proceed in horizon differentiation in most if not all soils. Thus, the processes in horizon differentiation in

Podzols would be the same as those in Latosols, Chernozems, or Desert soils. Following this line of thought, there would be some solution and transfer of sesquioxides in all of these soils, though not necessarily the same amounts. There would also be additions of organic matter, transfers of humus within the profile, and losses through decay in all of the soils. There would be one or more additions, removals, transfers, or transformations of silicate clay minerals. The same combinations of processes would be operating in horizon differentiation in all of these soils.

It is further postulated that the relative importance of each process operating in horizon differentiation is not uniform for all soils. The relative importance of the several processes differs from one soil to another. The relative importance may also change with time in a single profile. For example, the solution and transfer of sesquioxides is far more important in the differentiation of horizons in Podzols than in Chernozems. Additions of organic matter are important in the development of A horizons in Humic-Gley soils and much less important in Red-Yellow Podzolic soils. Differences in relative importance of any process in the full combination are small when two similar soils are compared. The differences are much larger between soils that are themselves unlike in many ways.

The combination of processes operating in horizon differentiation and the balance among them may be illustrated by a diagram consisting of arrows of different lengths, as in Figure 2. The length of each arrow indicates the importance of a single process. The balance among the several processes is suggested by the relative lengths of the arrows. This balance can be altered by changes in the length of any

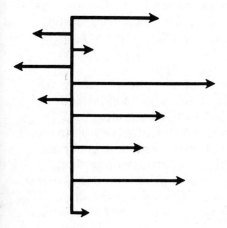

Figure 2.   Horizon differentiation processes.

one arrow or by changing the lengths of several simultaneously. Similarly, the relative importance among the processes may be altered by
changes in one or more of those processes. It should further be recognized that in certain combinations some processes may be of little
importance. By and large, however, the full variety of processes
seems to leave its imprint on soil character.

Further examples as applied to a few specimen groups of
soils may be helpful. In Desert soils, there are small losses of soluble
salts and carbonates from the profile, downward transfers of salts
and carbonates into deeper horizons, small additions of organic matter,
limited transfers and transformations of clay minerals, and limited
transfers of sesquioxides. In Podzols, there is much greater removal
of salts and carbonates, appreciable gains in organic matter, marked
transfers of sesquioxides and organic matter, limited losses of sesquioxides and clay minerals, and some loss of silica. In Latosols, there
are marked removals of salts and carbonates, appreciable additions
of organic matter, some losses of sesquioxides, marked losses of silica,
and transformations and losses of clay minerals.

The balance among individual processes in a given combination
thus becomes the key to the nature of a soil. The relative importance
of each process in the combination is reflected in the ultimate character
of the soil itself. Additions of organic matter are of little importance
in the combination of processes that differentiate horizons in Desert
soils. Removals and transfers of sesquioxides are also of little importance. On the other hand, these same processes are of great importance
in horizon differentiation in Latosols. This further illustrates the importance of the balance among processes in any given combination.

The variety of changes proceeding during the differentiation
of horizons in a profile depend themselves upon a host of simpler processes such as hydration, oxidation, solution, leaching, precipitation,
and mixing. These simpler and more basic reactions proceed in all
soils. They are controlled in their turn by factors such as climate,
living organisms, parent materials, and topography.

Thus, the theory of soil genesis outlined in the preceding discussions requires a shift in emphasis from theories of soil formation
held in the past. The theory does not so much discard ideas held
earlier as modify them and place them in a different setting. Primary
emphasis is placed upon the operation of processes in combinations,
with some processes promoting and others offsetting or retarding
horizon differentiation. Major emphasis is also placed upon the balance
among processes in any combination. It is further suggested that shifts
in balance among combinations of processes are responsible for soil

differences rather than the operation of markedly different genetic processes. The emphasis on widespread operation of the same kinds of changes in horizon differentiation seems consistent with the existence of the soils of the world as a continuum over the land surface. It is also consistent with the common lack of sharp boundaries between one soil and the next. It can accommodate the existence of both local and regional differences among soils. Finally, it is consistent with the sharing of some properties by all soils.

SUGGESTED READINGS

Crocker, R. L. and Dickson, B. A. "Soil Development on the Recessional Moraines of the Herbert and Mendenhall Glaciers, Southeastern Alaska," *Journal of Ecology* 43 (1955): 427–448.

Jenny, H. *Factors of Soil Formation,* New York: McGraw-Hill, 1941.

Kellogg, C. E., *Development and Signficance of the Great Soil Groups of the United States.* Publication 229. Washington: U.S. Department of Agriculture, 1936.

Marbut, C. F. *Soils: Their Genesis and Classification.* Madison: Soil Science Society of America, 1951.

Nikiforoff, C. C. "Fundamental Formula of Soil Formation." *American Journal of Science* 240 (1942): 846–866.

—— "Weathering and Soil Evolution." *Soil Science* 67 (1949): 219–230.

Retzer, J. L. and Simonson, R. W. "Distribution of Carbon in Morphological Units from the B Horizons of Solonetz-like Soils." *Journal of the American Society of Agronomy* 33 (1941): 1009–1013.

Simonson, R. W., "What Soils Are." In *Soil: Yearbook of Agriculture, 1957,* pp. 17–31. Washington: U.S. Government Printing Office, 1957.

Taylor, N. H. and Cox, J. E. *The Soil Pattern of New Zealand.* New Zealand Soil Bureau Publication 113, 1956.

Thorp, J. "Effects of Certain Animals that Live in Soils." *Scientific Monthly* 48 (1949): 180–191.

Man as a Factor of Soil Formation

O. W. Bidwell and F. D. Hole
*Department of Soil Science, Kansas State University and
University of Wisconsin*

O. W. Bidwell and F. D. Hole, "Man as a Factor of Soil Formation," *Soil Science*
99 (1965), pp. 65–72, The Williams & Wilkins Company. Reproduced with some
deletions and modifications by permission.

Man's impact on the soil has increased with his multiplication
and diffusion and with his elaboration of technology. Man the tool-
maker and refuse-accumulator is also man the soil-manipulator, a
purposeful mammal. The technology of modern man can remarkably
increase soil fertility and it can also accelerate soil erosion. . . .

In the course of their endeavor to provide a favorable environment for life, human populations have manipulated the factors
of soil formation. By making value judgments, we can attempt to
characterize the results as beneficial or detrimental, at least from a
local view point. . . . The reclamation of Danish heath for agricultural
crop production illustrates the improvement of virgin soil by human
operators. In 'this instance the ortstein of a podzol was disrupted by
plowing 40 to 80 cm. deep, and 11 tons of limestone, 1 ton of super-
phosphate, 440 pounds of potash, and 88 pounds of copper sulfate
were added per hectare. . . . A single agricultural program, such as
irrigation farming, has affected all five factors (Table 1) of soil formation simultaneously.

Anthropic Influence on the Parent Material Factor of Soil Formation

Accumulation of shell and bone refuse in middens of early
man increased the phosphorus content of soils and raised their pH
levels. . . . In England bonemeal was first used as a soil amendment
in 1774; Peruvian guano in 1820. Lime was used as early as 1794 and
Chilean nitrate fertilizer in the 1840s in Virginia. . . . By burning prairie
and forest stands, man has concentrated ash on the soil surface and
drastically accelerated the biocycle of plant nutrients. These additions
of mineral fertilizer material may be regarded as increments of fresh
soil parent or initial material. . . . Spectacular improvements in the
capacity of deficient soils to support livestock have resulted from
additions of trace elements, such as cobalt and molybdenum, to some
soils of New Zealand and Australia. Artificial drainage and the additions of gypsum to make the soil more productive have, at the same
time, altered its chemical nature by removing excess alkali.

A negative value may be assigned somewhat arbitrarily to certain other changes made by man in the parent material factor of soil formation that inhibit growth of desirable organisms. The removal through harvest of more nutrients than are replaced is a form of soil exploitation. Anthropic accumulation of toxic amounts of salts, alkalis, excessive amounts of trace elements like boron, and chemicals like copper sulfate are detrimental to the ecosystem. Three major occurrences of salinity, ascribable at least in part to mismanagement by people, are recorded in Mesopotamia in, respectively, 2400 to 1700 B.C., 1300 to 900 B.C., and 1200 A.D. Drainage of sulfide-containing soils, called "katekleis" by Dutch technicians has usually resulted in producing sulfuric acid in the soil and a soil pH below 2.5.

Anthropic Influence on the Topographic Factor of Soil Formation

Practices that check soil erosion have ranged from a roughening of the soil surface on a small scale to major landforming in order to shape terraces, diversions, and waterways. Fields have been leveled to expedite flood irrigation. The manual labor involved in making and maintaining agricultural terraces in parts of the Philippines and the continent of Asia is staggering. By means of fill, either of wastes or borrow materials, the level of the land surface has been raised locally by man. On the average there are 12 to 15 feet of "made ground," including ashes and discarded bricks, in the city of London. Not all aspects of these processes have been beneficial. Land leveling for irrigation, for example, has, in some localities exposed cemented pans and calcareous subsoils deficient in major and minor plant nutrient elements.

Subsidence of wetlands after aritificial draining has been particularly marked in bog soils; topographic reversal has resulted in parts of the Netherlands and in California. Mining operations have caused local collapse of soil bodies. Acceleration of soil erosion by man has modified topograhy and the affected soil bodies. Excavation by man has removed hills and lowered plains. . . .

Anthropic Influences on the Climate Factor of Soil Formation

A body of fertilized but droughty Plainfield fine sand in the northcentral United States has, with irrigation, competed successfully with prairie soils of Iowa and Illinois in corn production. By 1954 nearly 30 million acres were being irrigated in the United States, chiefly in the West. Flooding of soils has been practiced on rice paddy soils. Man has removed water from wetlands by drainage and has di-

Table 1. Suggested effects of the influence of man on five classic (though arbitrary) factors of soil formation.

Classic Factors	Beneficial Effects*	Detrimental Effects*
Parent material	(a) Adding mineral fertilizers (b) Accumulating shells and bones (c) Accumulating ash locally (d) Removing excessive amounts of substances such as salts	(a) Removing through harvest more plant and animal nutrients than are replaced (b) Adding materials in amounts toxic to plants or animals (c) Altering soil constitutents in a way to depress plant growth
Topography	(a) Checking erosion through surface roughening, land forming, and structure building (b) Raising land level by accumulation of material (c) Land leveling	(a) Causing subsidence by drainage of wetlands and by mining (b) Accelerating erosion (c) Excavating
Climate	(a) Adding water by irrigation (b) Rain-making by "seeding" clouds (c) Release of CO_2 to atmosphere by industrial man, with possible warming trend in climate (d) Heating air near the ground (e) Subsurface warming of soil, electrically, or by piped heat (f) Changing color of surface of soil to change albedo (g) Removing water by drainage (h) Diverting winds	(a) Subjecting soil to excessive insolation, to extended frost action, to exposure to wind, to compaction (b) Altering aspect by land forming (c) Creating smog (d) Clearing and burning off organic cover

	Beneficial	Detrimental
Organisms	(a) Introducing and controlling populations of plants and animals (b) Adding organic matter (including "night-soil") to soil directly or indirectly through organisms (c) Loosening soil by plowing to admit more oxygen (d) Fallowing (e) Removing pathogenic organisms, as by controlled burning	(a) Removing plants and animals (b) Reducing organic matter content of soil through burning, plowing, over-grazing, harvesting, accelerating oxidation, leaching (c) Adding or fostering pathogenic organisms (d) Adding radioactive substances
Time	(a) Rejuvenating the soil through additions of fresh parent material or through exposure of local parent material by soil erosion (b) Reclaiming land from under water	(a) Degrading the soil by accelerated removal of nutrients from soil and vegetative cover (b) Burying soil under solid fill or water

*The terms "beneficial" and "detrimental" imply a value judgment and the table is admittedly oversimplified and patently biased, but as a device to stimulate discussion, the presentation of such a table is felt to be justifiable.

verted desiccating winds by establishing shelter belts. By 1946, more than 100 million acres of United States farm land had been drained. To protect cranberry plants from frost, operators have flooded cranberry bogs systematically, and drained them again after the danger passed. Smudge pots have been set burning in citrus orchards to heat the air near the ground when frost threatened. In Iceland, natural hot waters have been circulated through pipes in soil to lengthen the growing season. Darkening of the soil, as by burning off the vegetation, or by spreading a film of asphalt or coal dust has raised soil temperature by decreasing albedo, and in temperate and subarctic regions has lengthened the growing season. In the United States horticulturists commonly use black plastic to increase soil temperature in the spring.

Man's manipulation of the soil in agriculture has included a removal of organic cover, with subsequent excessive insolation, extended frost action, exposure to wind, and compaction by machinery and livestock. Steinbrenner and Gessel found that tractor logging reduced soil permeability by 93 percent on the skid rows that occupied a quarter of the forest area in southwestern Washington. . . . Landforming procedures have in some instances changed the direction of slope. Urban smogs have affected the soil climate of cities by increasing the temperature and reducing the humidity.

Anthropic Influences on the Organic Factor of Soil Formation

The wide extent, particularly in the Old World, of soil horizons formed by the work of man is recognized by three new terms in the new (7th Approximation) soil classification of the United States Department of Agriculture: (1) *the anthropic epipedon,* which is high in content of phosphorus; (2) *the plaggen horizon,* which is high in content of sod or forest litter; and (3) *the agric horizon,* which has formed at the plow sole. Rice growers of China, especially those who use night soil as fertilizer, have for centuries maintained an artificial equilibrium with respect to organic matter and other soil constituents. In North America, European settlers worked the forest soils first, and waited until the second quarter of the past century to develop an iron plowshare capable of turning the resistant prairie sod. In many instances plowing of soil has admitted more oxygen to the soil, which stimulates growth of microorganisms in the more porous parts of the plow layer. Man has profoundly influenced the soil by introducing and controlling populations of plants and animals, by adding organic matter to the soil, and by removing pathogenic organisms through chemical treatments or controlled burning. Stubble mulching has protected soil against erosive action of wind and water. Pliny in the first century A.D., discussed in some detail the application of dung to land. Fallowing has been a part of the human control of population of organisms on land in soil. Moses directed the people of Israel to rest the land every 7 years.

Man's activities have, in some instances, reduced populations of beneficial organisms, such as earthworms; such activities have also reduced the organic matter content of the soil by excessive aeration or by allowing overgrazing, fostered pathogenic organisms, and increased the content of radioactive substances that affect organisms. Some 1200 years before Christ, Joshua (Joshua 17: 17) directed the people to cut down forests in the hill country of Canaan. Hobbs and Brown have presented data on the loss of nitrogen from soils of Kansas after the prairie sod was broken (Figure 1). . . .

Anthropic Influence on the Time Factor of Soil Formation
Rejuvenation of soil by man is accomplished by adding fresh parent material, by exposing parent material through accelerated erosion, or by reclaiming land from under water.

Depletion of soil by accelerated removal of nutrients from it and from vegetative cover has, in places, reversed the process and effectively aged the soil. Man has buried soil under solid fill and under water. Dutch polders were flooded by man in 1945 and by storms in 1953.

Conclusion
Alterations of the face of the earth by man have been examined in various works. Man's effects on the soil vary with the nature and properties of the soils and with the uses to which he puts the soils. . . . The human race is ever dependent on seasonal harvests of produce from the soil. Dokuchaev suggested that each major soil landscape has left its imprint on the culture and even on the attributes of the people living in it.

It may be concluded that man is at the same time an agent of dispersal and of concentration. By his "entropic" activity, he disperses natural resources such as ore, oil, uncontaminated water, and soil itself over the face of the earth into countless village and city dumps and valleys and even into epicontinental seas. Human negentropic processes concentrate nitrogen from the air, sources of atomic energy from the rocks, and metals from the sea, and keep fertile soil in place. Man witnesses and increasingly conducts competition between forces of disorganization and forces of organization. He has it within his grasp to see that the forces of organization predominate in his ecosystem. . . .

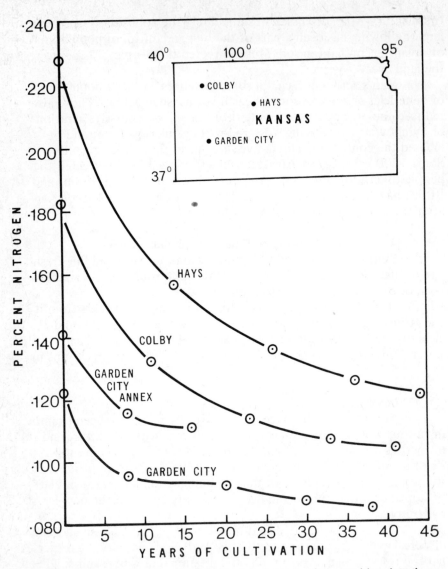

Figure 1. Nitrogen losses under cultivation from Ap horizons of some prairie sods at three sites in western Kansas.

In this context, the pedosphere or soil sphere of our planet is seen not only as the excited skin of the earth's crust influenced by conditions at the interface between the lithosphere, atmosphere, and land-associated hydrosphere, but also as being molded by what we may call the psychosphere, that discontinuous layer that contains the loci of minds where ideas and motivations develop. In the psychosphere man has the opportunity to plan activities to make both soil conservation and the development of optimal ecosystems real and enduring possibilities.

SUGGESTED READINGS

Akin, W. E. "Reclamation of the Danish Heath." *Journal of Soil and Water Conservation* 18 (1963): 97–102.

Albrecht, W. A. "Physical, Chemical and Biochemical changes in the Soil Community." In *Man's Role in Changing the Face of the Earth*, edited by W. L. Thomas, Jr. pp. 648–673. Chicago: University of Chicago Press, 1956.

Amemiya, M.; Robinson, C. W.; and Cowley, E. W. "Reclamation of a Saline Alkali Soil in the Upper Colorado River Basin." *Soil Science Society of America Proceedings* 20 (1956): 423–426.

Edelman, C. H. and Van Staveren, J. M. "Marsh Soils in the U.S. and in the Netherlands." *Journal of Soil and Water Conservation* 13 (1958): 5–17.

Hobbs. J. A. and Brown, P. L. *Nitrogen and Organic Carbon Changes in Cultivated Western Kansas Soils,* Bulletin 89. Manhattan: Kansas Agricultural Experimental Station, 1957.

Jacks, G. V., "Man: the Fertility-Maker." *Journal of Soil and Water Conservation* 17 (1962): 147–148.

Jacobson, T. and Adams, R. M. "Salt and Silt in Ancient Mesopotamian Agriculture." *Science* 128 (1958): 1251–1258.

Jenny, H. "Role of the Plant Factor in the Pedogenic Functions." *Ecology* 39 (1958): 5–16.

Nikiforoff, C. C. "Reappraisal of the Soil." *Science* 129 (1959): 186–196.

Satchell, J. E. "Earthworm Biology and Soil Fertility." *Soils and Fertilizers* 21 (1958): 209–219.

Simonson, R. W. "The Soil under Natural and Cultural Environments." *Journal of Soil and Water Conservation* 6 (1951): 63–69.

Steinbrenner, E. C. and Gessel, S. P. "The Effect of Tractor Logging on Physical Properties of Some Forest Soils in Southwestern Washington." *Soil Science Society of America Proceedings* 19 (1955): 372–376.

CHAPTER 7

Biota: The Complex Web of Life
Introduction

Living systems are open systems exchanging energy and matter across their boundaries and cycling matter within their boundaries. In a lake, for example, solar energy flows in and heat energy escapes; water flows in and out; plant nutrients are carried in and out by water; animals (insects, turtles, fish) migrate in and out. The plants and animals grow, mature, and die. After and during decomposition, their chemical elements become available for reuse by a new generation through cycling.

The natural ecosystems of the earth have built and now maintain the biosphere as we know it. Over time they have stored energy and matter because photosynthesis has slightly exceeded respiration. We use the term "web of life" to emphasize the fact that many interrelated strands are unified into a harmonious whole. Man is an integral part of the complex web of life and he is dependent on it.

Ecosystems can be analyzed by breaking them down into independent and dependent elements. The independent elements are largely beyond control of the system, that is, they are elements of the external environment. These independent elements are: (1) the macroclimate, or causal flows of energy and matter; (2) the available geological materials, or the minerals (nutrients) in storage; (3) the organisms available in a given area which evolved or migrated there over a long period of time, that is, the genetic pool; (4) man and his activities. The dependent elements modifiable within the ecosystem are: (1) the plant producers; (2) the animal consumers; (3) man's activities; (4) the decomposers (mostly bacteria and fungi); (5) microclimate; (6) soils.

Man alone of the earth's species must be considered both an independent and a dependent element. By what he does he can affect all other systems of the natural environment as well as himself and his own environment. Because human activities play a crucial and unique role in modifying the environment, natural systems should be studied with a view to man's effect on them. In this chapter, productivity studies of systems affected by man and of systems untouched by man are presented. The reader can compare the results of the two studies.

In the first article, Jordan studies productivity in major global ecosystems. Productivity refers to the rate at which biomass is being fixed by the producers, the green plants. What is important for consumers is the net production, that which is surplus above respiration (or maintenance). Net production is the food produced by a system, be it grass, leaves, insects, mice, or steer. Jordan has collected data from the limited number of productivity studies. He analyzes the general pattern of energy distribution or fixation in plants and relates it to the weather-climate and water subsystems. For comparative purposes, a relative value of the ratio of wood production (long-lived tissue for storage) to litter production (short-lived tissue for cycling) is used. Wood production is relatively constant with increases in solar radiation, but it declines with increases in precipitation. On the other hand, litter production diminishes with increasing solar radiation but is relatively constant as precipitation increases. Thus, a tropical rainforest fixes much more energy (in its leaves) than does a northern fir or spruce forest. In the rainforest much litter material is available for regular cycling and storage seems to be a minor problem. Jordan provides us with insights into the way plants use solar energy and how these patterns of energy use evolved.

In the second article, Woodwell outlines the effects of pollution on the structure of ecosystems. He and his group studied the effects of radioactive matter on vegetation in the field. Comparisons were made with: (1) those stresses naturally occurring in severe physical environmental gradients like mountain heights, salt spray zones, decreasing water availability zones; (2) those stresses occurring in ecosystems subject to recurring fires; (3) those stresses occurring as a result of harmful air pollution (oxides of sulphur); (4) those stresses occurring from herbicide applications in Viet Nam.

The results were similar in all cases. The deterioration of a terrestrial ecosystem causes trees to die first, then shrubs, then herbs and grasses; lichens and mosses are most resistant. A major physiological factor causing trees to die first is that size is limited by bark surface/leaf surface ratios. Leaves die as they are affected by radioactive matter and photosynthesis decreases but respiration continues since trees cannot do anything about their bark surface. Compare these results with those on productivity reported by Jordan. In both studies we find that a hostile environment can cause reduced diversity, decreased stability, lack of maintenance power, increasing entropy, and depletion of nutrient cycles in a system. We have commented in several places that ecosystems approximating steady-state conditions also approximate closed systems in nutrient cycling. With deterioration, nutrients are lost. Once lost from the cycling system, such nutrients can be replaced only by import or weathering of soil parent material, which is a very slow process. Degraded vegetation resulting from man's activities in many parts of the world reflects this ecological principle. Notable examples include the Mediterranean lands, Scotland, the Mexican plateau, the American Southwest.

In the third article, Arnold reviews the existing state of knowledge about Lake Erie, a regional lake threatened by pollution. The drainage basin contains many agricultural and industrial developments which are still intensifying. Even on the relatively undeveloped Ontario eastern basin shore of Lake Erie, a large steel plant, an oil refinery, and a large thermal electrical plant are planned or under construction. Manmade developments are increasing near lakes everywhere, and the results are almost always detrimental to the lakes.

Arnold reveals how flows of matter affect the structure of an aquatic ecosystem. He outlines the main factors causing changes in this structure, including the effects of sediment inputs and of warming of the water. Pollution effects are discussed under three headings: silt, domestic sewage, and industrial wastes. To date the main damage has been to the small and shallow western basin of Lake Erie. This area of the lake has received the greatest amount of pollution and is least able to handle it. Chemical changes, oxygen depletion, phytoplankton changes, changes in bottom invertebrate species, all suggest deterioration of the lake, as do records of fish yield and changes in fish species. By and large, through man's activities, it is becoming a richer lake for certain kinds of life but not the life generally desired by man. Most of the effects of deteriorating structure identified by Woodwell and Arnold apply to all other major aquatic and terrestrial ecosystems as well as to Lake Erie.

Unwanted and often unexpected deterioration of water and biota occur in and around many small natural lakes used intensively as recreation resources. Similar deterioration can be expected to occur even more quickly in manmade reservoir lakes. Such lakes, surrounded by man's activities, will usually receive great amounts of industrial waste and nutrient and sediment inputs. Similar dangers threaten local estuaries in all parts of the world. Yet estuaries, along with tropical rain forests and swamps and marshes, have the highest net primary production among ecosystem types of the world. It is these ecosystem types which are currently facing an onslaught of man's activities (for example, the Amazon Basin rain forests). Man's impact could easily exceed critical thresholds beyond which these ecosystems will permanently deteriorate.

In our selected readings on the biotic subsystem we have not emphasized "natural" terrestrial or aquatic life, that is, life forms which have had little interference from man. Instead, we have emphasized those parts of the ecosystem dominated by man. We strongly feel that a major concern of physical geographers and other natural and physical scientists should be the total living system, the ecosystem.

A World Pattern in Plant Energetics

Carl F. Jordan
Associate Ecologist, Argonne National Laboratory, Argonne, Illinois

Reprinted with some deletions and modifications by permission of the author and
the publisher from *American Scientist* 59 (1971), pp. 425–433.

The community energetics approach to ecology permits the
comparison of ecosystems of different structure. A comparison of
rates at which an oak forest, a tomato patch, and a rice paddy convert
solar energy into chemical energy, for example, could yield insights
into the structure and function of these ecosystems and how the
plants in them are influenced by climatic and edaphic factors. The
approach, used in many agricultural and forestry studies, of measuring
only economically useful plant parts, in contrast, does not give as much
information concerning the nature of plant communities.

Insights into energy flow in forest ecosystems throughout
the world have been gained by comparing ratios of leaf fall to litter
accumulation on the forest floor. Near the equator the ratio of leaf
fall to litter accumulation is high, and at higher latitudes the ratio is
low. This pattern is a result of high rates of leaf production and small
amounts of litter accumulation in the tropics, and low rates of leaf
production and large amounts of litter accumulation at higher latitudes.
Productivity of leaves and litter accumulation are related, in turn, to
climatic and edaphic factors.

Few worldwide patterns such as that of the leaf fall/litter
accumulation ratios have emerged from the many studies of community
energetics (often called "productivity studies") now in the ecological
literature. Recognizing worldwide patterns in plant production is
difficult because of the large local variations in production, which are
caused, in turn, by local variations in soil moisture, soil fertility,
climate, and other factors.

My objective here is to find a worldwide pattern of terrestrial
plant energetics that would provide a basis for calculating the productive potential of land areas of the world. The major problem in
recognizing such a pattern is the elimination of confusing irregularities
in the data resulting from local environmental variations. This problem
is solved by forming ratios, because ratios eliminate variations in absolute values, and consequently patterns are more easily recognized.

After studying the published data it became apparent that,
while absolute amounts of production depended greatly upon local
conditions, energy distribution within plants followed certain worldwide environmental gradients, regardless of local conditions. By energy

244

distribution within plants, I mean how the plant allocates the energy which is available for synthesizing parts. For example, a plant can allocate a lot of energy to wood and little to leaves, or vice versa. Because many ecological productivity studies include both total wood and leaf and other litter production, energy distribution can be quantified by forming a ratio of amount of energy bound in wood per year to amount of energy bound in leaves and other litter.

There is a rationale in attempting to look for a world pattern in the ratios described above. Energy stored as wood in the trunk and large branches of trees is bound in parts which remain intact for most of the life of the plant. Energy stored as leaves and other litter, including fruits, flowers, bark, and twigs, is energy that is quickly available to herbivores and decomposers. Under certain conditions, it seems possible that the environment would select in favor of plants which use a large proportion of the energy available as relatively permanent tissue, and under other conditions, it would select in favor of those which use only a small proportion as such tissue. Later I will discuss some of the possible selective mechanisms.

THE RATIOS

The ratios discussed here are of amounts of energy bound in long-lived tissue per year to amount of energy bound in short-lived tissue per year. They are calculated as follows:

$$\frac{(P_w)\,(C_w)}{(P_l)\,(C_l)}$$

where P_w = rate of wood production, C_w = caloric concentration (calories per gram, dry weight) in wood, P_l = rate of litter production, and C_l = caloric concentration in the litter. The ratio indicates how energy utilized by the plant for tissue synthesis is allocated. A high ratio indicates that a relatively high proportion of energy is bound in parts which remain intact for most of the life of the plant, including trunks and large roots of woody trees and rhizomes of certain perennial herbs and grasses. A low ratio indicates that a high proportion is bound in parts that are short-lived relative to the life of the plant, including leaves, fruits, and flowers, and in some cases bark and twigs.

Because the caloric concentrations in leaves and wood are similar and because leaves make up most of the litter, it is possible to cancel C_w and C_l in the above ratio, and to approximate it by the ratio of wood production to litter production. The data required for the latter ratio are more commonly found in the literature than those required for the former and, therefore, the latter are presented in this paper.

By comparing the ratios of wood to litter production we should be able to find a worldwide pattern in plant energetics. Because patterns in nature are a result of adaptations to environment, according to evolutionary dogma, recognizing major environmental patterns should help in finding patterns in biological data.

Two major environmental factors which form somewhat regular patterns are solar radiation and precipitation. Maps of annual amount of solar radiation reaching the earth's surface show that annual solar radiation generally decreases as latitude increases. Precipitation patterns are somewhat more complex, but still are predictable in relation to prevailing winds, mountains, and land masses.

All other environmental factors fall into two categories: (1) They are a result of one or both of the two major factors and therefore have the same approximate world patterns as the major factors. Examples are temperature and length of growing season, which are functions of the amount of solar radiation and, therefore, have the same general pattern of world distribution as solar radiation. (2) They form patterns so complex that correlation with ecological productivity is impossible because of the limited number of productivity studies. An example is geological formations. While annual amounts of solar radiation reaching the earth decrease with increasing latitude, the amount of solar radiation that can be used by plants may follow a slightly different pattern, and it is this pattern that determines the pattern of energetics to be shown here. An example of the difference is as follows: The British Isles are at a latitude of about 55°N, and presumably have many areas that receive less annual solar radiation than areas in the north-central part of the United States, at a latitude of about 45°N. Because of the warming influence of the Gulf Stream, however, the British Isles may have a longer growing season, and, as a result, there would be more usable solar radiation there than in the north-central United States. The amount of solar radiation impinging on the plant *during the growing season* determines the plant's response, not simply the amount *per year.* . . .

Before ratio patterns and environmental patterns can be compared, two biological factors must be considered. One factor is that the ratio of wood production to litter production is a function of age of community as well as a function of environment. Later it will become evident that even-aged forests (forests composed of trees all about the same age) which are either young or old have ratios lower than those of both intermediate even-aged forests and forests that have trees of all ages. Rate of wood production in young forests could be limited by the cambial area of the trees, causing the ratio in these communities to be low. In communities where most of the biomass occurs in old trees, the ratio also is low. As trees reach old age, their rate of wood production decreases faster than their rate of leaf production.

The other biological factor that influences the world pattern of wood/litter production ratios is that vascular plants have two basically different structures. In trees and shrubs, energy used as wood is stored mainly above ground. In herbs and grasses, energy used as wood or woody-like tissue is stored below ground. Trees and grasses growing in the same region can be subjected to the same environmental forces and yet have different ratios because of their basically different structure. For this reason, a pattern of ratios in forest communities is considered separately from a pattern in grass and herb communities. In areas where forests and grasslands are intermixed, forests often replace grassland through the process of succession.

Methods of measuring litter fall and wood production have not been standardized; consequently some variation in the ratios results from variations in methods. The difference in ratios of forests caused by nonstandard litter collections is probably small, because leaves comprise by far the greatest bulk of the litter that falls from trees, and all authors included leaves in their litter fall term.

Rate of wood production is given in more than half the forest productivity papers, while the annual increment in total standing biomass, including an increase in leaves attached to the tree, is shown in the rest. Errors in ratios arising from the use of change in standing crop per year, instead of annual wood production, are small, because leaf biomass changes very little in most trees after an age of about 20 years, while wood biomass increases almost till the tree dies. It appears that, in forest studies where shrub data were not included in the term wood production, the shrub component comprised an insignificant part of total production, and therefore errors from this source probably are small. In the calculation of ratios for grassland and herb communities, wood production is assumed to be the growth of rhizomes and roots, and litter production, the growth of above-ground parts. . . .

THE PATTERN

Available Solar Energy Gradient

The ratio of wood production to litter production in forests generally increases along a gradient of decreasing solar energy available during the growing season as shown in Figure 1. The ratios in this figure are from Table 1, and the available light energy was calculated as explained above.

Four of the communities plotted in Table 1 are of special interest because their ratios differ greatly from other forests of the same latitude. Community 14 is on Long Island, New York, where, because of the ocean's warming influence during the winter, the growing season is longer than at inland locations. Consistent with the hypothesis, the ratio is one of the lowest for temperate zone forests. Communities 23 and 24 are at a relatively high altitude where the growing season is short and, in keeping with the hypothesis, their ratios are relatively high. Community 17, which has the highest ratio for tropical communities, is noteworthy because its growing season is not governed by temperature but by a winter dry season.

Not all communities in Table 1 are included in Figure 1. Some are excluded because they are young or old even-aged communities or because the ratio was affected by precipitation, a factor in the world pattern considered later. Communities 6 and 9 have ratios relatively low for their location because they are young even-aged stands. Community 13 has a low ratio because it is an old even-aged stand. In communities 10, 11, and 16, the rate of fall of dead trees is approximately the same as the term "real primary production," suggesting that there is little annual increase in total plant biomass in the forest, a condition that would prevail in an old even-aged forest. Community 8 has a low ratio for a temperate forest, but it is located where precipitation is light. A low ratio is correlated with low precipitation as well as with high amounts of available light.

Only community 27 has a ratio that drastically departs from the general pattern. The leaf fall data in this study may be in error, because the author's estimate of leaf fall was not based on direct measurement but on correlations made by other authors from trees at other locations.

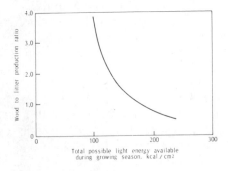

Figure 1. Ratio of wood production to litter production in forest communities as a function of amount of light energy available during the growing season.

The ratios of wood production to litter production in grass, herb, and sedge communities, like the ratios in forest communities, increase along a gradient of decreasing available solar energy, as indicated by type and location of community. The data in Table 2 show that the ratio in a tundra community is higher than ratios in temperate grassland communities. Aging apparently has the same effect on the ratios of grass and herb communities as on forest communities. The ratios are low when the community is young (Table 2, community 4) and old (communities 1 and 2).

Precipitation gradient

The ratio of wood production to litter production decreases as precipitation decreases. The ratios for mesic temperate forests is between about 2.0 and 4.0 (Table 1). For savannah forests, the ratio is about 1.5 (Table 1, communities 7 and 8). For the prairie community, the one ratio available is 0.87 (Table 2, community 5). In an Arizona desert shrub community, annual wood production was 6.3 grams per square meter per year, and litter production was 133 grams per square meter per year, giving a ratio of 0.05.

With a worldwide pattern of plant energetics established, it is easier to recognize worldwide patterns in absolute production values. Although data in the wood production column of Table 1 varies, there seems to be no relation between productivity and available solar energy (as indicated by latitude and altitude). The variations in wood production apparently are caused by local variations including soil moisture and fertility. Extremes in soil moisture and fertility could cause a reduced rate of growth in the species dominant throughout the region, or they could result in the local dominance of other species better adapted to the extreme conditions. On a worldwide scale, the absolute rate of wood production in mesic forested areas would be almost constant if variations in such local factors as soil moisture and fertility were eliminated.

In contrast, litter fall values in Table 1 decrease with increasing latitude and/or altitude. Litter fall decreases from approximately 2,000 grams per square meter per year in the tropics to just over 200 grams per square meter per year in north temperate latitudes or on mountain tops. In grassland communities (Table 2) absolute rates of wood production appear to be generally lower than in forest communities (Table 1), as might be expected considering the structure of the two groups of plants.

In contrast, litter fall seems to be similar in the two types of communities. No statistical test would show a significant difference between the litter fall columns of Tables 1 and 2.

Table 1. Rate of wood production and rate of litter production in various forests, and the ratio between the two rates.[3]

Community Number	Type of Community	Location	Age (in years)	Wood Production g/m^2/yr	Litter Fall g/m^2/yr	Wood Production/Litter Production
1	Tropical rain forest	Thailand	Mature	533	2322	0.23
2	Broadleaf evergreen forest	Japan	?	920	1140	0.80
3	Tropical rain forest	Puerto Rico	Intermediate	486	547	0.88
4	Tropical rain forests	Average of several	?	1650	1600	1.03
5	Subtropical forests	Average of several	?	1250	1200	1.04
6	Ash plantation	Denmark	12	410	330	1.46
7	Dry savannah	Turkmenistan Russia	?	440	290	1.52
8	Oak forest	Steppe zone, Russia	?	550	350	1.57
9	Beech plantation	Denmark	8	480	270	1.77
10	Fir	Mid taiga, Russia	?	450	250	1.80
11	Fir	Southern taiga, Russia	?	550	300	1.83
12	Beech forest	Germany	?	850	450	1.88
13	Beech plantation	Denmark	85	740	390	1.89
14	Oak-pine forest	Long Island, New York	40	783	406	1.92
15	Pine forest	Virginia	17	940	490	1.93
16	Fir forest	Northern taiga, Russia	?	300	150	2.00
17	Tropical seasonal forest	Ivory Coast	?	900	440	2.04
18	Beech plantation	Denmark	25	960	390	2.46
19	Beech plantation	Denmark	46	960	390	2.46
20	10 Angiosperm forests	England	20–50	369	137[1]	2.70

21	10 Angiosperm forests	Europe	?	770	280	2.75
22	18 Cold temperate forests	varied	varied	890	290	3.07
23	10 Angiosperm forests	Mts. of Tennessee	varied	1014[2]	320	3.16
24	13 Gymnosperm forests	Mts. of Tennessee	varied	889	267	3.32
25	7 Gymnosperm forests	Europe	varied	1050	270	3.88
26	22 Gymnosperm forests	England	20–50	892	228[1]	3.90
27	Tulip tree stand	Mts. of Tennessee	?	2407[2]	410	5.87

[1] Calculated from non-leaf/leaf production ratios given by Bray and Gorham.
[2] Above-ground portion only.
[3] Data sources are provided in the complete article by Jordan in *American Scientist* 59 (1971): 428.

Table 2. Rate of woody tissue production and rate of litter production in various perennial herb and grass ecosystems, and the ratio between the two rates.[1]

Community Number	Type of Community	Location	Age (in years)	Wood Production g/m²/yr	Litter Fall g/m²/yr	Wood Production/ Litter Production
1	Old field, upland	Michigan	30	0	312	0
2	Old field, swale	Michigan	30	0	1003	0
3	Perennial herbs	Japan	?	294	1484	0.19
4	Perennial grass	Georgia	8	148	461	0.32
5	Tallgrass prairie	Missouri	?	452	520	0.87
6	Old field	Michigan	14	1023	668	1.53
7	Mesic alpine tundra	Wyoming	?	302	162	1.86

[1] Data sources are provided in the complete article by Jordan in *American Scientist* 59 (1971): 429.

To summarize the features of the world pattern of absolute production values we can say that, along a gradient of decreasing available solar energy, wood production is constant but litter production decreases; along a gradient of decreasing precipitation, litter production is constant but wood production decreases.

World patterns of plant efficiency (calories of solar energy required to produce plant material with an energy equivalent of one calorie) can be recognized by using data already presented. Communities 1 through 5 receive approximately twice the solar energy during the growing season as communities 18–26, yet there is no significant difference in rates of wood production between the two groups of communities (Table 1). This means that communities at higher latitudes and altitudes produce wood more efficiently than communities at lower ones.

Efficiencies of litter production, in contrast, might be fairly constant throughout the world, or perhaps even decrease at higher latitudes and altitudes. Litter production in communities 1–5 is roughly 3 to 5 times greater than in communities 18–26 (Table 1) yet, as mentioned above, they have available only about twice the solar radiation as the latter communities. Where precipitation becomes severely limiting to plant growth, efficiency of solar energy utilization would be low regardless of amounts of solar energy.

Ecological Aspects of the Pattern

In the previous section, I pointed out that efficiency of wood production increases as amounts of available solar energy decrease, while efficiency of litter production appears to change very little. This increase in efficiency of wood production, coupled with an almost constant efficiency of litter production, causes the pattern of increasing wood to litter production ratios along gradients of decreasing available solar energy. One explanation for this pattern might be that fast growth (that is, efficient wood production) is or was a greater competitive advantage in areas with relatively little light, as in the taiga, than in areas with relatively high levels of available light, as in the moist lowland tropics.

Another adaptive mechanism that could result in high ratios at high latitudes and altitudes is the maximizing of the rate of wood production. This would be an adaptive advantage for plants in highly stressful environments, such as those of high altitude and latitude, if larger plants were more resistant to these stresses than small plants. A larger tree has larger roots and possibly more energy reserves to withstand low light levels, defoliation, or an unusually short growing season, events more common at high latitudes than in the warm lowland tropics.

Since the wood to litter production ratio decreases along a gradient of decreasing precipitation, in temperate zone communities, a low ratio is usually the result of a low rate of wood production, not a high rate of litter production (see Tables 1 and 2). Plants of prairie and steppe communities have a low rate of wood production because of the adaptive advantage of small plant size in dry areas: the smaller the plant, the less water it requires. Low rates of wood production are found in woody plants of dry areas because these plants have been selected for the ability to survive while maintaining very slow growth rates. The desert shrub community studied by Chew and Chew, for example, produced woody material at the rate of only 6.3 grams per square meter per year.

I have already suggested that wood production in mesic forests of the world is fairly uniform, excluding local variations caused by local environmental conditions. But we can ask: Does uniform wood production result from equal rates of production by all species or from the average production of all species in each community being equal? Either could be hypothesized from data cited in this paper, which represent total production from all species in various communities.

Not all species have equal rates of wood production. The predominant and largest tree species in all mesic forests of the world may have equal rates, and it is possible that their production outweighs the production of other species to the extent that the pattern of plant energetics is determined by their production. For example, spruce trees in the taiga and oaks in southern temperate regions could have similar rates of production (on a unit area of forest floor basis), and their rates might be so large in comparison to shrub and other tree production that variations in the latter production would not affect the pattern.

On the other hand, should the more or less uniform wood production throughout mesic forests of the world result from the average production of all species in each community being equal, some sort of community evolution would be implied. The implication arises from the improbability of equal production occurring by chance. While the possibility of coevolution of at least two species is evidenced by the positively mutualistic association of algae and fungi in lichens, no evidence exists that entire communities can evolve or have evolved as some sort of supra-organism.

Other aspects of the ratios of wood production to litter production, although not directly related to the overall pattern presented so far, are of ecological interest. One is the change in ratio during succession. In mesic environments, abandoned farms or cut-over forests initially are invaded by grasses and herbs. Later, trees replace the grass and herbs. During this succession, the ratio of wood production to litter production increases. . . .

A second aspect of these ratios is a consideration of the maximum ratio possible. Within limits, the greater the proportion of available energy bound as wood to that bound in leaves and other litter, the faster a woody plant grows, considering plant growth to be the rate of increase of biomass over a period of years. If a plant has bound too much energy in wood, it would have insufficient energy to support production of photosynthetic apparatus, and eventually would cease to grow and would die from insufficient energy for metabolism. The highest ratio of wood production to litter production listed in Table 1, with the exception of community 27 discussed earlier, is 3.90. This figure may represent the balance of production between wood and litter that results in the fastest growth of woody plants.

Another aspect of the ratio of wood to litter production is also of ecological interest. It has been hypothesized that evolutionary selection has modified the manner in which plants distribute energy between long-lived and short-lived tissue. This idea can be extended to include annual plants. Annuals devote all their available energy to materials required only through the growing season, except for the seeds. The annual plant's seeds may represent its adaptation to stress. While perennial plants and trees have adapted to stress by producing woody tissue at a high rate, or by putting woody tissue underground, annual plants have adapted to stress by producing an especially resistant seed. Seeds of annuals always must endure stressful cold or dry seasons on or in the soil; the seeds of many perennials, on the other hand, are protected by the vegetative stage of the life cycle until just before the seed germinates. Exceptions, including oaks and members of the rose family, have seeds especially adapted to over-winter.

The difference in energy utilization between annuals and perennials would account for the decrease in productivity of above-ground biomass in an abandoned field after the first year of abandonment. During succession, as perennials replace annuals, less energy is used in succulent above-ground tissue and more is stored in woody underground tissue, and above-ground production decreases. . . .

Caloric Concentrations

In 1961 Golley was first to point out that there was a general increase in caloric concentration (calories per gram of dry weight) in plants with increasing latitude, but also noted some exceptions. Too few studies were available at that time to recognize the various factors

involved in a world pattern of caloric concentrations. Data now available permit the formation of a pattern that encompasses all values:
this pattern is identical to the world pattern of ratios of wood production to litter production.

It is easier to see patterns in the caloric data than in the ratio
data (Tables 1 and 2), for two reasons. (1) Sampling and analytic
techniques for determining productivity of biomass are not as standardized as techniques for measuring caloric values. The less the variation in data due to technique, the easier it is to see the variations caused
by environmental factors. (2) Caloric values do not change much
during the life of an individual plant, but changes in the wood/litter
production ratio during the life of individual plants complicate the
world pattern of these ratios.

Caloric concentrations in plants increase along a gradient of
decreasing amounts of available solar radiation, as can be seen in
Figure 2. Caloric concentrations in this figure are from Tables 3 and
4. . . . Only caloric values of nondomestic vegetation and plants native
to the respective areas were included in Tables 3 and 4. Communities

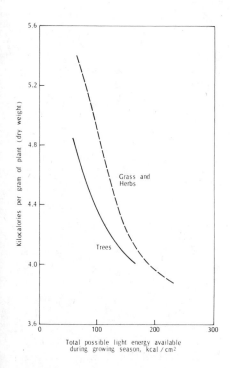

Figure 2. Caloric concentrations in plants
as a function of amount of light energy available during the growing season.

Table 3. Average energy values of trees in natural ecological communities, listed in order of increasing value.[1]

Community Number	Community or Species	Location	No. of Samples	Calories per gram	
				Leaves	Entire Plant
1	Tropical moist forest	Panama	4	3732	
2	Gallery forest	Panama	4	3879	
3	Tropical rain forest	Puerto Rico	15		3897
4	Pre-montane tropical forest	Panama	4	4060	
5	Oak forests	France & Spain	?		47-4900
6	Angiosperm forests	England	8	4759	
7	Scotch pine	England	14		4787
8	Poplar	N. W. Territory, Canada	2	4700	4800
9	Willow	N. W. Territory, Canada	2	4600	4800
10	Savanna	Minnesota	Composite	4846	
11	Oakwood	Minnesota	Composite	4916	
12	Gymnosperms	England	17	4926	
13	Oak	Minnesota	"few"	4930	
14	Alder	N. W. Territory, Canada	2	4800	5130
15	Cedar	Minnesota	"few"	5250	
16	Larch	Minnesota	"few"	5260	
17	Pine	Minnesota	"few"	5290	
18	Alpine shrub	New Hampshire	30	5367	

[1] Data sources are provided in the complete article by Jordan in *American Scientist* 59 (1971): 432.

8, 9, and 14, Table 3, were not plotted in Figure 2 because they are influenced by low amounts of precipitation, and community 4, Table 4, was not plotted because of the difficulty of determining available solar radiation at the site of that study.

Just as in the world pattern of wood to litter production ratios, it is the amount of solar energy available for the plant to use, not total annual solar radiation, that is the important environmental factor. Plants in an alpine shrub community (Table 3, community 18) and in an area with a cold continental climate (Table 3, communities 13, 15–17) have higher concentrations than plants at a higher latitude but in a location with a maritime climate and a longer growing season (Table 3, communities 6, 7, 12). The higher concentration in English gymnosperms (community 12) than in Minnesota angiosperms (communities 10 and 11) results from differences in the two plant groups to be discussed below.

The pattern of caloric concentration along a gradient of precipitation is similar to the pattern of ratios along a precipitation gradient: both decrease with decreasing precipitation. Plants in communities 2 and 4, Table 4 (both dry area communities), have lower caloric concentrations than plants in the temperate mesic communities of Table 3. In tundra regions, the same pattern occurs: in Table 3, plants in communities 8, 9, and 14 have lower concentrations than community 18. At the site of the former three communities, precipitation is light 10–20 inches of annual precipitation fall in the general region. At the latter site, annual precipitation is 73 inches per year.

It is evident from Figure 2 that, within a given locality, grasses and herbs have lower caloric concentrations than trees. This pattern coincides with the pattern of ratios (Tables 1 and 2) in that both the ratios and caloric concentrations are lower in herbs and grasses than in trees.

Because the world pattern of caloric concentrations coincides with world patterns of available light and precipitation, the caloric pattern must reflect evolutionary adaptations to those environmental factors. The adaptive advantage, in a region of limited light, of a plant that concentrates energy in its wood and leaf tissue is not readily recognized. High caloric concentration in wood and leaves would not necessarily make them more resistant to physical destruction or chemical decay. Resins of northern gymnosperms have a high caloric content, but gums and resins are also synthesized by tropical trees. It may not be the structural tissue or the presence or absence of resins that are responsible for higher caloric values but the energy concentration in the carbohydrates used for respiration. It seems possible that a high

Table 4. Average energy values of perennial herbs, grasses, and sedges in natural ecological communities, listed in order of increasing values. Cultivated plants, or plants not native to areas are not included, because they deviate from the natural distribution pattern of caloric values.[1]

Community Number	Community or Species	Location	No. of Samples	Calories per gram	
				Leaves	Entire Plant
1	Perennial grass	Georgia	143		3905
2	Prairie grass	Missouri	Composite	4071	4072
3	*Spartina* marsh	Georgia	14		
4	Desert grass	Utah	24	4080	4177
5	Old field herbs	Georgia	35		
6	Perennial herbs	Michigan	Composite	4315	
7	Perennial grass	Michigan	Composite	4384	
8	Prairie herbs	Minnesota	Composite	4471	
9	"Ground flora"	Minnesota	"few"	4680	
10	Alpine meadow	New Hampshire	3		4711
11	Alpine *Juncus* dwarf heath	New Hampshire	2		4790
12	Alpine sedges & herbs	New Hampshire	40	4796	

[1] Data sources are provided in the complete article by Jordan in *American Scientist* 59 (1971): 432.

energy concentration in fuel could result in greater efficiency of energy use by the plant, because the plant would have to process relatively less fuel material in order to obtain a given amount of energy for metabolic purposes. Another advantage of a high energy concentration in carbohydrates would be that more energy can be stored per gram of root.

The reason that caloric concentrations decrease along a gradient of decreasing precipitation is also difficult to determine. If metabolic efficiency and/or concentration of energy in storage tissue are the factors involved, then at the lower end of the precipitation gradient high values of these factors confer less of an advantage than at the higher end of the precipitation gradient. High metabolic efficiency and high storage concentration might be less of an advantage to plants in areas of low precipitation because, in these areas, plants are often smaller and generally have less biomass to support per unit area of leaf surface than in areas of high precipitation.

Gymnosperm vs. Angiosperm

There is an aspect of the world pattern of wood production to litter production ratios and of the pattern of caloric concentrations that is of interest to plant geographers, because it helps explain the world distribution of two great plant groups. That aspect is the difference in ratios and caloric concentrations between gymnosperms (such as pine and fir trees) and angiosperms (broad-leafed trees like oak). A comparison of communities 20–26 in Table 1 indicates that within a general region there may be a higher ratio in gymnosperms than in angiosperms, but there are exceptions to this pattern, possibly caused by gymnosperm communities that are young (community 15) or old (communities 10, 11, and 16). There are no ambiguities in the differences between gymnosperms and angiosperms in Table 3. In Minnesota, gymnosperms (communities 15–17) have higher values than angiosperms (communities 10, 11, and 13), and in England the same pattern is clear (communities 7 and 12 are higher than 6).

In previous sections, adaptive advantages of high ratios and high caloric concentrations have been hypothesized for plants in regions of limited solar radiation. If gymnosperms generally have higher ratios and caloric concentrations than angiosperms, it would suggest why gymnosperms replace angiosperms along a gradient of decreasing solar radiation from the tropics to the taiga, or with increasing altitude in the mountains of mesic regions. The less the available solar radiation within a general region, the greater the advantage of gymnosperms over angiosperms.

Along the gradient between taiga and tundra, small plant size apparently replaces efficiency of wood production as the most important adaptive mechanism. Also apparent is that no small gymnosperm species capable of surviving in the tundra have evolved, but some small angiosperms have become adapted to tundra conditions.

Conclusions
A pattern of plant productivity and caloric concentrations that encompasses naturally occurring terrestrial plant communities appears to be correlated with worldwide gradients of available solar radiation and precipitation. The relationship between the pattern of productivity, caloric concentrations, and the environmental factors is summarized in Figure 3.

One objective of science is to seek order in the universe; when we find order, we gain the ability to predict. When we find order in plant production on a worldwide scale, we are able to predict the productive capability of the world. The importance of finding the pattern of plant energetics is that it provides a basis on which the productive capability of the continents can be calculated.

One of the objectives of the International Biological Program, in which biologists from many countries are participating, is "to estimate existing and potential plant and animal production in the major

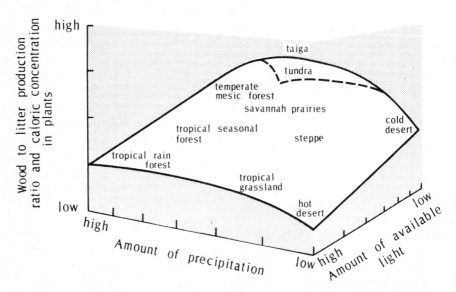

Figure 3. Production ratios and caloric concentrations as a function of amount of light available during the growing season and amount of precipitation.

climatic regions, particularly in relation to human welfare." The pattern presented is a step in the realization of this objective.

SUGGESTED READINGS

Bray, J. R. and Gorham, E. "Litter Production in Forests of the World." *Advances in Ecological Research* 2 (1964): 101–157.

Chew, R. M. and Chew, A. E. "The Primary Productivity of a Desert-Shrub (*Larrea Tridentata*) Community." *Ecological Monographs* 35 (1965): 355–375.

Dahlman, R. C. and Kucera, C. L. "Root Productivity and Turnover in Native Prairie." *Ecology* 46 (1965): 84–89.

Golley, F. B. "Energy Dynamics of Food Chains of an Old Field Community." *Ecological Monographs* 30 (1960): 187–206.

—— "Energy Values of Ecological Materials." *Ecology* 42 (1961): 581–584.

—— "Caloric Value of Wet Tropical Forest Vegetation." *Ecology* 50 (1969): 517–519.

Olson, J. S. "Energy Storage and the Balance of Producers and Decomposers in Ecological Systems." *Ecology* 44 (1963): 322–331.

Ovington, J. D. and Lawrence, D. B. "Comparative Chlorophyll and Energy Studies of Prairie, Savanna, Oakwood and Maize Field Ecosystems." *Ecology* 48 (1967): 515–524.

Rodin, L. E. and Basilevic, N. I. "World Distribution of Plant Biomass." In *Functioning of Terrestrial Ecosystems at the Primary Production Level,* pp. 42–52. Proceedings of Copenhagen Symposium, UNESCO, 1968.

Scott, D. and Billings, W. D. "Effects of Environmental Factors on Standing Crop and Productivity of an Alpine Tundra." *Ecological Mongraphs* 34 (1964): 243–270.

Whittaker, R. H. "Forest Dimensions and Production in the Great Smoky Mountains." *Ecology* 47 (1966): 103–121.

Whittaker, R. H. and Woodwell, G. M. "Structure, Production and Diversity of the Oak-Pine Forest at Brookhaven, New York." *Journal of Ecology* 57 (1969): 155–174.

Effects of Pollution on the Structure and Physiology of Ecosystems

G. M. Woodwell

Senior Ecologist, Biology Department, Brookhaven National Laboratory

Reprinted with some modifications by permission of the author and the publisher from *Science* 168 (April, 1970), pp. 429–433. Copyright 1970 by the American Association for the Advancement of Science.

      The accumulation of various toxic substances in the biosphere is leading to complex changes in the structure and function of natural ecosystems. Although the changes are complex, they follow in aggregate patterns that are similar in many different ecosystems and are therefore broadly predictable. The patterns involve many changes but include especially simplification of the structure of both plant and animal communities, shifts in the ratio of gross production to total respiration, and loss of part or all of the inventory of nutrients. Despite the frequency with which various pollutants are causing such changes and the significance of the changes for all living systems, only a few studies show details of the pattern of change clearly. These are studies of the effects of ionizing radiation, of persistent pesticides, and of eutrophication. The effects of radiation will be used here to show the pattern of changes in terrestrial plant communities and to show similarities with the effects of fire, oxides of sulfur, and herbicides. Effects of such pollutants as pesticides on the animal community are less conspicuous but quite parallel, which shows that the ecological effects of pollution can be anticipated in considerable detail.

      The problems caused by pollution are of interest from two viewpoints. Practical people — toxicologists, engineers, health physicists, public health officials, intensive users of the environment — consider pollution primarily as a direct hazard to man. Others, no less concerned for human welfare but with less pressing public responsibilities, recognize that toxicity to humans is but one aspect of the pollution problem, the other being a threat to the maintenance of a biosphere suitable for life as we know it. The first viewpoint leads to emphasis on human food chains; the second leads to emphasis on human welfare insofar as it depends on the integrity of the diverse ecosystems of the earth, the living systems that appear to have built and now maintain the biosphere.

      The food-chain problem is by far the simpler; it is amenable at least in part to the pragmatic, narrowly compartmentalized solutions that industrialized societies are good at. The best example of the toxicological approach is in control of mutagens, particularly the radionuclides. These present a specific, direct hazard to man. They are much more important to man than to other organisms. A slightly enhanced rate of mutation is a serious danger to man, who has developed through medical science elaborate ways of preserving a high fraction of the genetic defects in the population; it is trivial to the rest of the biota, in which genetic defects may be eliminated through selection. This is an important fact about pollution hazards — toxic substances that are principally mutagenic are usually of far greater direct hazard to man than to the rest of the earth's biota and must be considered first from the standpoint of their movement to man through food webs or other mechanisms and to a much lesser extent from that of their effects on the ecosystem through which they move. We have erred, as shown below, in assuming that all toxic substances should be treated this way.

Pollutants that affect other components of the earth's biota as well as man present a far greater problem. Their effects are chronic and may be cumulative in contrast to the effects of short-lived disturbances that are repaired by succession. We ask what effects such pollutants have on the structure of natural ecosystems and on biological diversity and what these changes mean to physiology, especially to mineral cycling and the long-term potential for sustaining life.

Although experience with pollution of various types is extensive and growing rapidly, only a limited number of detailed case history studies provide convincing control data that deal with the structure of ecosystems. One of the clearest and most detailed series of experiments in recent years has been focused on the ecological effects of radiation. These studies are especially useful because they allow cause and effect to be related quantitatively at the ecosystem level, which is difficult to do in nature. The question arises, however, whether the results from studies of ionizing radiation, a factor that is not usually considered to have played an important role in recent evolution, have any general application. The answer, somewhat surprisingly to many biologists, seems to be that they do. The ecological effects of radiation follow patterns that are known from other types of disturbances. The studies of radiation, because of their specificity, provide useful clues for examination of effects of other types of pollution for which evidence is much more fragmentary.

The effects of chronic irradiation of a late successional oak-pine forest have been studied at Brookhaven National Laboratory in New York. After 6 months' exposure to chronic irradiation from a Cesium 137 source, five well-defined zones of modification of vegetation had been established. They have become more pronounced through 7 years of chronic irradiation. The zones were:

1. A central devasted zone, where exposures were > 200 Roentgens/day and no higher plants survived, although certain mosses and lichens survived up to exposures > 1000 Roentgens/day.
2. A sedge zone, where *Carex pensylvanica* (a) survived and ultimately formed a continuous cover (> 150 Roentgens/day).
3. A shrub zone in which two species of *Vaccinium* and one of *Gaylussacia* survived, with *Quercus ilicifolia* toward the outer limit of the circle where exposures were lowest (> 40 Roentgens/day).
4. An oak zone, the pine having been eliminated (> 16 Roentgens/day).
5. Oak-pine forest, where exposures were < 2 Roentgens/day, and there was no obvious change in the number of species, although small changes in rates of growth were measurable at exposures as low as 1 Roentgens/day.

The effect was a systematic dissection of the forest, strata being removed layer by layer. Trees were eliminated at low exposures, then the taller shrubs (*Gaylussacia baccata*), then the lower shrubs (*Vaccinium* species), then the herbs, and finally the lichens and mosses. Within these groups, it was evident that under irradiation an upright form of growth was a disadvantage. The trees did vary — the pines (*Pinus rigida*) for instance were far more sensitive than the oaks without having a conspicuous tendency toward more upright growth, but all the trees were substantially more sensitive than the shrubs. Within the shrub zone, tall forms were more sensitive; even within the lichen populations, foliose and fruticose lichens proved more sensitive than crustose lichens.

The changes caused by chronic irradiation of herb communities in old fields show the same pattern — upright species are at a disadvantage. In one old field at Brookhaven, the frequency of low growing plants increased along the gradient of increasing radiation intensity to 100 percent at 1000 R per day. Comparison of the sensitivity of the herb field with that of the forest, by whatever criterion, clearly shows the field to be more resistant than the forest. The exposure reducing diversity to 50 percent in the first year was more than 1000 R per day for the field and 160 R per day for the forest, a greater than fivefold difference in sensitivity.

The changes in these ecosystems under chronic irradiation are best summarized as changes in structure, although diversity, primary production, total respiration, and nutrient inventory are also involved. The changes are similar to the familiar ones along natural gradients of increasingly severe conditions, such as exposure on mountains, salt spray, and water availability. Along all these gradients the conspicuous change is a reduction of structure from forest toward communities dominated by certain shrubs, then, under more severe conditions, by certain herbs, and finally by low-growing plants, frequently mosses and lichens. Succession, insofar as it has played any role at all in the irradiated ecosystems, has simply reinforced this pattern, adding a very few hardy species and allowing expansion of the populations of more resistant indigenous species. The reasons for radiation's causing this pattern are still not clear, but the pattern is a common one, not peculiar to ionizing radiation, despite the novelty of radiation exposures as high as these.

Its commonness is illustrated by the response to fire, one of the oldest and most important disruptions of nature. The oak-pine forests such as those on Long Island have, throughout their extensive range in eastern North America, been subject in recent times to repeated burning. The changes in physiognomy of the vegetation follow the above pattern very closely — the forest is replaced by communities of shrubs, especially bear oak (*Quercus ilicifolia*), *Gaylussacia*, and *Vaccinium* species. This change is equivalent to that caused by chronic exposure to 40 R per day or more. Buell and Cantlon, working on similar vegetation in New Jersey, showed that a further increase in the frequency of fires resulted in a differential reduction in taller shrubs first, and a substantial increase in the abundance of *Carex pensylvanica*, the same sedge now dominating the sedge zone of the irradiated forest. The parallel is detailed; radiation and repeated fires both reduce the structure of the forest in similar ways, favoring low-growing hardy species.

The similarity of response appears to extend to other vegetations as well. Research done at the Savannah River Laboratory has shown recently that the most radiation-resistant and fire-resistant species of twenty-year-old fields are annuals and perennials characteristic of disturbed places. An interesting sidelight of his study was the observation that the grass stage of long leaf pine (*Pinus Palustris*), long considered a specific adaptation to the fires that maintain the southeastern savannahs, appears more resistant to radiation damage than the mature trees. At a total acute exposure of 2.1 kR (3R per day), 85 percent of the grass-stage populations survived but only 55 percent of larger trees survived. Seasonal variation in sensitivity to radiation damage has been abundantly demonstrated, and it would not be surprising to find that this variation is related to the ecology of the species. Again it appears that the response to radiation is not unique.

The species surviving high radiation-exposure rates in the Brookhaven experiments are the ones commonly found in disturbed places, such as roadsides, gravel banks, and areas with nutrient-deficient or unstable soil. In the forest they include *Comptonia peregrina* (the sweet fern), a decumbent spiny *Rubus,* and lichens, especially *Cladonia cristatella.* In the old field one of the most conspicuously resistant species was *Digitaria Sanguinalis* (Crabgrass) among several other weedy species. Clearly these species are generalists in the sense that they survive a wide range of conditions, including exposure to high intensities of ionizing radiation — hardly a common experience in nature but apparently one that elicits a common response.

With this background one might predict that a similar pattern of devastation would result from such pollutants as oxides of sulfur released from smelting. The evidence is fragmentary, but Gorham and Gordon found around the smelters in Sudbury, Ontario, a striking reduction in the number of species of higher plants along a gradient of 62 kilometers (39 miles). In different samples the number of species ranged from 19 to 31 at the more distant sites and dropped abruptly at 6.4 kilometers. At 1.6 kilometers, one of two randomly placed plots (20 by 2 meters) included only one species. They classified the damage in five categories, from "Not obvious" through "Moderate" to "Very severe." The tree canopy had been reduced or eliminated within 4.8 to 6.4 kilometers of the smelter, with only occasional sprouts of trees, seedlings, and successional herbs and shrubs remaining; this damage is equivalent to that produced by expousre to 40 R per day. The most resistant trees were, almost predictably to a botanist, red maple (*Acer rubrum*) and red oak (*Quercus rubra*). Other species surviving in the zones of "Severe" and "Very severe" damage included *Sambucus pubens, Polygonum cilinode, Comptonia peregrina,* and *Epilobium angustifolium* (fire weed). The most sensitive plants appeared to be *Pinus strobus* and *Vaccinium myrtilloides.* The pine was reported no closer than 25.6 kilometers (16 miles), where it was chlorotic.

This example confirms the pattern of the change — first a reduction of diversity of the forest by elimination of sensitive species; then elimination of the tree canopy and survival of resistant shrubs and herbs widely recognized as "seral" or successional species of "generalists."

The effects of herbicides, despite their hoped for specificity, fall into the same pattern, and it is no surprise that the extremely diverse forest canopies of Viet Nam when sprayed repeatedly with herbicides are replaced over large areas by dense stands of species of bamboo.

The mechanisms involved in producing this series of patterns in terrestrial ecosystems are not entirely clear. One mechanism that is almost certainly important is simply the ratio of gross production to respiration in different strata of the community. The size of trees has been shown to approach a limit set by the amount of surface area of stems and branches in proportion to the amount of leaf area. The apparent reason is that, as a tree expands in size, the fraction of its total surface devoted to bark, which makes a major contribution to the respiration, expands more rapidly than does the photosynthetic area. Any chronic distrubance has a high probability of damaging the capacity for photosynthesis without reducing appreciably the total amount of respiration; therefore, large plants are more vulnerable than species requiring less total respiration. Thus chronic disturbances of widely different types favor plants that are small in stature, and any disturbance that tends to increase the amount of respiration in proportion to photosynthesis will aggravate this shift.

The shift in the structure of terrestrial plant communities toward shrubs, herbs, or mosses and lichens, involves changes in addition to those of structure and diversity. Simplification of the plant community involves also a reduction of the total standing crop of organic matter and a corresponding reduction in the total inventory of nutrient elements held within the system, a change that may have important long-term implications for the potential of the site to support life. The extent of such losses has been demonstrated recently by Bormann and his colleagues in the Hubbard Brook Forest in New Hampshire, where all of the trees in a watershed were cut, the cut material was left to decay, and the losses of nutrients were monitored in the runoff. Total nitrogen losses in the first year were equivalent to twice the amount cycled in the system during a normal year. With the rise of nitrate ions in the runoff, concentrations of calcium, magnesium, sodium, and potassium ions rose several fold, which caused eutrophication and even pollution of the streams fed by this watershed. The soil had little capacity to retain the nutrients that were locked in the biota once the higher plants had been killed. The total losses are not yet known, but early evidence indicated that they will be a high fraction of the nutrient inventory, which will cause a large reduction in the potential of the site for supporting living systems as complex as that destroyed — until nutrients accumulate again. Sources are limited; the principal source is erosion of primary minerals.

When the extent of the loss of nutrients that accompanies a reduction in the structure of a plant community is recognized, it is not surprising to find depauperate vegetation in places subject to chronic disturbances. Extensive sections of central Long Island, for example, support a depauperate oak-pine forest in which the bear oak, *Quercus ilicifolia,* is the principal woody species. The cation content of an ex-

tremely dense stand of this common community, which has a biomass
equivalent to that of the more diverse late successional forest that was
burned much less recently and less intensively, would be about 60
percent that of the richer stand, despite the equivalence of standing
crop. This means that the species, especially the bear oak, contain,
and presumably require, lower concentrations of cations. This is an
especially good example because the bear oak community is a long-
lasting one in the fire succession and marks the transition from a high
shrub community to forest. It has analogies elsewhere, such as the
health balds of the Great Smoky Mountains and certain bamboo
thickets in Southeast Asia.

The potential of a site for supporting life depends heavily on
the pool of nutrients available through breakdown of primary minerals
and through recycling in the living portion of the ecosystem. Reduction of the structure of the system drains these pools in whole or in
part; it puts leaks in the system. Any chronic pollution that affects the
structure of forests in Southeast Asia by herbicides has dumped the
nutrient pools of these large statured and extremely diverse forests.
The nutrients are carried to the streams, which turn green with the
algae that the nutrients support. Tschirley, reporting his study of the
effects of herbicides in Viet Nam, recorded "surprise" and "pleasure"
that fishing had improved in treated areas. If the herbicides are not
toxic to fish, there should be little surprise at improved catches of
certain kinds of fish in heavily enriched waters adjacent to herbicide-
treated forests. The bamboo thickets that replace the forests also reflect the drastically lowered potential of these sites to support living
systems. The time it takes to reestablish a forest with the original diversity depends on the availability of nutrients, and is probably very long
in most lateritic soils.

In generalizing about pollution, I have concentrated on some
of the grossest changes in the plant communities of terrestrial ecosystems. The emphasis on plants is appropriate because plants dominate
terrestrial ecosystems. But not all pollutants affect plants directly;
some have their principal effects on heterotrophs. What changes in the
structure of animal communities are caused by such broadly toxic
materials as most pesticides?

The general pattern of loss of structure is quite similar, although
the structure of the animal communities is more difficult to chart. The
transfer of energy appears to be one good criterion of structure. Various
studies suggest that 10 to 20 percent of the energy entering the plant
community is transferred directly to the animal community through
herbivores. Much of that energy, perhaps 50 percent or more, is used

in respiration to support the herbivore population; some is transferred to the detritus food chain directly, and some, probably not more than 20 percent, is transferred to predators of the herbivores. In an evolution-arily and successionally mature community, this transfer of 10 to 20 percent per trophic level may occur two or three times to support carnivores, some highly specialized, such as certain eagles, hawks, and herons, others less specialized, such as gulls, ravens, rats, and people.

Changes in the plant community, such as its size, rate of energy fixation, and species, will affect the structure of the animal community as well. Introduction of a toxin specific for animals, such as a pesticide that is a generalized nerve toxin, will also topple the pyramid. Although the persistent pesticides are fat soluble and tend to accumulate in carnivores and reduce populations at the tops of food chains, they affect every trophic level, reducing reproductive capacity, almost cer-tainly altering behavioral patterns, and disrupting the competitive relationships between species. Under these circumstances the highly specialized species, the obligate carnivores high in the trophic structure, are at a disadvantage because the food chain concentrates the toxin and, what is even more important, because the entire structure beneath them becomes unstable. Again the generalists or broadniched species are favored, the gulls, rats, ravens, pigeons and, in a very narrow short-term sense, man. Thus, the pesticides favor the herbivores, the very organisms they were invented to control.

Biological evolution has divided the resources of any site among a large variety of users — species — which, taken together, confer on that site the properties of a closely integrated system capable of con-serving a diversity of life. The system has structure; its populations exist with certain definable, quantitative relationships to one another; it fixes energy and releases it at a measurable rate; and it contains an inventory of nutrients that is accumulated and recirculated, not lost. The system is far from static; it is subject, on a time scale very long compared with a human lifespan, to a continuing augmentive change through evolution; on a shorter time scale, it is subject to succession toward a more stable state after any disturbance. The successional patterns are themselves a product of the evolution of life, providing for systematic recovery from any acute disturbance. Without a detailed discussion of the theory of ecology, one can say that biological evolu-tion, following a pattern approximating that outlined above, has built the earth's ecosystems, and that these systems have been the dominant influence on the earth throughout the span of human existence. The structure of these systems is now being changed all over the world. We know enough about the structure and function of these systems to predict the broad outline of the effects of pollution on both land and water. We know that as far as our interests in the next decades are concerned, pollution operates on the time scale of succession, not of evolution, and we cannot look to evolution to cure this set of problems. The loss of structure involves a shift away from complex arrangements of specialized species toward the generalists; away from forest toward hardy shrubs and herbs; away from those phytoplankton of the open ocean that Wurster proved so very sensitive to DDT, toward those algae of the sewage plants that are unaffected by almost everything including DDT and most fish; away from diversity in birds, plants, and fish toward monotony; away from tight nutrient cycles toward very loose ones with terrestrial systems becoming depleted, and with aquatic systems becoming overloaded; away from stability toward instability especially with regard to sizes of population of small, rapidly reproducing organisms such as insects and rodents that compete with man; away from a world that runs itself through a self-augmentive, slowly moving evolution, to one that requires constant tinkering to patch it up, a tinkering that is malignant in that each act of repair generates a need for further repairs to avert problems generated at compound interest.

This is the pattern, predictable in broad outline, aggravated by almost any pollutant. Once we recognize the pattern, we can begin to see the meaning of some of the changes occurring now in the earth's biota. We can see the demise of carnivorous birds and predict the demise of important fisheries. We can tell why, around industrial cities, hills that were once forested now are not; why each single species is important; and how the increase in the temperature of natural water bodies used to cool new reactors will, by augmenting respiration over photosynthesis, ultimately degrade the system and contribute to degradation of other interconnected ecosystems nearby. We can begin to speculate on where continued, exponential progress in this direction will lead: probably not to extinction — man will be around for a long time yet — but to a general degradation of the quality of life.

The solution? Fewer people, unpopular but-increasing restrictions on technology (making it more and more expensive), and a concerted effort to tighten up human ecosystems to reduce their interactions with the rest of the earth on whose stability we all depend. This does not require foregoing nuclear energy; it requires that if we must dump heat, it should be dumped into civilization to enhance a respiration rate in a sewage plant or an agricultural ecosystem, not dumped outside of civilization to affect that fraction of the earth's biota that sustains the earth as we know it. The question of what fraction that might be remains as one of the great issues, still scarcely considered by the scientific community.

SUGGESTED READINGS

Bormann, F. H., Likens, G. E., Fisher, A. W., and Eaton, J. S. "Nutrient Loss Accelerated by Clear-Cutting of a Forest Ecosystem." *Science* 159 (1968): 882–884.

Buell, M. F. and Cantlon, J. E. "Effects of Prescribed Burning on Ground Cover in the New Jersey Pine Barrens." *Ecology* 34 (1953): 520–528.

Gorham, E. and Gordon, A. G. "Some Effects of Smelter Pollution upon Aquatic Vegetation near Sudbury, Ontario." *Canadian Journal of Botany* 41 (1963): 371–378.

Phillipson, J. *Ecological Energetics.* New York: St. Martin's Press, 1966.

Ryther, J. H. "Photosynthesis and Fish Production in the Sea." *Science* 166 (1969): 72–76.

Slobodkin, L. B. *Growth and Regulation of Animal Populations.* New York: Holt, Rinehart and Winston, 1961.

Tschirley, F. H. "Defoliation in Vietnam." *Science* 163 (1969): 779–786.

Whittaker, R. H. and Woodwell, G. M. "Surface Area Relations of Woody Plants and Forest Communities." *American Journal of Botany* 54 (1967): 931–939.

Woodwell, G. M. "Effects of Ionizing Radiation on Terrestrial Eco-systems." *Science* 138 (1962): 562–577.

—— "Radiation and the Patterns of Nature." *Science* 156 (1967): 461–470.

Woodwell, G. M. and Whittaker, R. H. "Gamma Radiation of Plant Communities." *Quarterly Review of Biology* 43 (1968): 42–55.

The Ecological Decline of Lake Erie

Dean E. Arnold
Department of Biology, Pennsylvania State University

Reprinted with some deletions and modifications by permission of the author and the publisher from *New York Fish and Game Journal* 16 (1969), pp. 27–45. This paper was prepared while the author was affiliated with the Section of Ecology and Systematics, Cornell University.

In recent years, interest in the pollution and degradation of natural waters has become widespread and fashionable among both scientific and popular writers. In such writings, it is common to apply the label of "eutrophication" to the deterioration process, whatever its cause and means. To the classically-trained limnologist, "eutrophication" refers only to an increase in nutrient content, not to aging of lakes in general, nor to most types of pollution. For examples of eutrophy, one usually turns to small, shallow, weed-choked lakes and ponds, and it is indeed in such environments that the typical conditions are most easily seen. On the other hand, large lakes are the classic examples of oligotrophy, or low nutrient conditions. It has been widely held that the vast dilution factor characteristic of the largest lakes would prevent any clear indication of eutrophy in them. Recent studies, however, have forced a reconsideration of this idea. Perhaps the best-documented case is that of Lake Erie, the eleventh largest lake in the world in surface area. From the human viewpoint, this lake is rapidly deteriorating, not only by becoming more eutrophic, but in other ways to be discussed in this paper.

GEOLOGICAL AND PHYSICAL CHANGES

Early Lake Erie was formed about 12,400 years ago. Its level was about 30 meters below that at present, but it rose rapidly when the area around its outlet at Buffalo was uplifted following the retreat of the last glacier. The present level of about 174 meters above the sea was attained 9,000 to 10,000 years ago and has changed little since. The hard rock at Niagara Falls controls the level of the lake by preventing vertical erosion of the outlet, acting as a natural weir. However, the falls are being eroded away horizontally and thus are moving upstream. It is estimated that this horizontal erosion will intersect the eastern basin of the lake in approximately 25,000 years at the present rate. The lake will then empty, leaving litttle more than a marshy stream. By that time, however, other processes now becoming apparent will have destroyed the lake for human enjoyment, unless they are checked.

At present, the lake consists of three basins (western, central and eastern) that become less productive and deeper from west to east (Figure 1). The central basin is generally considered as the area between a line connecting Point Pelee, Ontario, and Sandusky, Ohio, and a line extending from the base of Long Point, Ontario, to Presque Isle (near Erie, Pennsylvania). The western basin includes the island area and is nowhere deeper than 18 meters. It is almost always completely mixed by wind action and is the most productive of the three basins. The central basin has a maximum depth of slightly less than 30 meters and exhibits summer stratification, as does the eastern basin which has a maximum depth of 64 meters. The mean depth of the lake as a whole is less than 28 meters. Average depths of the other Great Lakes are much greater, particularly in proportion to their areas.

The chief process in the aging of a lake is filling with sediments. This is a serious problem in Lake Erie despite its large volume. All of the large tributaries and most of the external material brought in enter the lake in the western basin, tending to decrease further its already shallow depth by adding sediments. Although the Detroit River (outlet of the upper lakes) contributes 90 percent of the inflow (55,000 cubic meters per second), the Maumee River contributes most of the silt load and nutrients. This is largely due to the draining of the Great Black Swamp in the late nineteenth century, which created rich but easily eroded farmlands. Most of the northern and some southern shores consist of high clay cliffs subject to wave erosion which contributes large amounts of sediments to all three basins. The shore of the lake is sinking at a rate of about 1 meter per 300 years due to shifting of the earth's crust, and this increases erosion and sedimentation. In addition to man's acceleration of sedimentation through cultivation and abuse of the land, he has built harbor jetties and erosion-control structures all along the shore. These seem to have increased the total shore erosion and silt load. There seem to be no published estimates of the rate of filling of the lake with sediments. The sediment load is reflected in light-penetration readings. In the Maumee River, Secchi disc readings average less than 1 meter. In the open water of the western basin, this increases to 2 meters due to mixing with the relatively clear water of the Detroit River and water from the central basin which enters through the Bass Island passages. Except for temporary seiche effects, there is a clockwise circulation of the waters of the western basin, and all of the outflow is through the Pelee Passage along the north shore. The average turnover time for western basin water is 2

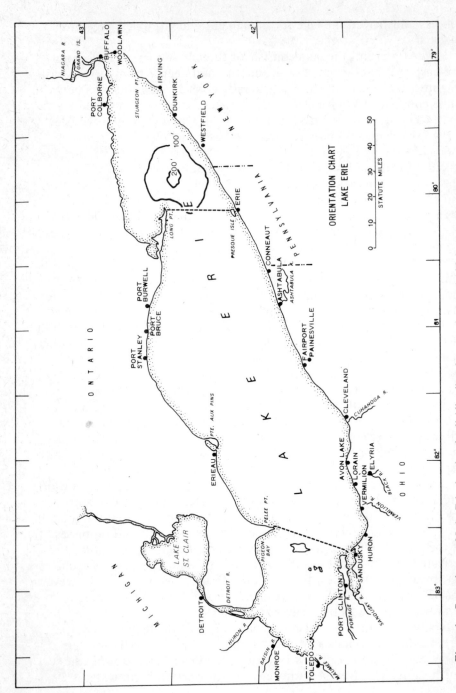

Figure 1. General map of Lake Erie showing the dividing lines between basis and 100-foot depth contours.

months. By the time the water reaches the eastern basin, its transparency has increased greatly, so Secchi disc readings are 4 to 8 meters. The latter readings are characteristic of the other Great Lakes; only western Lake Erie is not relatively clear. There have been no significant changes in transparency since the 1920s, but an overall average increase of 50 percent in turbidity occurs from summer to early winter each year.

There has been a gradual warming of both the lake and the climate of the surrounding area. The increase in average lake temperature has amounted to about $2°F$. since 1920 and there have been several open winters recently. This is not necessarily a symptom of eutrophication, but contributes to it by accelerating biological processes and to some extent by making the habitat less favorable for some species and more favorable for others.

POLLUTION

Pollution, in the broad sense, is responsible for most of the changes in the chemistry of Lake Erie. Three kinds of pollution may be considered important to the lake: (1) silt, as already mentioned, which changes the character of the bottom and reduces light penetration; (2) domestic sewage, which adds nutrients, lowers dissolved oxygen and causes health problems; and (3) industrial wastes, which may do all of the foregoing as well as cause injury or death to living organisms. Serious pollution enters the lake from the lower Detroit River, the western shores, along the south shore and at the eastern end. Vessels on the lake and dredging operations also contribute significant amounts of pollution.

Most of the effects of domestic sewage are seen in the western basin. This area is particularly susceptible to pollution for three reasons: (1) the large industrial communities on the Maumee, Raisin and Detroit Rivers; (2) its shallowness and consequent small water volume; and (3) its semi-isolation caused by two peninsulas and numerous islands which tend to prevent free outflow of water to the rest of the lake. Each day, the American shore discharges 32 million kilograms of waste solids plus 228,000 kilograms of dissolved phosphate and nitrogen into the Detroit River. On the Canadian side, much of Windsor's sewage is dumped into the river without chemical treatment. The same is true for the wastes of over 13,000 persons on the Michigan shore alone. The population in this area is increasing at the rate of 26 percent per decade, and the bacterial load at the outlet of the Detroit River has increased more than threefold since 1913. Maximum coliform counts in the area now reach 500 per milliliter, whereas in 1913 they were approximately 2 per milliliter. In all, the Detroit River receives 6.1 billion liters of waste per day.

Apparently there has been little if any increase in bacterial load in the central and eastern basins, except along populated shores. In a report on an early eastern basin survey, Zillig wrote: "The presence of B. coli in such small numbers, the repeated absence of this species and other gas-forming organisms in some parts of the lake, and the low bacterial counts at all stations, tend to eliminate pollution as a factor affecting fish in the open waters of Lake Erie."[1] Recent open-water samples in the eastern and central basins have shown similar results.

Little detailed documentation is available for the industrial waste discharges into Lake Erie, but they are known to be of increasingly large magnitude, and are probably responsible for many of the increases in dissolved ionic material in the lake. A significant amount of these wastes is in the form of airborne particles from smokestacks and trash burning which settle on the lake. Nitrogen in particular seems to be added in this way.

Chemical Changes

Except for the two constituents (Si and Fe) known to be involved in the mineral nutrition of at least some of the phytoplankton, all the chemical constitutents of Lake Erie have increased during the past century. Beeton summarized the changes in the major ions in parts per million, since 1906 as follows:

Calcium from 31.0 to 36.7
Magnesium from 7.6 to 10.2
Sodium + Potassium from 6.5 to 9.4
Sulphate from 13.0 to 23.0
Chloride from 8.7 to 26.0
Silica from 5. 9 to 1.6

Total solids from 133 to 183

(Not all the values are from the same location, but the differences are minor compared with the total change in concentration). . . .

There is some controversy about both the causes and the effects of these changes. Beeton stated that they are probably of no consequence to the biota and that they must be due to materials in the inflowing water. The Maumee River alone carried in over 125 metric tons of phosphates per year; these act as fertilizer for phytoplankton. . . . So do increases in nitrates in the runoff to Lake Erie. Harlow found that in the Michigan area of the lake, municipal wastes contributed 90 percent of the nutrients, with land drainage a minor factor. On the other hand, much of the increased concentration of soluble salts in the lake appears to be due to loss of water through evaporation (a component of natural lake aging). . . . It seems that the true cause of the chemical changes must involve both evaporation and inflow and that they must have some effect on the phytoplankton if not on other biota.

Dissolved Oxygen

Perhaps the most serious environmental change in Lake Erie has been in the dissolved oxygen levels at the bottom. Regardless of the average dissolved oxygen concentration in a body of water, a single instance of anaerobic conditions or levels below the lethal limit will kill all the benthic organisms and have many far-reaching consequences, lasting until new populations have been established by immigration. Such conditions are usually associated with thermal stratification over a bottom high in organic matter. The three basins of Lake Erie differ in these respects. The western basin is high in organic matter but is too shallow to stratify, the eastern basin stratifies but is low (although increasing) in organic matter, while the central basin stratifies and has accumulated sufficient organic matter to cause oxygen depletion to become the usual summer condition in recent years.

Low levels of dissolved oxygen have been observed in the central basin several times since 1930 and might have been more commonly detected with better sampling and analysis. Depletion has become gradually more extensive over the past three decades. At present over 70 percent of the central basin (more than 415,000 hectares or about 1,600 square miles) has less than 1 ppm dissolved oxygen at the bottom from mid-July through September. . . .

Oxygen depletion in the western basin occurs only when thermal stratification is set up by long, warm, windless periods. Bottom productivity is so high, however, that only 5 days of stratification are now required for the dissolved oxygen to drop below 3 ppm, whereas 28 days were required in 1953. The results of such an occurrence are discussed under the following topics in relation to invertebrates.

Phytoplankton and Other Algae

It is difficult to draw conclusions regarding changes in the algal flora of Lake Erie because of insufficient studies and a large amount of seasonal variation. However, the total abundance of phytoplankton

has increased almost threefold, and some shifts in dominant species
have been documented. . . . Analysis of records from 1919 to 1963 for
the central basin showed that there had been a consistent increase in
the average quantity of phytoplankton. The vernal and autumnal
phytoplankton maxima had consistently become more intensive and
had lasted longer. The periods of minimum phytoplankton in winter
and summer had become shorter and less well marked, until the winter
minimum failed to develop at all in some of the latest years. Blue-
green and green algae had partially displaced the diatoms in autumnal
pulses, and a bloom of blue-green algae covering 206,500 hectares
(about 800 square miles) of the western basin was observed for two
days in September 1964. This bloom was composed of *Anacystis,
Oscillatoria, Carteria, Aphanizomenon* and *Anabaena.* It is generally
agreed that these genera are good indicators of eutrophy, and they are
now among the dominants in Lake Erie.

Attached and floating algae (mostly filamentous) have also
increased. Since the early 1930s complaints have grown of decompos-
ing, malodorous accumulations of *Cladophora* along the shoreline,
particularly around the Bass Island and the eastern basin.

Benthic Invertebrates

The changes in benthic populations in the western and central
basins revolve around the naiad of the mayfly *Hexagenia limbata*
(*Ephemeroptera*), a clean-water inhabitant which until 1953 was the
dominant benthic organism. . . . From September 1–4, 1953, Britt
observed an unusual thermal stratification due to hot, calm weather.
In the western basin, oxygen concentrations as low as 0.70 parts per
million near the bottom had a catastrophic effect on *Hexagenia* populations. . . . Since then in both the western and central basins, the
plague of adult mayflies that was characteristic in summer around the
lights of south-shore cities has been absent. Caddisflies (*Trichoptera*),
also formerly abundant, had decreased to less than 1 per square meter
by 1957.

As might be expected, other organisms, more tolerant of adverse conditions, appeared to occupy the niche left by the mayflies
and caddisflies. *Oligochaete* worms (mostly *Tubificidae* or "sludge-
worms"), which had occurred at a density of about 12 per square meter
in 1929, had already increased to 551 per square meter by 1957 and
averaged over 2,000 per square meter in 1961 in the western basin,
with individual collections ranging up to 29,164 per square meter.
This group also increased in the central basin, although all organisms
except nematodes have decreased greatly there in the last few years

due to the anaerobic conditions. . . . The changes in the western basin in the preceding 31 years are summarized as follows: a ninefold increase in *Oligochaeta*, fourfold increase in *Chironomidae*, twofold increase in fingernail clams (*Sphaeriidae*), sixfold increase in snails, (*Gastropoda*), 400-fold decrease in *Hexagenia* and an increase in the area of heavy pollution from 263 to 1,020 square kilometers. Obviously, not all of these changes are the result of the catastrophic oxygen depletion of 1953, but such conditions certainly accelerated the process. Similar changes in fauna, although less extreme in numbers, have occurred in the central basin. Little is known of the extent of change in the eastern basin benthos.

Fisheries

Nearly all the available data on changes in the fish fauna of Lake Erie stem from the commercial catch. Naturally, such data may not show important changes in species which are not commercially profitable, but much information has been gathered on those which are. Five main hypotheses to explain the decline and extinction of the most valuable Lake Erie species have been proposed and advocated by various schools of thought: (1) high temperature, (2) oxygen depletion in the central basin, (3) overfishing, (4) pollution and (5) new predators or competitors. All of these are interrelated and probably mutually responsible in various degrees. The most desirable species have, in succession, undergone rapid population declines from which they have not permanently recovered. Since the proposed causes for these crashes are in most cases similar, it may be simplest to examine the history of each population and then the controversy over causes.

The first species to decline was the lake herring (cisco) (*Coregonus artedi*), which began to be exploited in the 1880s, fluctuated, exhibited a large yield in 1923 and 1924, suddenly collapsed in 1925, stayed minimal to the present. This collapse, being the first of lakewide importance, stimulated much concern among fishermen and public officials, who were inclined to suspect pollution and other factors, rather than overfishing, as the cause. Three studies were initiated. . . . The first two came to the conclusion that overfishing was at fault, and all three agreed that pollution was not the cause. Van Oosten determined that most of the ciscos present in 1923 and 1924 were concentrated in a small area of the central basin, probably because of adverse conditions elsewhere, and thus were easily "cleaned out" by the fishermen, accounting for the heavy yield followed by collapse.

The whitefish (*Coregonus clupeaformis*) fishery in the western basin greatly decreased about 1890 and practically vanished about

1920. It remained productive in the rest of the lake until about 1954. The sauger (*Stizostedion canadense*) fishery, which was generally a secondary one, declined about 1946.

The populations of walleye (*Stizostedion vitreum vitreum*) and the so-called "blue pike" (*Stizostedion vitreum glaucum*) seem to have some inverse correlation in abundance. The blue pike seem to have been restricted to the colder waters of the lake and were probably placed at some disadvantage as these waters become smaller and less habitable. After exhibiting several large fluctuations, the catch declined from 8,550,000 kilograms in 1956 to about 226 kilograms in 1958 and later years. Reflecting this decline, the growth rate of the remaining blue pike increased eightfold between 1951 and 1959, but the few pike caught in 1963 were mostly over 10 years old, inspiring little hope for recovery of the population.

The walleye fishery showed an upward trend in production from 1929 to 1956 (910,000 to 7,100,000 kilograms) but declined rapidly after 1960, producing only 325,000 kilograms in 1965 and now is fluctuating. The growth rate of the remaining population has increased markedly since its collapse, as has that of the blue pike.

Another species which has disappeared from the commercial catch is the lake sturgeon (*Acipenser fulvescens*). These were mostly removed at an early date because of their ability to wreck fish nets, and were destroyed or used as fuel or fertilizer until their value as food was realized; by which time, however, their numbers were severely reduced.

As the commercially important species have declined, other, less desirable species have increased. The exotics such as gizzard shad (*Dorosoma cepedianum*), alewife (*Alosa pseudoharengus*), white bass (*Roccus chrysops*) and smelt (*Osmerus mordax*) have become common, and native "rough fish" such as carp (*Cyprinus carpio*) and sheepshead or freshwater drum (*Aplodinotus grunniens*) have increased in numbers and percentage of the catch. The yellow perch (*Perca flavescens*) has to a large extent replaced the higher valued species (Figure 2) in the fishery, but its lower unit price causes the net income to be much lower than previously, and thus the number of fishermen has decreased.

The total catch of all species in Lake Erie has remained remarkably constant for many years because of the replacement of high-priced stocks with rough fish as the former have declined. . . . The fishing industry, however, has been hard hit by the species change because of its ultra-conservative attitudes, especially its reluctance to develop uses and markets for the newly abundant but unexploited species, and by the hodgepodge of regulations imposed by two federal and five state and provincial governments which have so far been unable to agree on uniform policies.

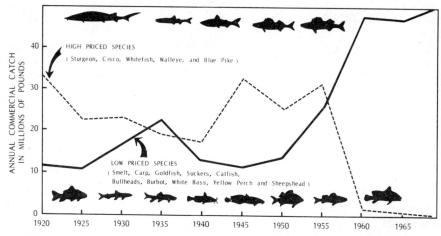

Figure 2. Annual commercial catch in Lake Erie from 1920 to 1968 according to groups of species. Broken line: sturgeon, cisco, whitefish, walleye and blue pike. Solid line: smelt, carp, goldfish, suckers, catfish, bullheads, burbot, white bass, yellow perch and sheepshead (low priced species).

The opinions as to the cause of the decline of major species have been centered around two camps, that of Van Oosten and that of Langlois. Van Oosten held that overfishing in the biological sense (that is, to the point where the stocks could not easily regain their former abundance) had definitely occurred in the case of the cisco and was a more likely explanation for the decline of the other species than the environmental factors blamed by the Langlois group. In this, Van Oosten has been supported to some extent by others. Regier and associates, in a recent extensive review, concluded that overfishing and poor management were largely responsible for the decline of the walleye population in the western end of the lake. Van Oosten and his followers do not deride the importance of environmental factors, but seem to view them as setting the stage for overfishing. He also mentioned disease, parasites and competition as possible negative factors. Regier pointed out that the more limiting the Lake Erie environment is, the more readily overfishing can occur.

Langlois and his supporters have held that environmental factors, particularly turbidity, related siltation on spawning and nursery ("key") areas, and temperature, are the controlling influence on the level of fish abundance in the lake and act essentially independently of fishing pressure. They also believe that stocking has been largely useless for the same reason. Temperature, in the form of the general warming trend, is largely responsible for the decline of the whitefish population which is at the southern limits of its range in Lake Erie.

FUTURE PROSPECTS

It is generally agreed that the hope for salvation of the fisheries and ecology of Lake Erie lies either in a return of the high-priced species through rehabilitation of the environment coupled with stocking, an increase in demand or price for remaining species, or introduction of new, desirable exotics. Rehabilitation of the environment seems almost impossible but is probably the approach most likely to be clamored for by the public and attempted by government agencies.

Langlois has proposed several remedial actions for the lake environment, all within the realm of feasibility from an engineering standpoint if not from a practical one. (Many already completed government resource-management projects seem to have this type of feasibility). These include (1) transferring sludge from shoal areas to low shorelines to lower the oxygen demand of the bottom and provide spawning beds; (2) aeration of the bottom waters by compressed-air hoses; (3) opening of the pre-glacial outlet of the lake west of the Welland Canal and installation of gates to permit periodic drawdown for aerating the bottom, controlling floods and facilitating levee construction; (4) a levee across the island region to carry a highway and permit drainage of the western basin for agricultural use, with only the ship channels maintained; and (5) alternate boat routes through channels dug north of the lake. A scheme has also been proposed for recirculating water from Lake Ontario to Georgian Bay and back through Lakes Huron and Erie for reuse in various ways. The potential effects of this and other schemes on the ecology of the lake are difficult to predict, but it is relatively certain that if changes of some sort are not made in man's use and misuse of the Lake Erie resource, he will lose it entirely.

REFERENCES

[1] A. M. Zillig, "Bacteriological Studies of Lake Erie," *Bulletin, Buffalo Society of Natural Science* 16 (1929): 51–59.

SUGGESTED READINGS

Ayers, J. C. "Great Lakes Waters, their Circulation and Physical and Chemical Characteristics." In *Great Lakes Basin,* edited by J. J. Pincus, pp. 71–89. Washington: American Association for the Advancement of Science, 1962.

Beeton, A. M. "Eutrophication of the St. Lawrence Great Lakes." *Limnology and Oceanography* 10 (1965): 240–254.

Beeton, A. M. and Chandler, D. C. "The St. Lawrence-Great Lakes." In *Limnology in North America,* edited by D. G. Frey, pp. 287–300. Madison: University of Wisconsin Press, 1962.

Britt, N. W. "Stratification in Western Lake Erie in the Summer of 1953: Effects on the *Hexagenia* (*Ephemeroptera*) Population." *Ecology*, 36 (1955): 239–244.

Doan, K. H., "Some Meteorological and Limnological Conditions as Factors in Abundance of Certain Fishes in Lake Erie." *Ecological Monographs* 12 (1942): 293–314.

Dymond, J. R. "The Fisheries of the Great Lakes." In *Fish and Wildlife,* edited by J. R. Dymond, pp. 73–92. Toronto: Longmans, 1964.

Harlow, G. G. *Major Sources of Nutrients for Algal Growth in Western Lake Erie.* Publication 15, pp. 389–394. Ann Arbor: Great Lakes Research Division, University of Michigan, 1966.

International Joint Commission. *Report of the International Joint Commission, United States and Canada on the Pollution of Boundary Waters.* Washington and Ottawa: 1951.

Langlois, T. H. *The Western End of Lake Erie and Its Ecology.* Ann Arbor: J. W. Edwards, 1954.

Powers, C. F. and Robertson, A. "The Aging Great Lakes." *Scientific American* 215 (1966): 95–104.

Regier, H. A. "A Perspective on Research on the Dynamics of Fish Populations in the Great Lakes." *Progressive Fish-Culturalist* 28 (1966): 3–18.

Regier, H. A.; Applegate, V. C.; Van Meter, H. D.; Wolfert, D. R.; Ferguson, R. G.; Ryder, R. R.; and Manz, J. V.: *The Ecology and Management of the Walleye in Western Lake Erie.* Special Report. Ann Arbor: Great Lakes Fisheries Commission, 1968.

Van Oosten, J. "Turbidity as a Factor in the Decline of Great Lakes Fishes with Special Reference to Lake Erie." *Transactions, American Fisheries Society* 75 (1948): 281–322.

CHAPTER 8

Application of Systems Principles Introduction

In studying any natural system, whether for theoretical or practical purposes, analysis should proceed in six steps. (1) The parts of the system (subsystems, elements) are identified and carefully described. (2) The structure of the system is derived, that is we discover how the parts fit together, how they are related. (3) The functions of the system are identified and carefully described. What are the flows of energy and matter like in kind, quantity, and quality? Given its structure, how does the system do what it is doing? It is at this stage that exchanges with the internal and external environments and feedback mechanisms must be identified. These three steps are absolutely essential and can provide an understanding of any natural system. For fuller understanding and more general applicability, the three final analytical steps are necessary, namely: (4) study of the evolution of the system, (5) study of its spatial patterns, and (6) study of its classification for comparison and integration with other systems. At a theoretical level, these six points of analysis provide the information necessary for attempts at mathematical models; at a practical level, they provide a valid basis for direct management attempts.

The systems approach can be used for more than theoretical study of the environment. The systems approach involves carefully organized research, but can be readily adapted for practical applications. It should be used in all of man's attempts to manage the environment. Almost all human activities affect the natural environment, and only when we recognize the interrelatedness of all the parts of the environment will we realize the true dimensions of the changes we have made. A systems approach as outlined above will give us the necessary understanding.

If we are to maintain and improve our natural environment, management of the various environmental systems must be accomplished in a systems context. Along with an emphasis on careful systems analysis to clarify management alternatives, three key ecological principles should be stressed. (1) The holocoenotic nature or wholeness of systems must be kept in mind. Diversity, stability, and dynamic equilibrium are the key concepts related to wholeness. (2) We must also remember the limiting factor principle. This principle has two facets: there are threshold limits beyond which fluctuations in energy and matter inputs cannot be tolerated; shortages of specific elements can limit productivity increases despite unlimited inputs of other elements. This principle emphasizes systems regulation and maintenance through negative feedback mechanisms. (3) There exist trigger factors which lead to a changed trajectory for the system. A dramatic change in the quantity or quality of inputs to a system will cause trigger factors to go into action, bringing a change in the state of the system.

Ecological principles have been applied in wildlife, rangeland, and forest management for a number of years. Often these applications did not include man as an integral part of the ecosystem. But today, the integration of human and natural systems is increasingly recognized, and more comprehensive approaches are applied to such problems as environmental deterioration or food and energy shortages.

We have selected four articles to demonstrate the applicability of a systems approach. Manmade systems can interact with natural systems without producing damage if ecological principles and systems concepts are given their proper place. Two articles deal with the importance of diversity and a land-ethic, land-policy framework. The other two illustrate direct applications of the systems approach.

Diversity is essential to a healthy ecosystem. If we are to have a quality environment we must maintain diversity in both manmade and natural environmental systems. The thrust of the first article is that we have reduced diversity by overemphasizing the need for high levels of efficiency and high levels of productivity. As noted by Odum in Chapter 2, the most productive ecosystems are not the most diverse ones. High levels of production mean low levels of protection (and diversity), while high levels of protection demand high levels of diversity. Diversity promotes stability, insures against risk, promotes better use of solar energy, and supports the mental well-being of human populations.

In the second article, Caldwell demonstrates that the ecosystem concept is the only valid long-range approach for handling land. While Caldwell's comments relate directly to American experience, the ecosystem principles on which they are based are universally applicable. American public land policy is based on historically derived legal, economic, and political assumptions. But this policy ignores ecological assumptions. Land policy should be based on scientific information that is fitted into a systems framework. Past legal rights and practice should be abandoned if in conflict with basic ecological principles.

Man's transgression of a physical environment continually subject to the strong forces of nature is the basis of Schuberth's article on barrier islands and their sandy beaches. This article illustrates how the physical processes of nature can lash back at man and also how essential it is that we integrate our knowledge of human society and the natural environment. Barrier beaches are vitally important recreational resources in Eastern North America. But, due to a lack of understanding and short-sighted solutions, man is threatening this resource through overuse and through poorly designed and visually displeasing technological fixes, for example, groins. We must learn how to recycle the sand that drifts down the beach from areas where it is wanted to areas where it is not wanted. To this end Schuberth suggests a beach nourishment approach, in which sand is pumped from the place where it drifts back to the area it came from. He sternly warns that man cannot alter the basic natural patterns at the beach interface between land and water; the energy forces are too vast. To protect his works man must, therefore, understand the rules. The hazard is human, not natural!

Our concluding article deals with the capacity of the natural environment to carry the human population. In the long run this is *the* survival problem. Odum makes the point that the natural environment serves man as a "supply depot" and as a "house." And two key principles related to quality of life are emphasized: (1) the optimum is almost always less than the maximum; (2) affluence reduces the number of people who can be supported by a given resource base.

Using the state of Georgia as a reasonable microcosm of the United States, he indicates that shortly after the year 2000, only 4 acres of land per person (instead of the current 10) will be available if the current birth rate is maintained. There is a great need for public action and pressure to put more land under public ownership or control. A reasonable goal would be to place about one-third of the land under protection.

Odum further stresses the need for pollution prevention. Such an approach will be much less costly in the long run. After all, pollution is basically the maldistribution of energy and matter in land, air, soil, and water. If pollution is prevented at the source, the need to repair environmental damage will largely be eliminated. Then the natural environment can long continue to be a good "supply depot" and "house."

Using an ecological systems approach to understand, restore, and wisely manage our natural environment has been the thrust of this book. A positive rather than a "fix-up" approach is essential to maintaining the quality of our environment and our lives. Much can be done with relatively little expense if ecosystem principles are used. For example, how much better it is to maintain nature in urban areas for our daily enjoyment rather than deleting nature from our cities so that we must escape to the country, mountain, or seashore for the weekend. Think how much energy could be conserved if these weekend pulses to find nature were largely unnecessary for urban dwellers. Much remains to be done to understand our environment and our role in it. In this book, we have tried to show how best to go about it.

Man's Efficient Rush
Toward Deadly Dullness

Kenneth E. F. Watt
Professor of Zoology, University of California at Davis

Reprinted by permission of the author and the publisher from *Natural History* 81
(February 1972), pp. 74–84. Copyright © 1972 The American Museum of Natural
History.

Is diversity of concern to people interested in natural history,
conservation, and the environment? To answer the question fully,
one must understand the exact meaning of diversity, the ubiquitous
loss of diversity in the world today, and the reasons for the value of
diversity.

An argument for preserving anything, particularly something
rare, often turns out to be an argument in disguise for diversity. Thus,
it seems worthwhile to provide natural historians with a handy kit of
powerful arguments for variety because all too often they feel defense-
less when confronted with the arguments of developers, which are
clearly supported by short-term economic benefits, at least for a few
investors.

The rapid loss of diversity in the world is a serious and pervasive
phenomenon. Everywhere we look, we see examples of a large number
of diverse entities being replaced by a small number of similar entities.
We all know about endangered species such as birds of prey and large
mammals, including all species of whales. Most of the world's commercial fish stocks are in danger, shell collectors are depleting tropical
beaches and coral reefs, and pollution will annihilate commercial
shellfish populations, resulting in simplification of our diets. But
progressive environmental simplification is far more widespread than
this. Half the butterfly species have disappeared in Holland in the
last few decades. Conversion of the Russian steppe from wild plants
to wheat fields has cut the number of insect species there by 58 percent.

In the economic sphere, there has been a tremendous reduction
in the number of manufacturers (think of the number of automobile
manufacturers in the United States in 1910). Our numerous corner
grocery stores have been replaced by a small number of huge super-
markets. In many fields, large numbers of small businesses have been
replaced by small numbers of large businesses, to the point where we
now have close to a monopoly in the manufacture of automobiles,
aircraft, and computing equipment. Similarly, in agriculture large
numbers of small farms have been replaced by small numbers of gigan-
tic farm corporations.

Textural and cultural diversity has declined in our cities, whether you compare different parts of the same city or different cities in different countries. Driving from an airport to the downtown section of a city, the signs tend to be in the same language (English) and to advertise the same products, whether one is in Rome, Beirut, or Singapore. Stores and banks seem to be stamped from a common mold.

Remarkably, the same process has occurred in the human population. An extraordinarily high proportion of the world's population is now very young. The variety once found when many human age classes coexisted in approximately equal numbers has gone.

There are too many examples of the decline of diversity for this situation to have come about by chance. There is indeed an underlying explanation: we live in an age, and a culture, that puts tremendous emphasis on efficiency and productivity as desiderata for mankind Since variety is inimical to these goals, variety has suffered and will continue to suffer. Unless powerful and compelling arguments can be offered to stop this loss of diversity, we will soon be living in a homogeneous — and boring — world.

The large number of specific arguments for maintaining the diversity of particular sets of plants, animals, or other items, all fall into four categories: (1) diversity promotes stability; (2) it insures against risks; (3) it utilizes more completely the sun's energy; and (4) it promotes the mental well-being of humans.

Stability

There are only two basic elements in all theoretical arguments as to why diversity promotes stability. The first is the idea of spreading the risk (the same idea applies when you buy insurance from the largest insurance company). If an organism feeds on many different species, the chances of all its food sources being wiped out in some catastrophe are less than if the organism feeds on a few, or only one, species. The second idea is that a system functions more harmoniously if it has more elements because it then has more homeostatic feedback loops.

This abstract language can be translated into concrete examples. The greater the variety of foods the human population has available for harvesting, hunting, or fishing, the less the likelihood of human catastrophe due to a disaster befalling a particular food species. A most chilling example was the potato famine in Ireland, where an entire human population was excessively dependent on one food species. The situation is fundamentally the same when an Indian tribe depends greatly on salmon at a certain time of year, and then something happens to the salmon population (pollution or modification of the environment in the spawning stream due to a hydroelectric installation, for example). What few people realize is that the entire human population is now setting itself up for the same situation. For example, as we rapidly deplete the stocks of more and more oceanic species through overfishing and pollution, we cut off optional food sources that we might need desperately in the future. The larger the human population becomes and the more the sources of food decline, the more precarious is our situation.

Our great preoccupation with productivity and efficiency and our lack of concern about diversity increase the precariousness of our economic lives, as well as of our food. Consider what happens when we try to maximize the manufacturing efficiency of aircraft. We are led, inexorably, to a situation in which a small group of corporations manufacture all aircraft in the United States. Each corporation is so large that it dominates the economies of the communities in which its plants are located. Thus, if a corporation meets with disaster, the community is in deep trouble. This is the case in Seattle, where Boeing sales slackened with saturation of the international aircraft market. Architectural writer Jane Jacobs discovered this principle of relating the economic stability of cities to their corporate diversity when she applied current ecological theories about the relation between diversity and stability to her urban studies.

In a most curious way, diversity appears to affect our economic, social, cultural, and political processes. For example, a slowly growing or nongrowing human population has a greater evenness of numbers in different age classes than a rapidly growing population. In a rapid-growth situation, young people are being added to the population so quickly that their numbers become unusually high relative to the numbers of older people. This strains society's ability to generate adequate educational taxes from the older group for the large younger group. It also is difficult for a rapidly growing society to create new jobs at the rate at which young people want to enter the labor force. . . .

The more even the numbers of people in different age classes, the easier it is to maintain good communication between generations. Thus, all the present discussion about a "generation gap" has its ultimate origin in the lack of diversity in human age classes.

Many similar arguments relating diversity and different forms of stability could be put forth. But the fundamental structure of all such arguments would be the same, whether the subject is a human society or a rare plant. The reason for preserving it is that it may, in

some unknown fashion, be important to the maintenance of stability
in a part of the planetary ecosystem.

Insurance Against Risk

The second class of arguments for maintaining diversity is
similar to the argument for buying life insurance. You don't really
want or expect to use it, but you buy it just in case. Similarly, a civilization does not expect its acts to harm the world, but just in case
they are destructive it would be nice to have at hand other things to
fall back on. For example, when we develop new strains of plants and
animals, we do not plan on producing lines that will deteriorate in
the future. We do not plan on producing strains of collie dogs in which
the females will have progressively more difficulty bearing viable
offspring, or strains of wheat that will succumb to rust, or berries that
after many generations will no longer have much flavor. When these
unintended events occur, we fall back on our "insurance policy,"
either by backcrossing our domestic strains to wild strains or by shifting our attention to new strains or species. But what if there are no new
strains or species to replace the unsatisfactory ones?

The insurance value of diversity applies to more than just
individual species or strains of plants and animals. Suppose a civilization irrigated farmland in such a fashion that long-term irreversible
destruction of the soil only showed up after a century. Suppose,
further, that the entire landscape of this civilization had been managed
in an identical fashion. Then when the entire landscape lost its fertility,
the civilization would be without land to produce food. Further, it
wouldn't even have any unmanaged land to compare with the managed
lands for scientific investigations. A simple example of the importance
of such comparisons is the few forest areas in Greece from which goats
have been excluded. The contrast between the grazed and ungrazed
lands is so startling that no argument from goat-lovers could withstand
visual comparison of forested areas with and without goats.

It is tremendously important for any civilization to set aside
areas where common cultivation practices are not adopted. If the same
techniques are used everywhere, we can never know the long-term
results of the practice. Thus, we can never know if intensive annual
pesticide sprayings have long-term deleterious effects on orchards,
forests, or woodlots unless we have unsprayed areas for comparison.

In short, a prudent civilization maintains the landscape under
many different management strategies, including parcels of each soil
and climate zone that are not managed at all. This landscape diversity
has two values. First, we have a yardstick for determining if something

unexpected or odd is gradually showing up in a managed area. Without the unmanaged areas, the odd or unexpected effect could be ascribed to something else, to a change in climate, for example. The unsettled arguments as to whether the changes in the landscape of the Mediterranean basin, the Middle East, North Africa, and northern India were due to climatic change or man's activities show clearly the importance of having unmanaged areas for checking. The second value of landscape diversity is that if a civilization unwittingly destroys its managed lands, it has other places on which to raise food while the destroyed areas are gradually rebuilt to productivity.

A generalization of this argument holds that an extremely prudent civilization would try to maintain other civilizations with different ideas about land use. Over the short term, the ideas of civilization A might appear vastly superior to those of civilization B. But over the long term it could turn out that the apparently "primitive" practices of civilization B were based on millennia of trial and error and incorporated deep wisdom that was unintelligible to civilization A.

Fuller Use of Energy

The third argument for diversity originates in the theory of modern ecologists that any habitat contains a set of "niches," or functions, that may be filled. If only part of the niches are filled, then the sun's energy that is captured by, and flows through, a system will be less than if all the niches were filled.

Perhaps the best known and most convincing illustration of this argument comes from Africa. Research shows that a mix of native animal species uses the landscape more economically than imported livestock. Each of the different types of antelope and other game consume slightly different mixes of food plants or parts of plants, so that a whole assemblage of different species uses the landscape more effeciently than, say, beef cattle would by themselves.

The same point has been demonstrated repeatedly in anaylses of the fish production per year per acre from different mixes of fish species. The more fish species there are in a body of water, the greater the gross production. Human understanding of this principle reaches its pinnacle in Oriental fish farming, where up to nine different species of carp are grown together in the set of proportions that makes best use of the resources in a pond.

Mental Well-being

Humanity has given far too little thought to the fourth argument for preserving diversity. How much diversity in the world around us is optimal for the human mind? Might the extent of environmental diversity have any relationship to the average level of mental health in a population? Could a certain level of diversity be most satisfying — emotionally and esthetically — to the human mind because of the conditions during human evolution? Diversity in an environment may have a much deeper significance for man than is generally recognized. We know that human beings tend to hallucinate when kept in confined quarters and deprived of sensory stimuli. This could be interpreted as a protective device by the mind to provide an otherwise unavailable need. Reports have been published indicating that extremely refractory mental patients, who had not spoken to anyone in years, showed an almost miraculous response when taken to wilderness areas.

The recent popularity of skin diving as recreation may convey a deep message. It may be that the rate of incoming sensory stimuli while skin diving is optimal for the human mind. I know that after several hours of constant interruption by the phone and visitors, I almost jump with each new phone call. But I also know that I can become bored amid all this stimuli. The extremely deep satisfaction I derive from exploring the ocean edge of a tropical island may be telling me something important about my mind and all our minds. We have evolved over a very long period so that our minds can cope handily with a certain rate of incoming sensory stimuli. We find the stimuli rate we can cope with in nature because we evolved there. Either sharply higher or sharply lower rates of incoming sensory stimuli are bad for our nervous systems.

This is only anecdotal evidence, but more carefully designed and measured research leads to the same conclusion. For some years, Prof. J. Lee Kavanau of UCLA has been conducting experiments on small mammal behavior in heavily instrumented cages. These cages are wired, enabling the animal to change its environment and recording every move the animal makes and every detail of the conditions in the cage. The animals learn to control their environment by pressing levers. Kavanau has discovered that animals will press levers to select other than optimal conditions. In other words, confronted with a choice of living constantly in an optimal world but being bored, or of living in a world that is only optimal part of the time and experiencing variety, even a small rodent will opt for variety. It is reasonable to assume that humans would opt even more strongly for variety rather than constant optimality. Perhaps diversity is not merely a luxury for us. It may be something we need.

If, upon reflection, you agree with my general line of argument as to the intrinsic value of diversity, then important implications follow for many aspects of our lives. Particularly, the argument has important political implications.

For example, if diversity breeds stability, then it is worthwhile for a government to regulate the rate at which different interest groups acquire wealth and power. Undue concentration of power and wealth allows a small group of people to change the landscape to suit themselves, even though the change may not suit others. For example, wilderness mountaintops and tropical islands have been overdeveloped for second homes because the prospective profits for developers were very large relative to the total costs for society. Costs were small for the developers because they were not equitably divided within the society. If something went sour with the development — the lots didn't sell after trees were bulldozed — or if subsequent sewage and pollution control costs spiraled, then someone else, not the developer, absorbed the costs. Thus, the developer reaped a great gain from subdividing, and someone else paid the price. Given this situation it is scarcely surprising that so much of the world is being destroyed or that diversity is diminishing so rapidly.

A comparable situation exists with respect to the oceans, which our culture treats as an international "common property resource." Since no one or no one nation owns the oceans or their contents, no one has a motive for perpetuating the living diversity of the oceans. Consequently, the precious living treasures of two-thirds of the earth may be less diverse or even depleted in a short time. And there are too many links between oceanic and terrestrial life for such a loss to occur without profoundly affecting humanity.

SUGGESTED READINGS

Dansereau, P. *Inscape and Landscape.* CBC Massey Lectures, 1972. Toronto: CBC Learning Systems, 1973.

Jacobs, J. *The Economy of Cities.* New York: Random House, 1969.

Leopold, A. *A Sand County Almanac.* New York: Oxford, 1949.

McHarg, I. L. *Design with Nature.* Garden City, N. Y.: Natural History Press, 1969.

Morris, D. *The Human Zoo.* London: Jonathan Cape, 1969.

National Academy of Sciences, Committee on Geological Sciences. *The Earth and Human Affairs.* San Francisco: Canfield Press, 1972.

United States, Council on Environmental Quality. *Environmental Quality.* First Annual Report. Washington: U.S. Government Printing Office, 1970.

United States, National Goals Research Staff. *Toward Balanced Growth; Quantity with Quality.* Washington: U.S. Government Printing Office, 1970.

The Ecosystem as a Criterion for Public Land Policy

Lynton K. Caldwell
Professor of Government, Indiana University, Bloomington

Reprinted with some deletions and modifications by permission of the author and the publisher from *Natural Resources Journal* 10 (1970), pp. 203–211, published by the University of New Mexico School of Law.

A public lands policy restricted to lands in governmental ownership has been politically expedient but ecologically unrealistic. The natural processes of physical and biological systems that comprise the land do not necessarily accommodate themselves to the artificial boundaries and restrictions that law and political economy impose upon them. The stress of human demands upon the land tends to displace natural processes throughout its ecosystems and to impair the capacity of the natural environment for self renewal. American public land policy is based upon a set of historically derived assumptions — legal, economic, and political — that provide no means for taking the fundamental ecological context of land use into account. It is, of course, necessary to cope with land problems within the conventional context of public attitudes, laws, and economic arrangements, inadequate though they may be to encompass all of the land-related needs of contemporary soceity. But it is also important to know that there is a larger context for policy with which laws and governments must ultimately reckon: it is the condition of the land as the physical base for human welfare and survival. If human demands upon the natural environment continue to mount, it will become necessary as a matter of welfare and survival to abandon present land policy assumptions for a policy of public management of human environment on ecologically valid principles. The proposed National Land Use Policy Act of 1970 (S.3354, Jackson) specifically indicates ecological factors as criteria for sound land use planning and establishes a national-state-local system for obtaining comprehensive land-use planning and management in which ecologically sound principles are favored.

How would a public land policy based upon ecosystems concepts differ from policies based upon other considerations? Public land policies here and abroad have traditionally been based on juridic, economic, or demographic concepts. Land planning based on sectoral analysis (essentially on economic and social uses) has been the predominant source of policy in those countries in which the rational allocation of natural resources in land has become an accepted public responsibility. Spatial planning, "which considers man and his natural environment in their geographical and historical associations" is an alternative complementary approach to land policy, but does not necessarily take ecological considerations fully into account. Ecological considerations, although not always by that name, have sometimes influenced land policies. But an ecosystems approach to public land policy has seldom been attempted on national or regional scales. The reason does not lie wholly in the complexity and ambiguity of ecosystems, although these are deterring factors. Failure to apply ecological criteria to land use policies is primarily the consequence of two related causes. The first is the inability of society, because of inadequate knowledge, insufficient wealth, or incompatible institutions, to build ecologically based land policies into a general system of environmental management. The second, and more obvious, is incompatible interests among competing land users.

An ecosystems approach to land policy encounters resistance to the degree that it is inconsistent with the values, assumptions, institutions, and practices that shape the prevailing social arrangement which affect the custody and care of the land. Ecological considerations may, in themselves, be compatible with specific aspects of traditional land use arrangements. For example, specific legal restrictions in Denmark, the Netherlands, and the United Kingdom are designed to protect and perpetuate certain traditional uses of the land for ecological reasons as well as for sentimental and esthetic purposes. Incompatibility among uses derives as often from the structuring of land use arrangements — from the way in which the various institutions influencing the use of land are related — as it does from contradictions among the uses themselves. Thus the factors involved in banking, taxation, insurance, and property law, when woven into a non-ecological matrix of public land policy, afford a very resistant, inadvertent barrier to an ecosystems approach. To establish rapidly a land policy in which ecological principles predominated would require that the conventional matrix be unravelled and rewoven in a new pattern. In a colony on the moon there would be an overwhelming presumption in favor of a predominately ecological approach. The arguments for survival would outweigh all others. On earth, ecological criteria will increasingly modify or replace other indices of value as the constraints of the closed-system environment of Spaceship Earth become increasingly apparent.

The context of land policy changes when the ecosystems concept is introduced. The discourse can no longer be confined realistically to lands in governmental ownership, but must take into account

whatever lands are included in particular ecosystems, regardless of
who holds title to them. This broadening of the policy context may be
opposed by persons committed to the inviolate right of private landownership, or who hold specific interests in land use that they believe
might be threatened by public action. Ecological principles are more
often and more easily applied to government lands than to private
holdings. Pressure for rapid economic return, and the financial or
technological inability of the private owner to apply ecological concepts, are the more common explanations. But if the management of
whole ecosystems becomes a matter of public policy, then the formulation of public land policy must proceed upon the basis of the proposition that all land is in some degree public.

　　　To conceive an ecosystems approach to public land policy,
one must have first arrived at an ecological viewpoint toward the
world of man and nature. But this is not the viewpoint from which
pioneers, land speculators, farmers, miners, stockmen, lawyers, bankers,
or local government officials have commonly seen the land. To institute an ecosystems approach to public land policy, a great many other
things besides land must be considered. An ecosystems approach is
essentially a total systems approach. It therefore includes in its pur-
view many things omitted in less comprehensive systems. It would impose constraints upon single purpose approaches to the environment
and would arouse hostility among individuals whose single purpose
pursuits would thereby be constrained.

IMPLICATIONS OF AN ECOSYSTEMS LAND POLICY

　　　Before examing more closely the ecosystem concept and the
opposition to its implied modification of rights of landownership,
the implications of the term "public land policy" must be identified, as
they are basic to the questions: What approach to land policy is most
consistent with the public interest? All things considered, what policy
is best? The term "best" arouses a multitude of subsidiary questions.
It is certain to arouse objections among persons unwilling or unable
to consider normative concepts. It may fail to interest persons who
believe that the only practical focus of public policy is upon the condition of things as they are. Nevertheless, goals and values are implicit in
the concept of "policy." The student concerned with the public interest
must examine the relevance of public policies to changes in the condition
of society and to future stability and welfare. Not all criteria for the
formulation and application of a policy afford equally effective means

to its specified ends. Moreover, not all goals or objectives serve equally well the general or long-term interests of society. For example, policies that permitted massive and continuing loss of top soil or encouraged price-escalating land speculation would not be a good public land policy under any criteria, however beneficial they might appear to be to the immediate interests of particular land users or owners.

In the United States, and particularly in the West, ambiguity can easily occur in the use of the expression "public land policy." Does the expression connote a public policy for land generally — all land? Or does it refer only to policies regarding lands in public ownership? Conventional American assumptions and word usage take the latter definition as the more practical and appropriate. Yet eminent domain, land use zoning, and sale of land for tax delinquency, make it clear that public jurisdiction over land is general and not confined to public ownership. An ecosystems approach to public land policy assumes a scope that embraces all land regardless of its ownership or custody under law. The metes and bounds of ecosystems are determined by physical, biological and cultural forces. Men may impose their own arrangements of natural systems, but engineers, surveyors, and lawyers neither amend nor repeal the so-called laws of nature. Ecosystems form a complex unity embracing the entire earth. And although men have never been able to deal with the ultimate unity of the ecosphere, they have been learning more and more about its interrelated workings. As more has been learned, the practicality of introducing ecological concepts into land use policy is enhanced. But the word "practicality" may be given two different interpretations. There is a conventional short-run practicality of socially sanctioned arrangements. There is also a long-run practicality that takes account of ecological trends, assesses the consequences of their continuation into the future, and estimates the effects of modifying forces that may impinge upon them.

Implicit in the ecosystems concept is recognition that maintenance of the ecosystem depends upon the consistency of manmade standards, laws, and boundaries with those that have evolved through natural processes. For example, man's structural works or artificial boundaries when forced into or across a natural system may alter, impair or destroy it. The Southern Pacific Railroad causeway altered the ecology of the Great Salt Lake, and land fills on the Eastern Seaboard estuaries are impairing numerous and valuable marine and salt-marsh ecosystems. Persistent mining of ground water has changed the ecology of soils and land surfaces in many parts of the United States, notably in central Arizona. It is obvious that manmade ecosystems will inevitably affect those of natural origin where civilized society exists. It is not obvious, however, that human changes must always be destructive to natural systems or that, with thoughtful planning, manmade and natural ecosystems could not more often co-exist in harmony.

But why this concern with an ecological basis for land policy? By what reasoning is an ecosystems approach to land use more useful or more valid than any other? Are ecological criteria merely the tools or overt expressions of a naturalistic ideology — an ecological mystique — which some nature lovers and a few apprehensive scientists would substitute for the economic common sense of people who know that the practical business of life continues to be the procuring of food, clothing, and shelter? Does an ecosystems concept impute some teleological design to nature? Is man required to seek out nature's purposes and adapt his laws and practices to nature's ends regardless of his own needs and purposes? The ancient Christian, substituting God's purposes for nature's, could have affirmed this proposition. Adherents to natural law concepts might still do so. But in the dominant societies of this technoeconomic age, mastery or manipulation of nature has become a goal that sometimes approaches a secular religion. Nature, if she has purposes, does not reveal them in language that contemporary man has been able to understand. Technological man, however, has defined and developed his own purposes in relation to nature. These purposes basically require the obtaining of food, clothing, and shelter from nature, and to this end man has organized his relationships with his environment on the basis of the uses he makes of particular components of the natural world. These components are the familiar "natural resources."

As long as man's numbers were few, his technology simple, and his demands upon the natural world limited, it was feasible to deal with the land and its products as if they were no more than discrete resources. Man was unable simultaneously to make both rapid and far-reaching changes in natural ecosystems. Major ecological changes, such as deforestation or the spread of cultivation over the grasslands required time, measured in Europe and Asia by centuries. Some of these changes, as in the brittle, sub-arid ecosystems of the Middle East were cumulatively destructive. Other changes, as in the clearing of forests for agriculture in Western Europe, largely substituted one ecological system for another of comparable stability and productivity. But modern science and technology have permitted man to upset longstanding ecological balances. His numbers have multiplied without restraint. His technology has become powerful and complex with unpredictable side effects, and his demands upon his environment have grown inordinate. Competition for resources has rapidly increased and conflicts among resource users have become a major phenomenon of politics.

If the categorizing of the products of nature into "natural resources" had been based upon a comprehending, selective utilization of the ecosystem, the implications of this "development process" for the integrity and survival of the ecosystem would have been available as a source for principles by which conflicts over resource uses might have been mediated. But ecosystems integrity as a criterion for policy choices has followed, not preceded, the natural resources concept of man-environment relationships. As a consequence, public land policy has shared in the contentiousness associated with the politics of natural resources, and the ecosystem concept has had as yet little mediating effect upon land-use conflicts. Neither in politics nor in administration has there been a generally accepted body of knowledge or doctrine by which conflicts over resource uses could be readily resolved. In the absence of an "ordering" or organizing concept, efforts to coordinate natural resources policies have been largely ineffectual or have been used as covers to impose or prevent one use over others. Prior to the recent intensification of the water pollution issue, the major impetus toward coordinative efforts in water policy may be seen as efforts to restrain the autonomous and arbitrary exercise of power by the Corps of Engineers, or it may be seen as efforts to reconcile differences between the Corps and competing agencies, most frequently the Bureau of Reclamation.

Public policy for land use, as for resources use generally, has been decided chiefly through trial by political combat. "Conservation" as a concept has been helpful principally as an intermediary proposition, midway between unrestricted competition among resource users and an ecologically based view of public responsibility for the self-renewing capabilities of the ecosystem. Aphorisms such as "conservation means wise use" are of little help in the absence of objective criteria for wisdom. An ecosystems approach to public land policy implies the possibility of public decisions based upon empirical principles of public interest in environmental quality and in the self-renewing capabilities of natural systems.

Availability of an objectively rational basis for land policy decisions (if such a basis is actually possible) does not imply, as a matter of course, that this basis will be accepted or acted upon. Human beings may be expected to act more often on a subjective level of rationality than upon more objective and enduring principles. But, until the ecosystems concept has been articulated and its amenability to practical application demonstrated, it is unavailable as a basis for policy. Yet, although the ecosystems approach to land policy remains largely on the theoretical level, it is nevertheless available for practical application at such time as it is perceived as a means of coping with the ecological predicament into which man has blundered.

To understand the ecological predicament of modern man is to begin to understand why an ecosystems approach may ultimately become necessary to human well-being and even to survival. Unfortunately, an understanding of the circumstances, now often described as the "ecological crisis," carries no automatic insight in how to correct or prevent conditions that are almost universally conceded to be harmful. If, as we shall presently contend, application of the ecosystems concept implies a wholly new way of organizing man's relations with the natural world, an ecosystems approach to public land policy implies fundamental changes in the rights and responsibilities of individuals and corporations in the possession and use of land.

It may not be too much to say that ecologically-based public policies imply a thorough-going transformation of some major sectors of the nation's political economy. The nature and scope of a public land policy based on ecological principles would be comprehensive and coordinative. The individual land-owner would lose certain rights and gain certain protections. Controversies over land use would be more often settled by administrative than by judicial means, and the criteria for settlement more often ecological fact than statutory law. Substantial changes could be expected to take place in the practical economics of land use. Application of ecological concepts would find a major obstacle in the treatment of land as a commodity. Private possession of land under ecological ground-rules could be made consistent with an ecosystems approach to land policy. But the freedom to buy, sell, or transfer land without regard to the ecological consequences of the intended or resulting action would not be consistent with an ecosystems approach. Laissez faire land economics, although deeply rooted in American folkways, is becoming increasingly inconsistent with the interests of the vast majority of citizens — a majority of citizens who live in great cities, own no land, and for whom the needs and amenities of life are becoming increasingly costly and difficult of access. . . .

THE SUBSTANCE OF AN ECOSYSTEMS APPROACH

The ecosystems approach has been advanced as a new way of defining public land policy. It would clearly be different from policies now dominant in the United States and to a large extent in other countries also. But the specific ways in which ecosystems relationships could be used as criteria for public policy for land must be defined before their operational feasibility can be assessed. The following summary of the salient properties of ecosystems criteria suggests some of the practical advantages to be gained from their application to land policies.

The first and essential characteristic of the ecosystems approach is its wholistic emphasis. In a pluralistic political-economy that has generally eschewed wholistic thinking, this comprehensive outlook and analysis is a salutary corrective to the tendencies of society to attack problems on a linear or single purpose basis. The novelty of wholistic analysis is now greatly reduced by the growth of systems thinking in government and industry. Indeed, ecosystems criteria may be taken as an application of systems thinking to relationships among natural and aritificial environments. Ecosystems criteria, for example, are absolutely essential to the construction of life-support systems for the exploration of the moon and outer space.

Secondly, ecosystems criteria are based on scientific knowledge, although science does not yet have adequate answers to all ecological problems. Public land policies are not notably based on scientific considerations. To enlist science in determining the goals of domestic policy is a departure from tradition, although science has often been invoked on behalf of policies adopted by other than scientific reasoning. For example, the Bureau of Land Management applies many scientific concepts in its administration of federal public lands, but there is much less science in the laws under which the total public land system operates. Obviously, science does not contain the answers to all policy questions, but in the present state of confusion and contradiction that characterizes land law, at least in the United States, scientific criteria might afford an objective basis for mediating otherwise irreconcilable disputes.

Thirdly, an ecosystems approach uses administrative means in preference to adjudication. This becomes possible to the extent that laws, policies, and actions are based on scientifically ascertainable facts rather than on political or technological fiat. Questions of fact become more important than questions of law (at least in a technical sense). Numerous issues, once litigated in the courts, cease to be issues when certain rights, practices or beliefs associated with land ownership are confirmed, modified, or extinguished by demonstrable evidence.

The substance of an ecosystems approach appears simple, although ecosystems are themselves infinitely complex. The approach begins with an assumption derived from scientific inquiry. The natural world is a composite of interrelating lifesystems subsisting in a highly improbable terrestrial environment. This environment — the ecosphere — is finite. Some of the components are naturally renewable, others are not. Of its renewable components (or resources) some are capable of restoration within a time dimension meaningful to man. But others, fossil fuels, for example, are incapable of renewal, although for some resources substitutes may be found.

The ultimate necessity of an ecosystems approach to environmental policy, including land, follows from the finite amount of land, water, air and other substances upon which the human economy depends, and the infinite character of human demands upon the environment. The heavier the stress of human demands upon the environment, the greater the degree to which those demands must be coordinated and policed in order that the economy continue to function. In an economy of scarce essentials and pressing demands, either the strong preempt resources and deprive the weak, or, where democratic collectivism prevails, socialization, rationing, licensing, and summary police action are instituted to insure fair shares. Political laissez faire in relation to the environment is feasible only when the demands that man makes upon it are relatively light and when natural ecological processes are permitted to operate, continually renewing the ecosystem so that what man uses today is replaced for his use tomorrow. The argument for ecological sophistication in public policies for land and the environment is no longer primarily the threat of shortages of food, energy or raw materials for industry that troubled the "classic conservationists." The more fundamental danger is to the quality of life and to human freedom — especially personal freedom — that will follow from a course of action that presses society to extremities in the maximum utilization of resources and space. Total resource utilization may well require total social control and the loss of choice and variety in life as the price of continuing subsistence.

Throughout nearly all human history man appears to have enjoyed a generally favorable ecological equilibrium. There were, of course, exceptional circumstances in which natural disasters or human errors disrupted a particular localized part of the ecosystem. Earthquakes, floods, droughts, epidemics and famines have disturbed the equilibrium, but the ecosphere as a whole has maintained its stability over thousands of years even though suffering and death have resulted from its localized oscillations. Technology and science have enabled man to cope more effectively with natural disasters, and in some measure to prevent them. But the very success of the human enterprise has created its greatest danger. Technoscience has now given man free rein to increase his numbers and his demands. The result has been a runaway increase in human populations and unremitting pressure on all resources, including land.

This rapid inflation of people and their demands has already impaired the quality of the human environment over large areas of the earth and threatens more serious damage in the years ahead. But at the present stage of human affairs, contemplation of the almost certain consequences of ecological folly is less painful than undergoing the changes that would be required to bring man-environment relationships into ecological balance. There may yet be time to preserve a margin of personal freedom, of environmental variety, and of unforeclosed opportunities that would be comparable to what man has experienced in the past. But the prospect of these conditions surviving into the next century is lessened every day. Science fiction, which often assumes a role of prophecy, presents the bleakest of prospects for human freedom and variety. The triumphs of science and technology do not seem to include the timely mastery by man of the cybernetics of his ecosystems. To accomplish this, he would first have to bring his impulses under control and to exercise a collective self-restraint that has not yet become one of man's strong characteristics.

The idea of instituting lesser controls now to protect basic values and to avoid more drastic measures later has little contemporary appeal. It is the American way, and indeed the human way, to react to crises rather than to forestall them. For who can be sure that the threatened crisis will actually materialize? There is no end to conventional wisdom on behalf of procrastination. What candidate for elective public office would advocate action in the face of dangers that were neither clear nor present in the perception of his constituents? How many politicians would commit themselves to the prevention of dangers that, if real, could only be prevented by an inconvenient rearranging of present institutions and relationships, and would cost prospective voters the happy prospect of something-for-nothing gains?

Contrary to allegations sometimes made by persons who see it threatening their particular interests, ecosystems policy is not anti-people. Human welfare, now and in the future, is its objective. But the welfare of the individual is ultimately dependent upon the viability of the life-supporting ecosystem. Impoverishment of an ecosystem means impoverishment of all society dependent upon it. For example, to preserve wetlands and estuaries from being drained or filled for dry land uses is not to prefer ducks and muskrats to people. It is rather to prefer the interests of the whole of society in a viable ecosystem to those self-centered interests that would jeopardize the ecosystem for immediate and personal monetary gain.

The substance of an ecosystems approach to land policy is to identify, to protect, and in the interest of human welfare, to manage the natural ecosystems upon whose continuing viability human welfare depends. So far as feasible, an ecosystems approach allows natural processes to carry on the work of self-renewal unassisted by human effort. To the extent that man can rely upon nature to renew the ecosystem, human effort that might otherwise be required for the management of nature is freed for other purposes. The pressure of human needs has forced man under certain conditions into the substitution of artificial for natural ecosystems. Elaborate systems of irrigation, drainage, and flood control are examples of artificial environments that are safe and productive only at the price of unremitting attention to maintenance of their systems. The great city is, of course, the most artificial and vulnerable environment of all and exacts from its inhabitants a heavy toll for systems maintenance.

To describe these systems as artificial is not to condemn them or to suggest that they are intrinsically inferior to natural systems. Civilization requires the construction of artificial ecosystems. The ecosystems approach to their management is not to return them to nature, but rather to benefit to the fullest extent from the operation of natural processes. The ecosystems approach implies an understanding of and respect for the potentialities of natural systems. To substitute wherever possible the economy of nature for human effort is the essence of economic as well as ecological good sense. Obviously, it is often necessary to channelize and direct natural forces in order to benefit from them. The extent to which human intervention in natural systems is economically or ecologically justifiable cannot be determined in the absence of demonstrable evidence. A particular high level dam, for example, may or may not be justifiable under an ecosystems approach and in comparison with optional ways of achieving its objectives. It is, however, safe to surmise that a blanket injunction to put all rivers under engineering management, or to ignore them altogether, would be very dubious ecological or economic wisdom.

When society works itself into an ecological straight-jacket, the ecosystem itself may be destroyed in efforts to break out of self-induced but unintended deprivations and constraints. Ecologically overstressed societies are impelled to further intensification of pressure on their environments in an effort to survive. Political leaders of over-populated, ecologically impoverished nations are seldom apt pupils in the school of resources conservation. Survival for them often means getting from the environment whatever can be gotten today, regardless of the consequences for tomorrow. An ecosystems approach to land policy thus also implies a policy of population control. Unless population pressure is manageable, no other aspect of the ecosystem can be freely managed indefinitely. Ultimately the pressure of sheer numbers and the attendant demands upon the ecosystem would force all environmental policies into serving the one overpowering objective of maintaining a minimal existence for the human masses.

There are alternatives to such a course of constrained futility. Among these might be one classed under the heading of unthinkable thoughts. This course would be for a tough-minded and ecologically sophisticated elite to impose ecological order on their less perceptive and self-disciplined brethren. How this might be done, however, is not clear. Unfortunately, political astuteness and charisma seem more often to be found among the ecologically illiterate members of society. Compulsory population control through biomedical science if possible, or Malthusian control if all other means fail, could very well be the outcome of the present unwillingness of human societies to assess their ecological predicament realistically. Land is a substantially inelastic resource and this means that as human population multiplies, land policy is increasingly determined by population policy. The inseparable connections between land use, population and the public interest are now evident.

Among the conflicts in our future-oriented technoscientific society is its fragmented and contradictory treatment of time. The relativity of time has become commonplace, and for certain purposes as in space flight, atomic technology, and medicine, very refined concepts of time are employed. With respect to the dynamics of the ecosystem, however, the time perceptions of modern man are perhaps less developed than those that characterized his agrarian ancestors. Modern man has not learned to perceive the world as a complex of dynamic interrelated systems. His behavior suggests that he believes the world to be an infinitely open system. Within this open system, time and change have a different meaning than they have when the system is closed. When closed, there is no escape from mistakes, and the consequences of a chain-reaction once started in time cannot be avoided by interplanetary flight. Space exploration has reinforced the illusion that the infinity of the cosmos offers a way out for earth-bound man. The reality for society in the ascertainable future is that the earth must be considered a closed system, even though it is in continual interaction with the galaxy.

Within this essentially closed system, change is continuous. Man's future is inextricably involved with changes in the air, water, and land which are the gross elements of the ecosphere. He has himself become a principal change agent. His numbers and technologies have the effect of accelerating changes in time, of wearing down land forms, of increasing the salinity of the sea, and of altering the chemistry of the atmosphere. Only the most comprehensive surveillance of the side effects of technology, and the most carefully evaluated application of science and technology to the ecosystem can prevent inadvertent damage to its self-regenerating capabilities. To be effective, management of the ecosystem must conform to the appropriate time table of nature, not merely to the convenience of man. To illustrate, a dollar crisis or a Far Eastern war may offer politically defensible but ecologically invalid arguments for delaying efforts to save the Great Lakes from death by pollution. Today there may be higher political priorities, but ecologically, tomorrow may be too late.

IN DEFENSE OF AN ECOSYSTEMS LAND POLICY

The intention in this article is not to describe the content of an actual ecosystems land policy. To attempt this without reference to specific places, times, and circumstances would be to contradict the very thesis that has been developed. It is the ecosystems approach to policy that has been introduced. It was conceded at the outset that no such comprehensive approach to land policy exists in the United States. If such a policy based on ecological concepts were to be adopted, some major changes in the laws, expectations, and governmental arrangements in American society would also have to occur. . . . If the implications of this article are correct, American society and indeed mankind generally will eventually be forced into something like an ecosystems policy for land.

In essence this article asserts that man's predicament is that of passengers on a spaceship whose destination is unknown, whose numbers and appetites are increasing, and who have been long accustomed to quarrelsome and improvident conduct. The passengers assume that the builders of the spaceship endowed it with self-renewing mechanisms so that they need take little thought of its maintenace. Moreover, because the ship is very large, they act as though it were infinite, although they are quite capable of calculating its carrying capacity for given levels of safety and convenience. They know that there may come a day when its resources will be taxed beyond capacity. But they are also possessed by the optimistic thought that before the day of disaster arrives, they will land on some habitable planet. And so there is doubt among them as to the practical necessity for restraint.

This is the paradigm of Spaceship Earth whose passengers are only now beginning to realize where they are. Only the ecologically informed among them are aware of the growing precariousness of their condition. Unfortunately, the practical men who are the leaders and managers of the enterprise, although well-informed in many important ways, are generally uninformed or misinformed in this important respect. Their attention is on the lesser mechanics of the enterprise and on the mediation of quarrels among the passengers that might destroy the ship prematurely. Is it then to be conceded that the outcome of the voyage is hopeless, that the passengers cannot be taught, and that the officers and crew are unwilling to learn? No incontrovertible evidence compels this conclusion. It is equally plausible to assume, because human civilization is in itself a highly improbable phenomenon, that the limits of improbability have not yet been reached. Unlikely as it may be, it is possible that American society, if not mankind generally, may reassess its circumstances with sufficient realism and insight to avoid ecological foreclosure. It is conceivable that people may voluntarily adopt ways of organizing their economy and of behaving in relation to the natural environment so as to bring the economy and the ecosystem into a dynamic, self-sustaining equilibrium.

It is hardly to be expected that the ecosystems policy can be made attractive to persons who would suffer real economic or psychological loss through its implementation. These persons, however, constitute a relatively small, although disproportionately influential, force in society. A greater number of Americans appear to have been wedded to certain fundamental concepts and institutions that do not serve them well. This incongruity between real needs and postulated values has been especially strong in matters of land use regulation and environmental management. Urban apartment dwellers appear in large numbers to subscribe to environmental policies appropriate only to the life and times of Daniel Boone. A more adequate understanding of the values, attitudes and understandings of urban Americans in relation to natural systems is greatly needed.

If present demographic projections are valid, the America of the twenty-first century, and even before, will be politically dominated by the residents of great cities. Their beliefs and wishes could reshape public policies toward land. Few of the millions of urban residents will be owners of land; few will have a personal stake in returns from its rental, sale or exploitation. But all would be in some measure dependent on it for the realization of other values. The great mass of urban dwellers are therefore not likely to be hostile to ecosystems concepts. They are likely to be totally unfamiliar with it, and to be unable to appraise its significance or its meaning for their lives. Defense of the concept among landless urbanites is thus largely a matter of including an understanding of ecology, and its implications for human welfare and public policy. . . .

A practical objection to the plausibility of an ecologically oriented public policy is the complexity of the ecosystems themselves. Taking as their target for criticism an exaggerated interpretation of ecology, critics say that because ecologists insist that everything relating to an ecosystem must be taken into account, nothing can be taken into account. This, they say, is because ecology provides no method for assessing priorities among the properties of ecosystems in relation to human values. The conclusion follows that the findings of ecological science are largely inapplicable (although not necessarily irrelevant) to the economics and politics of land policy. This criticism would have validity if an ecosystems approach to public land policy did in fact imply an extension of ecological concepts to everything having to do with land tenure and management, or required every aspect of an ecosystem to be examined in relation to every land use decision. But this totalitarian interpretation is neither necessary nor feasible. The fact is that ecologists are sometimes able to present alternative sets of policies for public consideration, together with their probable consequences. These may be reviewed by the public or by its representatives who may then establish priorities in public law policy.

It is doubtful that a public land policy designed to preserve and protect ecosystems would necessarily be more complex than the mass of laws, policies, and regulations affecting the ownership and use of land today. The effectiveness of an ecosystems land policy does not depend upon its mirroring the complexities of ecosystems. On the contrary, an ecosystems approach might simplify and clarify public land policy. A policy for the protection and ecologically intelligent management of ecosystems could, by the establishment of standards and guidelines, reduce the confusion, conflict, and uncertainty that characterizes land use policy throughout the United States. It may be unrealistic to believe that the American people will adopt an ecosystems approach to land policy on its merits, but an ecological approach would almost certainly be more realistic in its treatment of the real problems of land than are some of the present policies. For the truth is that a great part of public policy for land is only tangentially concerned with the land as a major element in the human life support system. Land policies are not necessarily framed with reference to the land itself, but are often consequent to decisions made in banks, bars, and bedrooms. In any case, land use policy has been and will continue to be instrumental to broader social objectives.

The nature of these objectives and their relevance to the continuing
maintenance of the land as an element in the ecosphere must therefore be taken into account in any serious effort to understand or
to modify land use policy and practices.

Public land policy does not begin with the land, but with
man's dependencies upon it. Measured by ultimate human welfare,
the most important of these dependencies is the basic function of land
in the ecosystems through which life on earth is sustained. But these
ecological functions are not the ones accorded the higher priorities in
our society. Matters of land economics, of law, of land use technologies, and of public relations are in the forefront of our attention.
Our concepts of public law and private property split our thought
and action so that we tend to think of public land policy only as
policy for publicly-owned lands. The idea of a public land policy for all
lands regardless of formal title would be consistent with ecological
realities. From a legal viewpoint, however, a public land policy for
"private" lands might appear to be a contradiction in terms. The
immediate and practical problems of land policy under the prevailing
laws and assumptions require attention, and most students of public
land policy will examine them in this context. Yet the larger view is
also needed. Our preoccupation with immediate and practical problems should not prevent our questioning whether we are indeed address-
ing ourselves to the right questions, at the right time, and in the right
way. Public land policy is amenable to treatment at several levels of
discourse. This article has sought a broad and theoretical level of
treatment on the premise that unless the context of public land policy
is consistent with ecological realities, specific land policies will ultimately prove to be ineffectual or harmful. The argument of this article
has been that the socio-political context of land use policy in America
has been ecologically unwise, unrealistic, and uneconomic. The conclusion follows that a fundamental change of public attitude will be required if the broad range of needs and interests of the American people
are to be served from the limited amount of land whose future use
has not already been determined by law or events. . . .

SUGGESTED READINGS

Berger, C. J. *Land Ownership and Use.* Boston: Little, Brown, 1968.
Boulding, K. "The Economics of the Coming Spaceship Earth." In *Envi-
ronmental Quality in a Growing Economy,* edited by H. Jarrett.
Baltimore: Johns Hopkins Press, 1968.

Caldwell, L. K. *Environment: A Challenge to Modern Society.* Garden City, N. Y.: Natural History Press, 1970.

Fellmeth, R. C., Project Director. *Politics of Land. Ralph Nader's Study Group Report on Land Use in California.* New York: Grossman, 1973.

Haar, C. *Land-Use Planning.* Boston: Little, Brown, 1959.

—— *Law and Land: Anglo-American Planning Practice.* Cambridge, Mass.: Harvard University Press, 1964.

Macinko, G. "Saturation: A Problem Evaded in Planning Land Use." *Science* 149 (1965): 516–521.

Milton, J. P. and Farvar, M. F., eds. *Proceedings of a Conference on the Ecological Aspects of International Development,* Warrenton, Virginia, 1968. St. Louis: Center for the Biology of Natural Systems, Washington University, 1970.

Reilly, W. K. *The Use of Land: A Citizens' Policy Guide to Urban Growth.* New York: Crowell, 1973.

Sears, P. "The Inexorable Problem of Space." *Science* 127 (1958): 9–16.

Senzel, I. "Public Land Laws and Effective Management." In *Proceedings of the 10th Annual Western Resources Conference,* July 1–3, 1968. Fort Collins, Colorado. pp. 127–139.

Soil Conservation Society of America. *National Land Use Policy: Objectives, Components, Implementation.* Anberg, Iowa: Soil Conservation Society of America, 1973.

Barrier Beaches of Eastern North America

Christopher J. Schuberth
Lecturer in Geology, The American Museum of Natural History

Reprinted with some deletions by permission of the author and the publisher from
Natural History 79 (June–July 1970), pp. 46–55. Copyright © The American
Museum of Natural History.

A slender ribbon of light-colored sand, about thirty miles long
and less than a mile wide, arches gracefully southward from Long
Island and pierces the dark blue waters of the Atlantic Ocean. Cartog-
raphers call it Great South Beach, but to most New Yorkers it is known
as Fire Island. Fire Island is the northernmost segment of an almost
continuous chain of low barrier islands that extends from New York
to Florida. Similar barrier chains line much of the Gulf Coast, the
North Sea coast of Holland, and the Baltic Sea coast of Poland. In the
United States a number of important industrial and resort cities —
Galveston, Miami Beach, Atlantic City, to mention three — have
developed on these islands.

Unlike the immobile rock ramparts of the New England coast,
the barrier beaches respond sensitively to the changing forces of the
coastal environment. Occasionally they founder temporarily beneath
the abnormally high tides and gale force winds that accompany intense
coastal storms or tropics-spawned hurricanes. But more often, these
fragile lines of sand maintain the mainland's outer defense against a
dynamic and aggressive sea.

Vacationists in ever increasing numbers continue to flock to
these islands. On Fire Island the growth of summer communities
has been so rapid that land for new seaside homes is almost nonexistent.
The Fire Island National Seashore, established in 1967, now maintains in a natural state all the undeveloped land of the barrier island
outside the borders of Smith Point County Park, Robert Moses State
Park, and the thirteen established communities. This has increased
the demand for land within the communities and has inflated prices
tremendously.

Natural, ocean-facing dunes of windblown sand, so vulnerable
to wave erosion during times of severe storms, yet so essential for
the protection of the island's interior, have become the most highly
prized parcels of real estate. Hundreds of summer homes, including
many expensive ones, have occupied these protective dunes. In many
places these homes, with their spindly supportive legs, now stand
exposed to the full fury of storm-driven waves. Senseless tampering

with protective dunes has made many of the island's interior communities susceptible to an invasion by the sea. Much is at stake, both in terms of personal financial investments — now totaling several tens of millions of dollars — and the stability of the island itself.

The geologic processes that shape a barrier island do not change with the arrival of man. The complex coastal processes — their broad patterns and detailed variations — are part of an ongoing history of physical change in which neither of the antagonists, waves nor beaches, gains a permanent victory. The process of sand transportation within the surf, for example, is a response by the beach to the changing pattern of breaking waves. The problem for man is not the movement of sand as such, but rather its movement away from areas where it is needed for the protection of expensive homes. When the oceanfront was unoccupied, the beach could shift without alarming anyone. Now, with the presence of houses and other fixed objects against which shoreline changes can be measured, island dwellers become dismayed by the loss of their sand.

In futile attempts to maintain shoreline stability and protect property on the barrier beaches of Long Island from wave damage, millions of dollars of private and public funds are periodically invested to replace sand removed by wave action. Dredged out of the shallow, backwater areas of Great South Bay, sand is pumped onto the oceanfronts of troubled communities. Within a few years, this expensive sand is swept away to collect, unwanted, in other areas. The endangered properties remain in the same hazardous position, and the additional sand often moves to inlets and other navigational channels where it is not wanted. To aggravate this situation, the source of dredgeable sand is not endless. Already nearly all available sand has been removed from some areas in Great South Bay.

The so-called erosional problem involves normal, well-understood geologic processes, which have been in operation since the barrier first formed some 5,000 years ago. These same coastal processes continue to reshape the shorefront despite the presence of man and his works. It is only when man comes to cross-purposes with the natural design of change, when his developed real estate is threatened by normal, ongoing geologic processes — volcanism, earthquakes, landslides, the shift of a barrier island — that these processes take on alarming new dimensions and become geologic hazards. But, if man presses closer to the flanks of active volcanoes or straddles regions of seismic instability (such as the San Andreas Fault in California), if he develops housing atop unstable rainsodden slopes in the Pacific Coast ranges, or pushes onto the protective dunes of the wave-moved barrier sands, does he have the right to consider the effects of these natural

processes as hazards? Since man is the transgressor, is it not more realistic to consider the hazards involved as human?

To cope with the problems of coastal erosion, we must define
three basic terms before we can understand the significant geologic
processes involved. A barrier island is an elongate ridge of unconsolidated sand, often dozens of miles long and between a few yards to
a mile wide, that generally parallels the mainland shore. Its sea-facing
dunes, if naturally formed from windblown sand, rarely rise more
than fifty feet above high water. The barrier is separated from the
mainland by a shallow bay, or lagoon, which may be several miles
wide. Each barrier island is separated from the next in the chain by a
tidal inlet, rarely more than a mile wide.

The geologist defines a beach as the whole downsloping zone
of oceanfront in which sand is in a near-constant state of movement
by ordinary wave action. Thus, a beach extends from the normal
high-tide line to a depth of water generally not exceeding 30 feet
below low tide. Below 30 feet in depth, wave motion, even during a
severe storm, rarely stirs the sand. The familiar part of the shore, the
near-horizontal terrace of heavily trampled sand that extends seaward
from the foot of the dunes to the high-tide line, is known as the berm.
It is built up by sand brought ashore through the turbulent action
of breaking waves.

The problems of oceanfront residents result from the energy
released by the continual breaking of ocean waves. More than 8,000
breakers pound Fire Island's beach every day — an average of six each
minute — with a force of as much as 2,000 pounds per square foot.
When ocean waves move into shallow water, usually less than 30 feet
deep, the circular orbit of their water particles is distorted. As each
wave steepens, and becomes asymmetrical, the distance between crests
decreases. Continuing landward, the ever steepening wave becomes
so distorted in the shallow water that its crest curls over, and the
wave breaks with a thunderous crash to form the white, frothy surf.
A swirling mass of sand-laden water, the swash, is hurled across the
exposed beach face. When the energy of the swash is spent, a less
turbulent flow of water returns to the sea and on out to the breaker
zone as a below-surface undertow, which is recycled landward with
the next breaking wave.

Most of the breaker's energy is released in the strong turbulence
of the surf and swash. In this turbulent zone, untold numbers of sand
grains are dislodged and moved about in such a pattern that they never
return to their original position. Moved, for example, a tenth of an
inch with each breaking wave, an individual sand grain could migrate
in the surf as much as 100 feet in a day.

A sand grain follows two broad patterns of movement along
the beach. The swash pushes a sand grain up the beach face, while
the backflow carries it seaward. But sand grains rarely follow a straight
up-and-down path. As each sand grain moves landward and seaward
it usually also moves parallel to the beach.

The distance and the direction that sand grains move are related
to the coastal conditions of summer and winter seasons. During the
summer, waves are usually low, the surf is not turbulent, and the corresponding swash is a thin sheet of gentle water. Few storms occur.
Under these quiet weather conditions, friction will hold sand grains
against the bottom during the gentle backflow of water, and most
are not carried back in the undertow to the breaker zone. As a result,
the net movement of sand is landward. Beginning in early summer,
billions of sand grains along the length of beach slowly build up a
broad terrace, known as the summer berm, which widens as the season
progresses. Throngs of bathers enjoy the wide berm and swim in the
gentle surf during July and August. And the widening summer berm
may relieve the anxieties of oceanfront property owners.

But the existence of a wide berm is short-lived. From late fall
to early spring coastal storms, often as many as one a month, churn
up the Atlantic waters. In the long run, these produce the great physical changes along the oceanfront. High waves force a great volume of
turbulent water across the beach and onto the summer berm. The
strong turbulence keeps sand in suspension so that the powerful counter-
currents of backflow carry the sand out to the breaker zone. Behind
the breaker zone, in the deeper, less turbulent water, most of the
sand accumulates. It forms an offshore bar, a low underwater ridge
of sand that parallels the shore. As the bar grows in height, the waves
break farther offshore and turbulence scours the top of the bar.
Although usually seen only at extreme low water, bigger waves break
initially over the offshore bar; lower waves re-form in the deeper
water landward of the submerged bar, only to break finally along
the winter beach.

Intense winter-spring storms with onshore winds of gale force
often produce high tides and chaotic patterns of breaking waves. A
turbulent surf and a powerful swash flood the winter berm and often
tear into the dunes, removing tens of thousands of cubic yards of
sand. During the March 6–8, 1962 storm, the surf, with unusually
high 30-foot waves, swept away 96 dune homes and severely damaged
another 195, from Fire Island east to Montauk Point. Waves breached
dunes at 50 places, exposing the back dune areas to intense wave
erosion. Three thousand feet of roadway at Westhampton Beach were
destroyed; a new tidal inlet, over 1,200 feet wide, was created where

formerly developed properties existed; and about 70 feet of beach, berm, and dunes were wiped off the map. An estimated 350 homes were destroyed as far south as Virginia, over 20,000 sustained major wave damage, and property losses exceeded $234 million.

Six years later, in November, a small coastal storm inflicted $2 million in property damage and removed over $900,000 worth of sand fill designed to protect ocean-facing homes along a half mile of Westhampton Beach. Thirteen months later, during the "Christmas Day Storm," an additional half dozen homes were destroyed in two Fire Island communities.

Yet, during this seven-year period, not a single hurricane threatened the coastal region, a most unusual and fortunate circumstance, for if one had, wave erosion and wind damage would have left the now-unprotected communities in shambles.

After each storm the beach and berm undergo partial recovery. The dunes may suffer more permanent damage because vegetation must take hold again to keep the blowing sand in place. Over the next several days a less turbulent surf, almost contritely, returns some of the offshore sand as each wave, stumbling over the submerged bar, lifts sand grains into suspension. Moved forward in the next breaking wave, the suspended sand slowly advances landward. The narrow, concave early poststorm profile of the shorefront is altered to a wider, convex late poststorm profile. However, this widening and filling in of the berm over the next few weeks is often interrupted by another storm. Over the entire winter-spring season, much of the sand of the summer berm remains in the submerged bar.

If the sand moved only in a straight line away from the shore in the winter and back in the summer; if, in other words, the same sand moved back and forth in a closed system, then beach erosion would be a simple problem. Unfortunately, sand also moves lengthwise along the beach. The system is not closed; it loses sand constantly. Therefore, sand must be added to one part of the system to replace the losses from other parts. Otherwise the barrier islands, in time, would disappear. Each year hundreds of thousands of cubic yards of sand leave the barrier island system and are deposited in other areas, particularly in the tidal inlets that connect the lagoonal waters with the open sea.

The sand particles move along the chain because waves rarely approach parallel to the beach. The angle at which waves approach the shore is determined largely by wind direction at the surface of the open ocean where waves build up. Northeast winds produce the largest waves, capable of moving the greatest volume of sediment, on the barrier beaches of Long Island.

A wave from the northeast breaks from east to west. The uprush of water from the breaking wave, plus the sand particles, moves obliquely up the beach face. But the return flow and the sand particles follow a straight path down the beach face. When moved by the next swash, the sand grains follow the same stepwise pattern. Multiplied by countless repetitions on a seemingly infinite number of sand grains, this action transports a vast amount of sand along the entire beach, primarily in the surf zone. This process is called beach drifting, and the movement of water is known as the littoral current.

On Fire Island the littoral current each year moves 600,000 cubic yards of sand westward. Most of it remains in the quieter waters of Fire Island Inlet and forms submerged sand bars, which quickly coalesce into low above-water accumulations. This sand persistently extends Democrat Point, the west end of Fire Island. Six hundred thousand cubic yards of sand is equivalent to a convoy of cement trucks dumping loads of sand at nine-minute intervals, 24 hours a day, year-round. The Fire Island lighthouse, erected in 1858 at the western-most tip of the island, now stands five miles inland. Democrat Point continues to extend westward at an average rate of 212 feet each year.

Beach drifting is man's major problem on any barrier island that undergoes intensive development. Coastal erosion costs the United States approximately $150 million annually. For many years, the accepted method of dealing with this problem was to build groins, dam-like rock structures a few feet high and about a hundred feet long, perpendicular to the shoreline. Sand is trapped on the updrift side of the groin, and the berm and beach widen quickly. But the sand supply is thereby reduced and, on the downdrift side, the beach and berm must retreat. So, another groin is needed "downstream" to trap whatever sand is available in the littoral current. The beach and berm begin to retreat downstream from the second groin. So another groin is built, and another, turning a former unsullied stretch of shore into a field of ugly groins. The groins create a series of curving, flotsam-retaining berms and beaches.

The effects of groins are local and temporary. Owners of ocean-front properties in immediate danger of being washed away are understandably eager to see fast action and quick solutions in the hope of restoring their beach. But too often changes are made without realizing the consequences. Groins may easily accelerate erosion. Eleven groins recently completed along Westhampton Beach had this effect. Intensified wave action on the downdrift side of the westernmost groin was the primary cause of the $2 million in property damage during the November, 1968, storm and an estimated $900,000 loss in sand fill.

Groin fields at Miami Beach have had little positive effect in stabilizing the shorefront. The first of many was installed after the disastrous 1926 hurricane. Yet all the groins combined have not stemmed the outflow of sand, which continues at the average rate of 150,000 cubic yards each year. Today, several shorefront hotels have no berm remaining, and their hastily erected seawalls send ocean spray into parking lots and swimming pools.

Because groins rarely provide a long-term solution, they should not be considered a preferred method for sustaining a beach and berm. In the long run they are usually more expensive and less effective than well-planned programs of beach nourishment, a method that integrates the natural forces in operation along the coast.

On Fire Island, some communities tried to nourish their beach and berm with sand dredged from Great South Bay. Each attempt to restore the berm met with failure simply because the volume of sand involved was insufficient to maintain the *entire* berm. The littoral current redistributed this small amount of sand along the complete stretch of beach to the west.

The only way to maintain a beach and berm is to consider the entire oceanfront, from inlet to inlet, as a single system. On Fire Island, for example, sand quickly accumulates along the updrift side of jetties constructed for the purpose of keeping Moriches Inlet, at the east end, and Fire Island Inlet, at the west end, free of sand. A sand-transfer plant could pump sand through a buried pipe. less than three miles long, from the east side of Moriches Inlet and discharge it onto the downdrift side — on the east end of Fire Island — into the headwaters of the littoral current. There, the sand would re-enter the littoral conveyor belt and, as a berm-widening wedge, continue down the beach all the way to the inlet at Democrat Point, 30 miles to the west.

Furthermore, the sand building up along the east side of Fire Island Inlet could be pumped back east ten miles or so and discharged into the littoral stream, where it would be recycled westward, supplying additional sand to widen the berm and beach. To keep the navigation channels free of accumulating sand, Fire Island Inlet is now dredged periodically and the sand hauled several miles out to sea and dumped. Why such valuable sand is removed permanently from the littoral current is somewhat obscure, particularly since some of this sand has, at great expense, already been dredged out of Great South Bay and added to the beach and berm in front of the troubled communities to the east. The least that could be done with this excess sand would be to transfer it across Fire Island Inlet and feed it into the littoral stream along the heavily eroded east end of Jones-Oak Beach.

The best natural defense of a barrier island coast is a continuously wide berm, and the least expensive way to achieve this is to rebuild and nourish it. In 1968, the Corps of Engineers authorized a beach nourishment project to redevelop and to maintain the shorefront of Miami Beach. With an initial investment of $30 million, the project would pump 15 million cubic yards of sand onto the entire ten miles of oceanfront between Government Cut and Bakers Haulover Inlet to produce a 2½-foot-high shelf, called a hurricane berm, that will extend about 20 feet beyond the present shoreline. From this berm, the beach will slope down to a new high-water line about 150 feet east of the present shoreline. Then, at an estimated expense of about $1 million each year, 200,000 cubic yards of sand will be dredged annually to nourish and maintain the 10-mile beach. Most of the sand will be obtained from the inlets, which will be kept free from sand accumulation. Wave action and the littoral currents would redistribute the sand along the entire shorefront. . . .

Man still cannot alter the basic natural patterns between land and sea. For thousands of miles across the open sea, energy stored from distant storms will be transmitted in neverending patterns of undulating swells and troughs. On nearing the coast, this energy will be transformed into steepened waves hurling thunderous breakers in one final, furious assault. And the land will continue to shift, either straightening its front to offer the least possible area for attack, or outmaneuvering the sea by redeploying material to an underwater position on which the waves must trip and sap their energies.

If man wishes to build his works on the fringes of such a battleground, he must understand that the rules of this ancient battle require the beach, the berm, and the dunes to shift constantly before the assault of the sea. If man tries to change these rules, he can only fail; and in his failure he may even undermine the fragile hold of these outposts against the powerful sea.

SUGGESTED READINGS

Davis, J. H. "Influences of Man upon Coastlines." In *Man's Impact on Environment,* edited by T. R. Detwyler, pp. 332–347. New York: McGraw-Hill, 1971.

Dury, G. H. *Perspectives on Geomorphic Processes.* Commission on College Geography, Resource Paper 3. Washington: Association of American Geographers, 1969.

Flawn, P. T. *Environmental Geology.* New York: Harper and Row, 1970.

King, C. A. M. *Beaches and Coasts.* 2nd ed. New York: St. Martin's Press, 1972.

Pitty, A. F. *Introduction to Geomorphology.* London: Methuen, 1971.

Steers, J. A., ed. *Applied Coastal Geomorphology.* London: Macmillan, 1971.

—— *Introduction to Coastline Development.* London: Macmillan, 1971.

Optimum Population and Environment:
A Georgian Microcosm

Eugene P. Odum
Director, Institute of Ecology, University of Georgia

Reprinted by permission of the author and the publisher from *Current History* 58 (1970), pp. 355–359, 365, 366.

The world seems to be getting smaller and more limited in its capacity to support human beings because the per capita use of resources in developed countries, and the per capita expectations in undeveloped countries, keep going up. Thoughtful persons everywhere are agreeing, perhaps reluctantly in many cases, that if a high quality human existence is to be achieved man must now "manage" his own population as well as the natural resources on which he depends.

To the ecologist, this means first and foremost that the population growth rate must be drastically reduced so that an equilibrium can be reached in the very near future if we are to avoid the very high risk of excessive population, reduction in the per capita availability of resources and a loss in the individual's freedom of action. If this is indeed the case, then the question of what constitutes an optimum population density for man becomes a key issue. An ecological approach to this problem involves considering the total demands that an individual makes on his environment, and how these demands can be met without degrading or destroying his living space or *lebensraum*.

Since the environment is both a "supply depot" and a "house" for man, the concept of the integrated system, the "ecosystem," is the basis for the relevant ecology of today. In the conduct of human affairs in the past, these two functions of the environment have been considered as separate and unrelated problems, as many writers are now pointing out. The dramatic change in peoples' attitude towards their environment and the rise of a sort of "populist" ecology in the 1970s stem from a general recognition that the quality of the *lebensraum* is so intimately interrelated with the rate of production and consumption of resources that the total "man-in-nature" ecosystem must now be the basis for intelligent management. Lewis Mumford places this concept in more general terms when he says that "Ideological misconceptions have impelled us to promote the expansion of knowledge, power, productivity, without inventing any adequate systems of controls," and that therefore "the problem of our age" is how to use quality to control quantity.[1] In actual fact, it will be much easier to "invent" controls than to agree on a "set point," or optimum level, for the "population-stat."

THE GEORGIAN MICROCOSM

In the fall of 1969, my class in advanced ecology at the University of Georgia elected to tackle the question of "the optimum population for Georgia" on the assumption that this state was large enough and typical enough to be a sort of "microcosm" for the nation and the world. The basic question asked was: How many people can Georgia support at a reasonably high standard of living on a continuing, self-contained equilibrium basis, in the sense that imports and exports of food and resources would be balanced? As it turned out, Georgia is a good microcosm for the United States because its present density and growth rate, and the distribution of its human and domestic animal population are close to the mean for the whole nation. Likewise, food production and land use patterns in Georgia are average. Furthermore, since pollution, overcrowding and loss of non-renewable resources have not yet reached very serious proportions, the state, like most of the nation, has the opportunity to plan ahead for a new kind of "progress," based on the right of the individual to have a quality environment and to share in the economic benefits of wise use and recycling of resources.

It is self-evident that such planning must start at the local and state level. The ecological and population situation is so varied in the nation as a whole that it is not likely that a nationwide plan for optimum population and environment can be initiated until states and regions take their inventories and set tentative standards. For example, the impetus to redesign the internal combustion engine to reduce air pollution started in California where the problem was locally acute. And once California sets rigorous control standards the nation must quickly follow because manufacturers have to meet maximum, not minimum, standards, since they cannot (for long, at least) build one kind of car for California and another for other states.

As background for the Georgia inventory, two general principles were adopted. The first principle can be stated as follows: "The optimum is almost always less than the maximum." In terms of human population density, the number of people in a given area that would be optimum from the standpoint of the quality of the individual's life and his environment is considerably fewer than the maximum number of people that might be supported, that is, merely fed, housed and clothed as dehumanized robots or "domestic animals." The same principle can be applied to automobiles; certainly the greatest number of cars that can be accommodated bumper-to-bumper on a freeway is not optimum for the forward progress of the individual automobile. Perhaps, then, the idea of the "greatest good for the greatest number" is not really a tenable principle. Maybe Dr. George Wald's slogan, "a better world for fewer babies" is more relevant to our times.

A second principle is that affluence actually reduces the number of people who can be supported by a given resource base. Thus, the optimum population for a highly developed, industrialized nation with a high per capita G. N. P. (gross national product) is very much lower than the population that can be supported at a subsistence level in an undeveloped nation, because the *per capita* consumption of resources and the production of wastes are so much greater in the developed countries. Thus, if one person in the United States exerts 50 times more demand on his environment than does an Asian, then it is obvious that no environment can support as many Americans as Asians without disastrous deterioration in the quality of that environment. Table 1 illustrates how sharply our world is divided into "developed" and "undeveloped" nations. The distribution of G. N. P. is strongly bimodal, with very few people living in intermediate (so called "developing") nations. Shocking as it may seem, the United States is now in as much danger of overpopulation at its level of per capita living as is India at her present standard of living. Population control must be an overriding issue in both the developed and undeveloped worlds, but the levels that are critical, the limiting factors and the strategy of control are quite different.

Table 1. World distribution of per capita G. N. P.

Per Capita G. N. P. ($)	Number of Countries	Percent World Population
40–149	31	56.5
150–299	25	8.8
300–599	15	4.7
600–2400	16	30.0

Source: Revelle in *Prospects of the World Food Supply* (Washington, D.C.: National Academy of Science, 1966) Table 1, p. 24.

Minimum American per Capita Acreage Requirements

Table 2 is the consensus estimate made by the students of the minimum acreage necessary to support one person at a standard of living now enjoyed by Americans, including a pollution-free living space, room for outdoor recreation and adequate biological capacity to recycle air, water and other vital resources. The per capita area required for food was obtained by taking the diet recommended by the President's Council on Physical Fitness and determining how much crop and grazing land is required to supply the annual requirement for each item. If Americans would be satisfied with merely getting enough calories and greatly reducing their consumption of meat, as little as a third of an acre per person would be adequate, but the kind of diet Americans now enjoy including orange juice, bacon and eggs for breakfast and steaks for dinner — all of which require a great deal of land space to produce — takes at least 1.5 acres per capita. Thus, the American "demands" from his agricultural environment 10 times the space that is required to produce the rice diet of the Oriental (assuming equally efficient crop production in both cases). The one-acre requirement for "fibers" is based on present per capita use of paper, wood, cotton and so forth, that equals the average annual production of one acre of forest and other fiber-producing land. The two acres for "natural area use" are based on the minimum space needs for watersheds, airsheds, green belt zones in urban areas, recreation areas (state golf courses) as estimated by recent land use surveys. Again, we could do with less by designing more artificial waste recycling systems and doing away with outdoor recreation, but at a high cost to society as a whole.

In considering the five-acre per capita estimate, two points must be emphasized: (1) If the per capita use goes up in the future, either more land is needed or greater production per acre must be forced by increased use of chemical controls that, in turn, tend to

Table 2. Minimum per capita acreage requirements for a quality environment.

Food-producing land	1.5 acres
Fiber-producing land	1 acre
Natural use areas (watershed, airshed, greenbelt, recreation, waste disposal, etc.)	2 acres
Artificial systems (urban, industrial, highways, waste treatment facilities, etc.)	0.5 acres
TOTAL	5.0 acres

pollute the total environment, creating a cost in taxes that would reduce the individual's "take home" pay. (2) The five-acre estimate is relevant only to an area such as Georgia that has a favorable climate (adequate rainfall and moderate temperature). The per capita area requirement would be much greater in regions with large areas of deserts, steep mountains or other extreme ecosystems.

The inventory of Georgia is summarized in Tables 3–6. The per capita density (Table 3) of 1 in 8 acres compares with the national average of 1 in 10 acres. The urban-rural distribution is comparable to the national average. A domestic animal population 5 times that of people is also close to the national average, as is the 10 percent of land devoted to agriculture (see Table 4). In considering the impact of man on his environment, the importance of the domestic animal is too often overlooked; yet such animals are actually consuming more "primary production" (i.e., photosynthetic conversion of sun energy to organic matter) than man, and they require huge amounts of land. Also, in this country, pets such as dogs and cats are estimated to consume enough food to support 5 million people. We could do away with all domestic animals, of course, and substitute people, but to the ecologist that would mean not only giving up meat in the diet, but also dehumanizing man to the level of a domestic animal. It is interesting that Georgia now produces enough food to feed 12 million people, provided that people actually consumed the crops directly. A diet of corn, other grains, soy beans, peanuts and vegetables could supply adequate calories and protein. In actual practice, of course, very little of Georgia's crop production is consumed directly; most of it is fed to animals or shipped out of state in exchange for food from elsewhere.

Table 3. Georgia: area and density, people and domestic animals.

Total area	37.7 million acres
Total people	4.8 million
Per capita density	1 in 8 acres
Population density –	
(31% Atlanta met. area:	
60% urban, 56% under 30 yrs. of age.)	
Domestic Animals	
Population equivalent*	21 million
Total Man-Animal	26 million
Population equivalent*	1 in 1.5 acres

*Population equivalent is a unit of animal weight equivalent in metabolism to one adult person.

Table 4. Georgia – land use in 1968

Land Use	(Percent)
Crops	
food	7.5
fiber	.8
idle (rotated)	3.7
Pasture	7.4
Forest	
private	66.3
public	4.5*
Recreation (public)	1.8*
Coastal wetlands	1.3*
Urban, etc.	4.5

*Total of these 3 categories or 7.6% is all land now set aside for "natural use" only (i.e., protected from exploitation).

Table 5. Food production in Georgia – 1969

	Kcal/year $\times 10^{12}$ *
Corn	8.5
Grain	0.6
Sweet Potatoes	0.03
Soy Beans	1.8
Peanuts	1.4
Vegetables	0.05
TOTAL	$\pm 12 \times 10^{12}$

*10^6 Kcal will support one person one year.

If we consider for the moment that one person in five acres is a reasonable per capita density, then Georgia is rapidly approaching that level. As shown in Table 6, the net growth rate is 2 percent which, if continued, would mean a doubling of the population (leaving only four acres per capita) in 35 years. Almost before we realize it Georgia is moving from what was considered essentially a sparsely populated state to one that is beginning to feel the adverse effects of population pressure. As emphasized, this pressure is due not so much to the number of people, but to the great increase in the per capita de-

Table 6. 1970 estimates of population growth-rate in Georgia

	(Per Year)
Birth rate	2.4%
Immigration	0.4%
Death rate	0.8%
Net growth rate	2.0%

mands on space and resources. It comes as a shock to everyone that Georgia and the nation could be badly overpopulated by the year 2000.

Natural Regulators

It is possible to prepare graphic models for population growth and stabilization to show how animal populations in nature normally regulate their density well below the limit that would be imposed by the food supply. In this event the quality of both the individual and the environment is insured, since the individual is neither likely to run out of food (or other resources) nor to "overgraze" or otherwise permanently damage his habitat in his efforts to obtain the necessities of life. In some populations, death controlled by predators, disease or parasites is the regulator; in other populations, birth control is the mechanism. In some of the best regulated species of the most highly evolved animals, namely the birds and the mammals, the essential control is behavior that restricts the use of space.

This sort of "territorial control" would seem to be relevant to the human population problem. Best of all, planned and controlled land use mutually agreed upon through the democratic process can be accomplished at the local and state level right now, while we continue the discussions about birth control and abortion in an effort to reach some kind of national and international consensus that can make these approaches effective nationwide and worldwide. Consequently, it certainly will be worthwhile to consider what we might accomplish along the lines of territorial control through land use planning.

Land Use Planning

In actual fact, Georgia is extremely vulnerable to overpopulation for two reasons: (1) the immigration rate is high and can be expected to increase as people flee from the crowded, polluted and deteriorated part of our country and (2) land is open to immediate exploitation on a huge scale because there are so few protective laws and so little land in public ownership. Many of these factors apply to other areas of the nation. Even if the birth rate drops in Georgia and other less crowded states, population growth rate would remain high because of immigration that will come as people discover the relatively cheap and quickly available "open spaces." As already indicated, a growth rate of 2 percent per year means that Georgians would be down to one man in 4 acres in thirty-five years.

A land speculation spiral that is economically ruinous to all but a few speculators could well result unless plans are made now, and control legislation is enacted. Georgia has a lot of open land now but very little has been set aside to remain so. Only about 7 percent of Georgia (see Table 4) is reserved in national, state or city parks, refuges, greenbelts or other protected categories; even our best farmland is vulnerable to real estate exploitation.

As citizens, what can Georgians do? First, they can instigate and support drives, both at the local and state levels, to get more land into public ownership (parks, state and national forests, greenbelts) and can work to have an "open space" bill passed that will enable private owners to establish scenic easements and other restrictions on the use of land that is valuable in its natural state. Second, they can work towards the establishment of metro-commissions and state-wide environmental commissions with strong zoning powers. The passage by the Georgia legislature of the marshlands protection bill early in 1970 was a step in this direction because almost half a million acres were put into a protective category with an agency empowered to insure the best and highest use of a natural resource that otherwise is very vulnerable to destructive types of exploitation.

If about one-third of the area of Georgia were in a protected category, then we would be well protected against against overpopulation, and we would have a big buffer that would make the technical problems of pollution control much easier. It is important to note that Western states are fortunate in that 40–50 percent of their land is already in public ownership. The battle there will be to mobilize public opinion to prevent overdevelopment and degradation of these lands.

The third function that citizens can perform is to be more selective about the type and location of new industry. Citizens will be doing industry and society a favor by establishing tough pollution standards and requiring advance waste treatment because it is much cheaper to engineer and internalize the costs of complete waste treatment, water and air recycling at the beginning than to take action later and also pay for repairing a damaged environment. There is no longer a need nor excuse for "dirty" industries that pollute and pay low wages. Any state can now attract industries that have the resources to pay good wages and the public conscience to do what is necessary in waste management.

In summary, our microcosm study makes a case for basing the optimum population on total space requirement and not on food as such. The world can feed more "warm bodies" than it can support high quality human beings.

REFERENCES

[1] L. Mumford, "Quality in the Control of Quantity," in *Natural Resources: Quality and Quantity,* edited by S. V. Ciriacy-Wantrup and J. J. Parsons (Berkeley: University of California Press, 1967), pp. 7–18.

SUGGESTED READINGS

Dasmann, R. F. *Planet in Peril? Man and the Biosphere Today.* Harmondsworth, England: Penguin, 1972.

Institute of Ecology. *Man in the Living Environment.* Madison: University of Wisconsin Press, 1972.

Irving, R. M. and Priddle, G. B., eds. *Crisis: Readings in Environmental Issues and Strategies.* Toronto: Macmillan, 1971.

Mumford, L. "Quality in the Control of Quantity." In *Natural Resources: Quality and Quantity,* edited by S. V. Ciriacy-Wantrup and J. J. Parsons, pp. 7–18. Berkeley: University of California Press, 1967.

Odum, E. P. "The Attitude Revolution." In *The Crisis of Survival,* pp. 9–15. New York: Morrow, 1970.

Simmons, I. G. "Ecology and Land Use." *Transactions, Institute of British Geographers* 38 (1966): 59–72.

INDEX

Aerosols:
  effects on climate, 94–96
Agriculture:
  effects of frost, 76–82; origins and
    dispersals, 53
Aircraft:
  effects on climate, 107–108
Air pollution:
  effects on ecosystems, 266; effects on
    urban climates, 104–107
Aswan Dam:
  effects on fisheries, 3
Atmosphere:
  description, 46–47; evolution, 87–88
Atmospheric circulation:
  effects on oceans, 23–25

Balance of nature, 49–50
Baltimore:
  effects of construction (on rivers), 197–199
Barrier islands:
  definition, 314
Beaches:
  definition, 314; erosion processes, 314–
    317; nourishment techniques, 318–319;
    stabilization (groins), 317–318
Biosphere:
  description, 47–48
Borneo:
  effects of DDT, 14–15
Brookhaven National Laboratory: 263
Budyko, M.I.: 88

Callendar, G.S.: 92

Carbon cycle: 215–216
Carbon dioxide:
  effects on climate, 92–93
Castle Creek Basin, Calif.:
  water balance, 66
Cesium: 137;
  effects on forests, 263–264
Cities:
  effects on climate, 99–107; definition, 61,
    87
Climatic change:
  effects of aerosals, 94–96; effects of carbon
    dioxide, 92–93; effects of volcanic dust,
    94; Philadelphia, 90
Climatology: 61–62, 68–69
Columbia, Md.:
  urban heat island, 100–101
Coulomb, J.: 103

Dams:
  biological effects, 143–144
Darwin, C.: 44
Davis, W.M.: 184
DDT:
  ecological effects (Borneo), 14–15
Desert soils: 230
Dokuchaev, V.V.: 32, 222
Drainage nets:
  geometrical relations, 182–183
Drought:
  U.S. eastern seaboard, 91–92
Dynamic equilibrium:
  definition, 11; forms, 11, 12; in geo-
    morphology, 186–187, 189–190

Early man:
  population density, 51–52
Ecological succession:
  definition, 40–41, 49; effects of fire, 265;
    relevance to planning, 41
Ecology:
  origin and development, 44–45
Ecosystem:
  approaches to study, 33–35; components,
    35–40, 38; concept development, 32–35;
    definition, 31–32; diversity, 10–11;
    efficiency, 252; productivity (measure-
    ment), 244–247; stability, 11; types, 260
Energy:
  definition, 9; forms, 9, 20
Entropy:
  definition, 9; in geomorphology, 185–186
Environmental quality:
  minimum standards, 324
Erosion:
  definition, 155
Erosion rates:
  cemeteries, 155; effects of climate, 156;
    effects of man, 158–162; effects of
    topography, 156; global estimates, 162–
    164; United States, 157–158, 159
Eutrophication:
  definition, 272; Lake Tahoe, 135–136

Fire:
  ecological effects, 265
Fire Island, N.Y.:
  beach nourishment, 318–319; storm
    damage, 315–316
Fire Island National Seashore, 312
Fluvial geomorphology:
  magnitude and frequency concept, 179
Fog dispersal: 98
Food chains:
  in streams, 144–146
Forbes, S.A.: 32
Forests:
  microclimate, 73–74; productivity, 250–
    251; effects of radiation, 263–265
Franklin, B.: 74–75
Frost:
  effects on agriculture, 76–82; types, 78–79

Geiger, R.: 69, 73, 82, 96
Geographical cycle: 184
Georgia:
  land use planning, 327–329; population
    pressure, 325–327
Gilbert, G.K.: 186
Glaciers:
  as indices of climatic change, 91; manage-
    ment, 119; role in water balance (budget),
    119–120
Grade: 184
Grasses and herbs:
  productivity, 251
Great Plains:
  irrigation and climate, 97
Greenhouse effect: 92

Habitat: 48
Hail suppression: 98
Hardin, G.: 33
Heat balance: 23
Heat budget: 64
Hellman, G.: 70
Herbicides:
  ecological effects (Vietnam), 266, 268
Hubbard Brook, N.H.:
  calcium cycle, 7–8
Human evolution: 50–51
Humphreys, W.J.: 94
Hurricane modification: 99
Hutchinson, G.E.: 33
Hutton, J.: 154
Hydrologic cycle: 25–26
Hydrology:
  definition, 123
Hydrosphere:
  description, 47

Interface:
  definition, 21
International Biological Program: 260–261
International Commission of Snow and
    Ice: 120
International Geophysical Year: 92
International Hydrological Decade: 114,
    115; research, 120–121
Irrigation:
  ancient civilization, 114–115; effects on
    microclimate, 96–97

Jefferson, T.: 96

Krakatoa: 94

Lakes:
  origins, 131–132
Lake Erie:
  algae, 277–278; commercial fisheries,
    decline, 279–281; conservation measures,
    282; dissolved oxygen, 277; invertebrates,
    278–279; physical geography, 272–275;
    pollution sources, 275–276; pollution
    types, 275; sedimentation, 273–275;
    water chemistry, 276

Lake Tahoe:
  dissolved oxygen, 134–135; eutrophica-
    tion, 135–136; life expectancy, 136;
    origin, 132; pollution, 136–139; pollu-
    tion abatement, 138–139; transparency,
    133; water budget, 123–129; water
    quality, 129–131; water temperature,
    133–134
Land ethic: 32
Landmass denudation cycle: 27
Land use:
  effect on sediment yields, 192–197
Land use planning:
  Georgia, 327–329
Land use policy:
  approaches, 295–301; ecosystems approach,
    301–307
Langbein, W.B.: 115
Latosols: 230
Least-work principle: 185
Leopold, A.: 32
Limiting factors principle: 48–49
Limnology:
  definition, 131
Linnaeus: 85
Lithosphere:
  description, 46

Marsh, G.P.: 32, 61
Miami Beach:
  beach erosion, 318; beach nourishment,
    319; U.S. Corps of Engineers, 319
Microclimate:
  effects of irrigation, 96–97; effects of
    man, 74–76; effects of reservoirs, 97;
    effects of soils, 71; effects of topography,
    71–72; effects of vegetation, 73–74;
    elements, 69–70; forests, 73–74; Neotoma
    Valley, Ohio, 72
Milankovitch, M.: 88
Mississippi Basin:
  water balance, 65–66
Mobius, K.: 32
Morozov, G.F.: 32

Natural environment: as a system, 2–3, 5, 74
Negative feedback: 13–14
Neotoma Valley, Ohio:
  microclimate, 72
Niche: 48
Nitrogen cycle: 214

Oceans:
  sedimentation rates, 165
Ocean circulation:
  effects of atmosphere, 23–25

Odum, H.T.: 37
Old-fields:
  effects of radiation, 264–265
Optimum population: 322–333
Origin of Species: 44

Paris:
  urban heat island, 101–102
Pesticides:
  effects on animal communities, 268–269
Phenology: 85–86
Philadelphia:
  climate change, 90
Phosphorus cycle: 216–219
Physical geography: 19
Podzols: 230
Poland:
  reservoirs (microclimate effects), 97
Positive feedback: 14–15

Radiation balance: 22
Range: 48
Remote sensing:
  hydrologic applications, 118–119
Reservoirs:
  effects on microclimate (Poland), 97
Rivers:
  definition, 169
River beds:
  as biological habitats, 143–144
River channels:
  effects of construction, 197–201; hydraulic
    relations, 171–179; sinuosity, 179–182
Rock cycle: 166–167
Role: 48

Schaefer, V.J.: 107
Schmidt, W.: 69
Snow ridging: 84–85
Soil:
  definitions, 206; effects of man, 234–235;
    effects on microclimate, 71; physio-
    chemical characteristics, 207–208; types,
    208–209, 223–224
Soil animals: 209–211
Soil formation:
  theories, 221–222
Soil microorganisms:
  types, 211–213; activities, 213–214
Soil moisture:
  conservation, 84–85
Soil profiles:
  development, 224–225; role of organic
    matter, 225–228
Solar constant: 22
Spaceship earth: 35, 307–308

Steady state: 21
Stream ecology:
    fish breeding, 146–148
Stream temperature:
    biological effects, 141–142
Sudbury, Ontario:
    ecological effects of smelting, 266
Sulfur oxides:
    ecological effects, 226
System:
    definition, 4
Systems approach: 1, 3–4; in physical
        geography, 19–20
Systems ecology: 34

Tansley, A.G.: 32
Territoriality: 52
Thermodynamics:
    laws, 9, 62
Thornthwaite, C.W.: 69, 84, 85, 96–97
Topography:
    effects on microclimate, 71–72

U.S. Corps of Engineers:
    beach nourishment (Miami Beach), 319
Urban climate, 99–107
Urban heat island: 99–103; Columbia, Md.,
        100–101; Paris, 101–102
Urbanization:
    effects on climate, 99–107

Urban rivers:
    management conflicts, 201–202

Vegetation:
    effects on microclimate, 73–74
Vietnam:
    ecological effects of herbicides, 266, 268
Voeikov, A.: 61
Volcanic dust:
    effects on climate, 94

Washburn, A. L.: 156
Water balance: 25;
    Castle Creek Basin, Calif., 66; Mississippi
        Basin, 65–66; N. America, 65; oceans, 65
Water budget: 64;
    global data, 117; Lake Tahoe, 123–129;
        measurement, 116–119; role of glaciers,
        119–120; United States, 169
Water pollution:
    Lake Tahoe, 136–139
Water quality:
    Lake Tahoe, 129–131
Water vapor:
    role in global heat balance, 25
Water year:
    definition, 126
Weather modification: 98–99
White, L.: 32
Wolfe, J.N.: 72